THE
143ᴿᴰ IN IRAQ

TRAINING THE IRAQI POLICE, IN SPITE OF IT ALL

BY
MARC YOUNGQUIST

EMERALD LAKE
BOOKS

The 143rd in Iraq
Copyright © 2016 Marc Youngquist
marcyoungquist.com

Second Edition

Book design by Green Frog Publishing

Cover design by Gerber Studio
gerberstudio.com

Cover stock photo by Stavchansky Yakov/Shutterstock

Books published by Emerald Lake Books may be ordered through booksellers or by contacting:
Emerald Lake Books
Sherman, CT 06784
emeraldlakebooks.com

ISBN: 978-0-9971207-8-3 (hc)
ISBN: 978-0-9971207-1-4 (pb)
ISBN: 978-0-9971207-2-1 (epub)
Library of Congress Number: 2016960082

Printed in the United States of America.

As a former Commander of the 143rd MP Company (1997-1999), this bare knuckle blow-by-blow account of how my former soldiers performed so magnificently in Iraq made me proud, made me laugh, and even made me cry. It kept me on the edge of my seat, wanting to read the next page, and wishing I were there with them every step of the way. Knowing MSG (retired) Youngquist as I do, this detailed and, at times, disturbing, account of the obstacles the 143rd MP Company faced is the gritty truth as only a soldier's NCO would tell it. To the soldiers of the 143rd: Well done and welcome home. I am grateful for this chronicle of your service, and proud of each and every one of you!

Colonel (Ret.) Stephan Picard
Operation Iraqi Freedom Veteran

MSG Younquist has again provided invaluable service to our nation with this book. His ability to relate personnel, equipment and training to mission requirements makes "The 143rd in Iraq, In Spite of It All" a must read for military professionals and civilian leaders alike. MSG Younquist's real life experiences accurately describe the challenges leaders face today. I wish I had had this book when I was teaching in ROTC.

Major Robert E. Henry
Judge Advocate, United States Army Reserve
Instructor, Command and General Staff College Officer Course

When America goes to war, she sends her serving sons and daughters into harm's way for the protection of her people and the security of the nation. In doing so, she sends the strongest of the faithful, her volunteers, the people who have the hearts of lions, who leave their homes and family for the greater good of us all.

And when America goes to war, she calls and asks, "Who will go?" Marc Youngquist, a former marine and serving National Guard trooper put up his hand and said, "I will".

Marc has written of his Connecticut Military Police National Guard unit as they deployed and saw action in Iraq in 2003 and 2004. His is a telling story that readers rarely see—the gritty clear-eyed truth that includes the chaos of organization, the apathy of command staff, the lack of critical need-to-have equipment, and the sometimes broken-down/obsolete vehicles, weapons, communications, adverse weather and health threats—even clothing necessary to do the job. Marc writes of this and more, not in complaint or anger, but as it is and what he and his fellow MP Unit still accomplished in an active and always dangerous combat zone.

Every American owes a measure of gratitude and respect for our military. Every American should read Marc Youngquist's account of our citizen soldiers and their missions—not only overcoming the challenge of a sometimes faceless enemy that uses buried and roadside car bombs, snipers, and guerilla warfare tactics to kill Americans, but how they prevailed and met the call of duty, "In Spite of It All."

Bruce W. Tully
Special Agent In Charge (Ret.)
Senior Foreign Service
Diplomatic Security Service
United States Department of State

ACKNOWLEDGEMENTS

First and foremost I want to thank the men and women of the 143rd Military Police Company of the Connecticut Army National Guard. Through their hard work, dedication, commitment and determination, the unit survived and successfully completed three combat deployments.

Next, many thanks to my beautiful wife, Marcia, who put up with weekend drills, annual training and one crazy deployment to the sandbox.

I would also like to thank Lieutenant Mike Grube, First Sergeant Chaun Jones, Sergeant First Class Dan Lawler, Sergeant First Class Roddy Porter and Sergeant First Class Marc Pucinski for use of their photographs and tireless fact-checking for the book. I also need to thank Sergeant First Class Bob Mongiat, Sergeant "Doc" Buonacore, Sergeant Chris Sweetwood and Sergeant Roger Roberge (to name a few) for reminding me of details I had forgotten. Sergeant Roberge, seemingly out of nowhere, found a publisher who was instantly interested in the book, after fifty publishers, for one reason or another, stated that they were not interested.

My thanks go out to President Bush and Secretary of Defense Robert Gates, who finally came up with a winning plan. When the 143rd Military Police Company deployed to Afghanistan, they were properly prepared and equipped for their mission.

Without the help of my nephew and editor, Geoff Bottone, this book might have never seen the light of day. I was fortunate enough to have two more follow-up editors, Geri Gormley and Charles Sweetman, who made me sound like I really did have a Master's Degree. I am also grateful to my first publisher, Kathy Bizzoco of Green Frog Publishing, for giving me an opportunity to tell our story. Gratitude goes to my new publisher as well, Tara Alemany of Emerald Lake Books, for stepping in when this book went out of print and picking it up so that the tale of these American heroes would not be cut short.

A special thanks to "The Voice of the 143rd Military Police Company," Jim Vicevich of WTIC News Talk 1080, who kept the 143rd Military Police in the news every day for well over a year. Even now, ten years later, he still talks about the Unit.

Dozens, maybe hundreds, of people sent us packages, cards and most of all, their support while we were deployed in Iraq. You will never know how important these gestures were. The insurance company I worked for, Middlesex Mutual/Middleoak, went out of its way to support me and my family while I was deployed. And on my return, they shut down the office, and held a welcome home ceremony. I am truly grateful for my colleagues.

FOR NON-MILITARY PERSONNEL

Non-military readers can find rank titles and military terms a bit confusing. While rank titles are not important to understanding this book, you will find a general Military Police Organization Chart (keeping in mind that the chain of command changed four times during the course of a year) in Appendix I, *Military Police Organization*, and what I hope are helpful definitions of military terms in the *Glossary*.

TABLE OF CONTENTS

LIST OF FIGURES

FOREWORD

The mothers and fathers of America will give you their sons and daughters...with the confidence in you that you will not needlessly waste their lives. And you dare not. That's the burden the mantle of leadership places upon you. You could be the person who gives the orders that will bring about the deaths of thousands and thousands of young men and women. It is an awesome responsibility. You cannot fail. You dare not fail...

General H. Norman Schwarzkopf
Eisenhower Hall Theater Speech to the Corps of Cadets
May 15, 1991

Promise me you'll always remember: You're braver than you believe, and stronger than you seem, and smarter than you think.

Christopher Robin to Winnie the Pooh
Winnie the Pooh

This book is not just my story; this book is the story of the 143rd Military Police Company. This is a story that almost no one knows.

Despite seeing combat almost every day for a year in Iraq, very few news articles were written about our unit's exploits. Those articles speak only in very general terms concerning what the unit did and who did it. No articles were printed in hometown newspapers about the awards the unit received; in no small part because those much-deserved awards were not forthcoming.

In addition, I have run into people who know the soldiers I served with. Not one of them knew any of the details about what their friends, coworkers, employees, or relatives had done in Iraq.

For the past several years, I have presented a Veterans Day talk at a local middle school. The core of that talk is about the bravery and dedication displayed by soldiers from the 143rd on one particularly hellish twenty-four-hour period during our 2003/2004 deployment in Iraq. Throughout this talk, I make mention of only one name—the name of the young lady who was killed on a very bad night. Her name was Rachel Bosveld. She was not assigned to the Connecticut National Guard, but was assigned to the active-duty unit we worked closely with.

During that attack, six soldiers from the 143rd went to the aid of Specialist Rachel Bosveld and the two soldiers who were with her. All three had sustained life-threatening injuries, and in Specialist Bosveld's case, her injuries were, unfortunately, fatal. Under fire, the three injured soldiers were carried across the open area of the Police Station compound into the protected confines of the station, where lifesaving first aid was performed.

Following one Veteran's Day presentation, a teacher at that school, approached to ask if I knew a very close friend of hers, who was stationed in Iraq. As it happens, her close friend was one of the soldiers who also survived the night Rachel Bosveld died. Her friend, along with five other soldiers, was awarded a medal for valor for rescuing the three wounded soldiers while under fire at the risk of their own lives. The teacher had never known this about her good friend, Staff Sergeant Andrea Cloutier.

I realized from our conversation that if a close friend didn't know about her actions, her boss, Governor Dannel P. Malloy, likely didn't know, either. The Governor was grateful that I wrote a letter to him, sharing the exploits of one of the Connecticut State Troopers assigned to his personal security detail. He knew that the trooper had been in the National Guard and had served in Iraq, but nothing more.

On another occasion, I was at a function and found myself sitting next to the Chief of Police for the City of Bridgeport. I told him that Alexander Wilde, one of my better soldiers, was currently working for him.

He told me that he knew Wilde and stated that he was a good officer, but he did not know until that moment that Wilde had saved the lives of two soldiers in a night attack at Abu Ghraib Police Station.

These conversations repeated themselves many more times, with the same response each time. No one knew. With this book, I am trying let everyone know.

Throughout this book, I mention some soldiers by name, but not all of them. Each of the soldiers has a story to tell, and unfortunately, I cannot cover them all. In some cases, the soldiers were so low-profile that they went about their business as good soldiers without any fanfare and without being noticed.

That is not to say that they were not valuable assets or that they did not face risks, just that they were quiet, unassuming troops doing a fantastic job. What I hope to accomplish is to inform people of the great job the 143rd Military Police Company did, in spite of all the factors that worked against them, seeking to foil their efforts at every turn.

Chapter One

COURAGE

Courage is fear holding on a minute longer.

General George S. Patton, Jr.

On December 27, 2003, while en route to the Iraqi Police Academy Range, Staff Sergeant Sullivan's Squad was hit by an IED. Staff Sergeant Sullivan's Squad was part of several squads from different Military Police Companies assigned to the range. The first blast damaged one of his two vehicles, injuring all three soldiers, one severely. The vehicle was so heavily damaged that it could not exit the kill zone to safety.

The driver, Private First Class Wabrek, received numerous wounds, despite the bullet-resistant glass and the flak jacket secured to the door to block incoming shrapnel. While Wabrek sustained injuries to the face and left eye, his Kevlar helmet stopped what would have been a fatal blow. The blast also shattered the magazine of his M-16, which was in a bracket next to his left leg, riddling his leg with fragments of bullets and the magazine itself. Private First Class Wabrek is one of the toughest individuals I have ever met; he never once complained.

Other pieces of shrapnel flew inside the vehicle and struck Team Leader Sergeant Jessica Walsh in the face. Days later, when Private First Class Wichowski was adjusting Sergeant Walsh's helmet for the night vision attachment, he accidently dropped the helmet and realized that something had cut into his hand, which was now bleeding. After examining the helmet, Wichowski found a jagged piece of shrapnel lodged in the helmet right at the location that protects the left temple. If Sergeant Walsh had not been wearing the helmet properly, she would have been instantly killed by that small piece of shrapnel.

Specialist Wichowski, the vehicle gunner, received a back injury when a piece of the explosive device blasted through the floor of the vehicle and up through the roof, striking him in the back ceramic plate of his body armor. Had it not been for the ceramic plate, chances are good that the shrapnel would have cut him in half. All three soldiers suffered hearing loss, and were extremely disoriented by the blast and concussion.

Shortly after, small arms fire began raking both the disabled vehicle and Staff Sergeant Sullivan's vehicle, which had stopped to assist his stricken team. At first, only three soldiers were capable of returning fire, and the heaviest weapon available was a Squad Automatic (SAW) M-249 with limited ammunition.

In an ambush like this, with a vehicle that cannot move, soldiers are drilled to deliver a heavy volume of fire on the attackers to achieve fire superiority and break up the ambush. However, neither the SAW nor the soldiers' M-16s had heavy enough rounds to punch through the walls that the attackers hid behind. Considering that ammunition was already limited, no one wanted to waste bullets making pockmarks in the walls. Fortunately, the limited number of U.S. soldiers with limited ammunition were able to drive the insurgents away with suppressive fire.

About this time, another U.S. unit came into the kill zone to assist, only to be hit by an IED—several soldiers were severely injured when they dismounted and attempted to make their way to the damaged vehicle. A radio call was made requesting an Air MedEvac helicopter to pick up the injured soldiers, but I don't know if that call ever went through. Most of the time, our radios did not have enough range for anything beyond a couple of miles; it is uncertain whether or not the aviation unit ever heard our call for help.

Staff Sergeant Sullivan managed to get his wounded soldiers, and the rest of his team, along with the injured soldiers from the other unit, to the combat surgical hospital.

Private First Class Wabrek, despite being seriously injured, was concerned about what his family would be told about his injuries. He wanted to let his mother know that he was okay. The last thing that he wanted was for his mother to find out that her son had been wounded in Iraq, from a chaplain and a team of officers standing at her front door. Unfortunately (or not), he was in no condition to talk; the pain and medication were just too much. If he had gotten on the phone, he would have caused his mother unnecessary concern.

Staff Sergeant Sullivan took care of his Squad like they were his family, because to him, they were. In direct violation of several orders, Staff Sergeant Sullivan borrowed a cell phone and called Wabrek's mother. He explained what had happened and that Steve was getting the best of care in a real hospital. Staff Sergeant Sullivan continued to explain that Steve would be flown out of Iraq and up to Germany shortly for further treatment, and then be evacuated to the States where he would most likely be admitted to the Walter Reed Army Hospital.

While Staff Sergeant Sullivan's actions violated several regulations, he had details about Wabrek that the Casualty Assistance Team did not. While they were a huge improvement over the telegrams that notified families in previous wars, the Casualty Assistance Team would not have firsthand knowledge of what happened to Wabrek. Sullivan knew that Wabrek's mother would rather hear from someone who actually knew her son, as opposed to hearing from an officer who had never met her son, and could offer only overly-rehearsed lines.

This secret of this short phone call was kept for years. The story we heard that day was that Private First Class Wabrek called his mother from a borrowed cell phone (no one would question a son calling his mother from a hospital bed).

Until Wabrek was sent to Germany, Sullivan and his Squad visited Steve at the hospital every chance they could get. They even escorted him to the airport to ensure his safety and see him off. Several others from the unit checked on Wabrek when he was in the recovery room, and waited with him for the transport that would take him to Germany, and back to the States. Wabrek insisted that Wichowski, his gunner, get a video camera to get footage of him in the CSH being treated.

Several days later the Squad packed up Private First Class Wabrek's gear and shipped it home; they knew he wasn't coming back.

Air Land Battle Manual

The military has detailed instructions for everything, from how to launch a nuclear weapon to how to dig a latrine. The overall direction comes from the *Air Land Battle Manual*, which gives general guidance for coordinating all Army units, and instructions on how the next war will be fought. The Military Police Corps has its own field manual that outlines what every soldier in a company should be doing, what they should be doing it with, and how they should be doing it. Some of these instructions come under the Table of Organization and Equipment that details each soldier's job, as well as the exact equipment that each soldier, from Private to Captain, should have. These details are followed by tactical operating procedures, and are handed down through orders issued by ranking officers.

When you're the low man on the totem pole, people above you can short circuit all these orders and directives, leaving you with no option but to suck it up and drive on. Some situations are more understandable than others—if you have a finite number of armored vehicles, and you are putting out more soldiers than the armored vehicles can accommodate, you make do with whatever vehicles are available. What you do not do is place soldiers who are in unarmored vehicles into more hazardous situations than the soldiers in armored ones. This common-sense concept, along with many others, was not followed.

It had taken twelve years to get to this point, where bureaucratic apathy, professional indifference, underestimating the situation, and just plain stupidity almost got three soldiers killed. Old, unarmored vehicles, radios that did not work, low ammunition supplies, decreasing squads from three teams of ten soldiers to two teams of six soldiers, light machine guns with limited penetration power, and lack of hand grenades all combined to bring us to a point where we came so close to losing three soldiers in one day. All of this could have been corrected if the Department of Defense, the active-duty Army, and the State of Connecticut had cared just a little bit. Unfortunately, this was not the first incident, and it would not be the last.

Figure 1.1   Private First Class Steven Wabrek

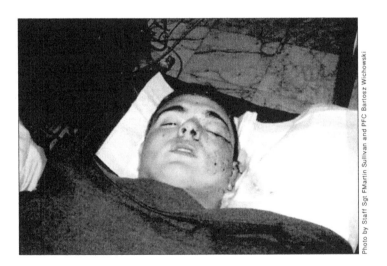

Figure 1.2   Private First Class Wabrek waiting for transport

Figure 1.3   2nd Platoon's damaged vehicle being inspected by
              Sergeant Karl Rhynhart

Figure 1.4   Private First Class Wabrek was sitting behind the door

Figure 1.5   Sergeant Walsh was sitting in the Squad Leader's seat when she was struck in the face

Figure 1.6   Wichowski was in the turret and struck in the back

Chapter Two

AUGUST 1991

Friends all tried to warn me, but I held my head up high
All the time they warned me, but I only passed them by
They all tried to tell me, but I guess I didn't care
I turned my back and left them standing there.

Mike Curb Congregation
Theme Song from *Kelly's Heroes*

August, 1991, was both my first drill with the 143rd Military Police Company and the company's first drill back in the States after being deployed in Operation Desert Storm. No one really thought that the war with Iraq was over; we all knew that the next one would start in a matter of months or years.

A Brief History

Following the collapse of the Soviet Union, the entire structure of the U.S. military began to change. With the potential for a large ground war in Europe off the table, the need for large numbers of active-duty troops was no longer necessary. This change caused a shift to a smaller but more lethal and professional military that would rely on technology and overwhelming firepower. With this change came the need for highly trained soldiers to man the new state-of-the-art equipment.

The Army understood that it could no longer staff all the support positions on the active-duty side, so support operations were shifted to the National Guard and Reserve forces. This shift was a big change, because previously, the assignments given to the Army National Guard had closely paralleled the assignments given to the active-duty Army.

The shift became apparent during Desert Storm when tens of thousands of Guard and Reserve troops were activated to support the mission in Saudi Arabia and Kuwait. The U.S. was no longer able to enter a conflict without activating Guard and Reserve forces. Units that used to be considered second string were now part of the first team, and without them, the first team could not have even gotten onto the battlefield.

After Desert Storm, this change in specialization accelerated even further, until active-duty was concentrated mainly on Infantry, armor and artillery, leaving the Guard and Reserve to focus on Military Police, medical, intelligence, aviation support, combat sustainment and engineering activities. While the Army did have these jobs in their active-duty units, they did not have the numbers required for a full-scale conflict—especially with other limited engagements like Bosnia and Kosovo, which also required the activation of Guard and Reserve units.

The Gulf War and the Return Home

After the Iraqi invasion of Kuwait on August 2, 1990, the U.S. military began ramping up to counter the attack, activating my unit on January 3, 1991. After little more than twenty days of Mobilization Training, the 143rd Military Police Company (which I was not yet assigned to) was sent to Saudi Arabia. The unit arrived in-theater on January 27, 1991, and after a successful assignment, left Saudi Arabia around May 5, 1991. It was one of the few units activated from the State of Connecticut; the Infantry, Artillery, and Engineers were all left behind in the States.

This time the 143rd was designated as an enemy prisoner of war unit. During Desert Storm, they handled approximately 35,000 Iraqi prisoners of war, keeping 3,000 to 5,000 POWs in their compound at any given time. They did their job during Desert Storm, did it well and without any serious incidents. They also had a very cocky attitude because they were one of the few units from Connecticut to actually be in Desert Storm.

The State of Connecticut didn't seem to think much of this attitude. Although the Infantry, Artillery and Engineers had remained stateside, those three units got more attention, newer equipment, better training and better deployments than what the Military Police had been getting and continued to get after their return. This apparent favoritism was because those units happened to make up the bulk of the Connecticut Army National Guard and had most of the more senior ranking officers, which gave them a greater ability to advocate for themselves than the Military Police ever could.

In Iraq, Saddam continued to violate the spirit of the cease-fire while conforming to the general letter of the law. He attacked Shia in the Basrah area and Kurds in the north, both groups that had supported the Coalition. Based on Saddam's actions, the unit knew that they would one day have to return to Iraq.

In the intervening years, the unit also kept coming up for active-duty deployments for operations such as Haiti, Somalia, Bosnia, Kosovo and missions to the Middle East. Even though these operations kept occurring, they somehow always left the 143rd Military Police Company on short notice and scrambling to be prepared. A flurry of activity would take place, causing equipment to come in, personnel to be assigned and training to be stepped up. Each time the deployment was cancelled, rather than maintain and increase readiness, the State Command and the Army (who are responsible for providing funding, equipment, training areas, etc.) allowed everything to go back to square one.

Duties of the MP Unit

As soon as anyone mentions the word 'police,' the assumption is that the duty of a Military Police unit is law enforcement. While this is true in some cases, we actually have four missions:

- Law Enforcement: This is where Military Police officers act as police officers just as though they were in a civilian environment, but perform their duties on a military base.
- Prisoner Control: Handling enemy prisoners of war or other detainees.
- Security: This is sometimes associated with sensitive locations, such as nuclear storage facilities.
- Battlefield Circulation Control: This is kind of like a combat traffic cop. The mission is to operate behind the U.S. front lines, ensuring that troops and equipment move forward, and that casualties and damaged equipment make their way to the rear in an orderly fashion. Circulation Control is accomplished in a variety of ways; sometimes it involves escort work, sometimes route control, other times deterrent patrolling.

All Military Police units are trained in each of these areas, and are then required to specialize in one specific area.

In any of the schools that the military has concerning Military Police, emphasis is always placed on how MP units must be able to shoot, move, and communicate. While these three components are key to almost all military operations, these components are essential to a Military Police operation when performing a battlefield circulation control assignment. MPs are expected to be able to move across the battlefield, covering a wide area (sometimes upwards of twenty miles or more), and report back to higher headquarters with their findings.

Following Desert Storm, the unit was re-designated as a BCC, changing the unit's entire configuration. While the numbers of soldiers in the unit would remain somewhat the same, their equipment, training, and focus would be going in an entirely different direction. With this change, a lot of training and a lot of re-equipping needed to take place. It came in small doses.

With equipment trickling in, the actual mission didn't change, and the unit required a certain number of vehicles, machine guns, and continued training to be combat ready. The re-designation was dragged out over ten years and never completed.

Command

A sense of bureaucratic apathy existed that left the Military Police always short of what they needed to be fully prepared for their next combat assignment. No one intentionally sabotaged our ability to get the job done; more likely they only did what was absolutely necessary to cover the basics and nothing more.

Much of the apathy could be attributed to the fact that we were assigned, at first, to an aviation unit that had no understanding of Military Police operations. Another factor was that we were a unit with no serious ranking officers, which meant that we had no higher command to champion our cause, even if Army doctrine supported our position. Getting a colonel to listen to a junior Captain for an explanation as to why something needs to get done in a discipline that is completely alien to the aviation field is, at best, difficult.

To say the least, support was lacking from higher headquarters. They had their own agendas, which did not include the Military Police unit, and they considered us more of a nuisance than an asset because we were not compatible with their type of operations. Assigning us to an aviation unit made little sense, but at the time, there was no one else for the company to be put under. Unfortunately, any other battalion unit we could have been placed with would have come with the same communication and command difficulties as being assigned to an aviation unit (a fact we discovered later on when assigned first to a Troop Command, and then to an Area Support Group, neither of which had any real understanding of our mission).

For years, the 143rd Military Police Company was the only Military Police unit in Connecticut. At full strength, the unit would have totaled 186 soldiers, where the Connecticut Army National Guard had several thousand soldiers. We were just a drop in the bucket.

Training

Most people are under the impression that National Guard training consists of one weekend a month and two weeks a year. While that may once have been true, extra time has been required from guardsmen ever since the conclusion of Desert Storm, usually without pay. They told us that we needed to give this extra time because we were doing it for the flag. The colonel, who made somewhere in the area of $1,200 a month, implored me, the other sergeants and lower-ranking officers to donate time without pay when we were making about $300 a month. Those of us who volunteered tried to justify the additional time commitment to ourselves by saying that the extra effort was needed, and we were the only ones who could do it.

Our only incentive for donating more time was that the U.S. promised to give us a quarter of a retirement point for each extra meeting we attended. These quarters would be added to our total retirement points, which would increase our retirement pay. I personally never saw the extra points when I put in for retirement.

If we had actually put serious effort into training one weekend a month and the two weeks a year, we might have had something. Unfortunately, there were certain mandatory tasks that took up our time and precluded us from doing any real mission training. These included: urine testing for drugs and alcohol, HIV testing, class "A" uniform inspections, the Christmas party, the company picnic, equipment inspections, firearms qualification, and the physical fitness test. HIV tests and urine tests were all done on an unannounced basis, so whatever training was scheduled for that day was interrupted and, in some cases, not done at all—invariably taking away at least one full day from training of a drill weekend. The class "A" uniform inspection almost always happened during Christmas time, followed by mandatory briefings and the company Christmas party, taking away a full weekend of training.

Each year, units must qualify with basic weapons (M-16 and the M-9 pistol). Our unit was always assigned to run the ranges in support of other units, such as medical or aviation, because we were more skilled in soldier-like duties than they were. While our soldiers were busy running the ranges, they were not given additional time on the range themselves, leaving them with approximately 45 minutes worth of actual training on a two-and-a-half day training weekend.

Preparing and packing up for the two-week annual training, as well as unpacking when the unit returned from training, used up two more weekends. Another weekend was lost to physical fitness testing and testing the soldiers on common tasks. Another full training day was dedicated to the company picnic, normally held sometime during the summer (the most ideal weather in which to train).

These tasks were important, in their own way, but they took days and weekends away from the actual training needed to prepare our unit for combat. Adding up all of the time devoted to these other tasks reveals that we used between eleven to thirteen days of approximately twenty-two potential training days during a year. The remaining days were ours for mission-oriented training, provided that no one else thought of something for us to do. Some training days were used for the governor's inauguration or the Memorial Day parade.

Other days were dedicated to performing preventive maintenance on vehicles, radios, weapon systems and other support equipment.

Even as war loomed closer, the Guard did not deviate from this type of training schedule. Still, at the unit level, we did try to provide realistic training in the wake of the then-current scenarios happening around the world.

Move

Initially, the unit was issued four-wheel-drive pickup trucks and four-wheel-drive Blazers as combat vehicles. This is completely against Army doctrine, which states that a battlefield circulation control unit is supposed to be equipped with Humvees. To make matters worse, the pickups and Blazers were hand-me-downs, coming from units that had been disbanded after Desert Storm, and were used up, old, and no longer functional for the mission at hand. Training with these vehicles was impossible because machine guns could not be mounted (as they could have been with Humvees) to offer battlefield circulation control protection.

The Command Sergeant Major of the Battalion whom we reported to was under the command of the aviation unit. He, like they, did not completely understand the role of the Military Police in the modern-day battlefield. When he was told that it would be impossible for us to train to standard or perform our mission using vehicles such as pickup trucks and Blazers, he said he would look into it and have a study done to see how this would impact the Military Police Company in performing their mission.

I told the sergeant major that assigning these vehicles to a Military Police Company was like issuing a heavy lift helicopter squadron 2.5 ton trucks instead of helicopters, and then assessing whether those vehicles would be able to perform the duties required of the heavy lift aviation company. After all, the squadron could go to a pickup zone with the trucks, which are far more cost effective than helicopters.

The sergeant major did not enjoy my comparison.

However, we did begin to receive Humvees sometime later. Unfortunately, these were also hand-me-downs from units deactivated after Desert Storm and had seen some very rough service time. Some of the vehicles came from units that had been deactivated in Germany, or from deactivated units in the Connecticut National Guard. The Connecticut units knew that their vehicles, as well as their units, would be going away at the end of their annual training cycle, so they beat the crap out of them.

The bulk of the Connecticut vehicles had come from a TOW missile unit and were equipped and mounted to carry TOW missiles (Tube Launched, Optically Tracked, Wire-Guided Missile). These mounts and brackets were not compatible with our mission because we carried completely different types of equipment and armament. Trying to load these vehicles with MP equipment proved difficult with all of the extra hardware.

I informed the sergeant major in charge of state-wide maintenance that we needed to remove the brackets. He informed me that we did not have authorization to remove the brackets or the storage equipment, because doing so would change the configuration of the vehicles. Despite explaining to him that we were having difficulty utilizing the vehicles to store equipment on racks that were neither useful nor functional for our mission, he was unimpressed and refused to give us authorization.

At this point, we got out our 9/16" socket wrenches, removed all the brackets and the mountings, piled them off to the side, and told the sergeant major where he could come and pick them up. I do not think the sergeant major cared for me any more after that, because I had violated a major rule of the Army National Guard—common sense is to be avoided at all costs.

From this point, we had a constant battle with maintenance just to keep our vehicles running. When they went in for service, instead of being repaired, they were made to just run. Getting vehicles "running" was the major concern of the State Maintenance Section, because once a vehicle was documented to be up and running, the positive activity flow was reflected on that unit's performance rating. If a vehicle had an electrical problem, the battery would be charged, but the source of the dead battery would never be investigated. If a vehicle leaked oil, the leak would be plugged without bothering to see what caused it in the first place.

On one occasion, the sergeant major ordered me to get up to the maintenance section because six of our vehicles had been fixed and needed to be removed. The sergeant major was very demanding, giving me the impression that I was somehow delaying recovery of my vehicles from his maintenance section, thereby taking up valuable space. At my first opportunity, the following drill weekend, I went to the maintenance section with several soldiers to retrieve our vehicles.

Two of the vehicles would not start. The first one, which I personally attempted to start, had been left idling to charge the battery for so long that the fuel had been exhausted and the glow plugs for the motor had burned out. This left the battery that they were attempting to charge completely dead and the vehicle unserviceable. The second vehicle would not start for reasons that no one could determine.

On the eight-mile trip back to the unit, one of the four drivable vehicles stopped running on the highway and had to be towed back to the maintenance facility. Upon arrival at our home station, we documented that one of the three remaining vehicles was now leaking oil profusely and could not be safely used. This vehicle was also towed back to the maintenance facility.

The Parking Brake Heater

Captain Picard, Specialist Settino (his driver), and I took a drive one freezing February night, heading from the Hartford Armory down to Camp Niantic. No matter what we did, we could not get the heat in the vehicle to come on. We eventually gave up and drove on through the cold, making a note to have the heater looked at by the maintenance section once we made it to Camp Niantic.

About an hour and one-half later, Specialist Settino pulled into a parking spot at Camp Niantic and engaged the parking brake before turning off the engine (standard procedure even though the vehicle had an automatic transmission). As soon as she raised the parking brake, we were startled by a strange noise; when Settino released the emergency brake, the noise stopped. We all stared at one another and at the dashboard, not believing our ears. When Settino put on the parking brake again, the noise came back again. She repeated this several times, and each time we were more amazed than the last.

Then we realized that the heat had come on. The Captain and Settino put their hands up to the dashboard vents, confirming that warm air was finally circulating. We could not figure out why pulling on the parking brake made the heat come on, but confirmed that was the only way to turn on the heat in that vehicle. We walked away shaking our heads and shrugging our shoulders. So it goes.

Shoot

Obtaining and maintaining appropriate vehicles for the unit wasn't our only concern. During this time period, our main battle weapon kept changing as well. Initially, each vehicle in an MP platoon was assigned an M-60 machine gun (a total of ten machine guns per platoon). The active-duty Army also decided to supply one 50-caliber machine gun per squad, designated as the squad leader's weapon.

From 1982 into the late 1990s, use of these weapons was based on the doctrine of the *Air Land Battle Manual*, which assumed that the weapons would be used fighting a major land war in Europe or Korea. These initial weapon assignments gave an MP platoon a balance of medium and heavy firepower, along with considerable range.

Then prior to the Iraq war, the main battle weapon was changed to the MK-19 automatic grenade launcher. All of our 50-caliber weapons and M-60 machine guns were removed from inventory. This change was, again, based on the Air Land Battle.

The concept behind the Military Police having the MK-19 grenade launcher was that it would be used in a rear battle situation to counter attacks by troops parachuting in or being transported by helicopter. The idea was that enemy troops, as American Rangers or paratroopers are, would be dropped in behind the front lines to attack supply and support operations and disrupt the forward movement of combat troops. The Military Police ranging across the battlefield with these MK-19 grenade launchers would be able to engage the enemy at distances greater than the enemies' small arms could reach. The MK-19 had an effective range of 1,400 meters and a maximum range of 2,023 meters with a rate of fire of 325 to 375 rounds per minute. The weapon weighed seventy pounds—not including the ammunition and the ammunition basket—and the tripod added an additional forty-four pounds.

The Military Police, operating in a squad formation, would position themselves out of small arms range and then rain 40mm grenades down on the landing troops. A squad of three vehicles would employ a tactic called "talking guns."

Initially, the guns would fire in sequence, sending out one to three rounds to determine their range, and ensure that a few rounds would make it down range at any given time. Once a squad leader determined that the guns had the correct range, the fire would increase, with each vehicle firing three to six grenades in sequence. Once the first gun fired, its team would assess its accuracy and do corrections while the second gun fired, followed by the third, and so on.

This type of fire causes an explosion amongst the landing troops down range every few seconds. Troops in the open and with limited ability to respond to the vehicles that are firing at them outside their effective range would be devastated. This, of course, assumed an open fighting environment, with no considerations given to any other combat scenarios, such as urban environments or other close combat fighting.

Because of their bursting radius, MK-19 rounds require a distance to travel before they arm. This safety feature protects both the troops who use the weapon and friendly soldiers nearby from rounds that could detonate early. The standard MK-19 round is a high explosive round that takes between forty-five- and ninety-feet to arm. In close combat situations, such as an urban environment, the rounds might not arm before striking buildings, making them basically big, slow-firing bullets.

To balance off the firepower of the MK-19, each MP team was assigned the following:

Team Leader

- **M-16 rifle**

  A standard-issue assault rifle has the option of firing blank rounds, allowing soldiers to train with nonlethal rounds in a simulated combat environment.

- **M-203**

  A grenade launcher (mounted under the barrel of an M-16 rifle), the M-203 gives soldiers dual capacity to engage targets and can launch 40mm high-explosive grenades, smoke rounds and flares.

- **M-9 Beretta pistol**

  A 9mm pistol assigned to Military Police officers. We were fortunate to have conversion kits for the M-9 that allowed us to fire non-lethal, paint ball-like rounds (for training).

Gunner

- **MK-19**

  A belt-fed, fully automatic weapon designed to not cook off. It fires 40mm grenades at a cyclic rate of 325 to 375 rounds per minute, giving a practical rate of fire of sixty rounds per minute (rapid) and forty rounds per minute, sustained. The MK-19 can launch a grenade at a maximum distance of 2,212 meters, though its effective range is about 1,500 meters. The MK-19A is a man-portable, crew-served weapon that can fire from a tripod-mounted position, or from a vehicle mount (with the latter preferred, as an MK-19A weighs 32.9 kilograms or 72.5 pounds.). The primary ammunition is the high-explosive dual-purpose M-430 grenade. On impact, the grenade can kill anyone within the radius of five meters, and wound them within the radius of fifteen.

- **M-249 SAW (squad automatic weapon)**
  A lightweight machine gun that fires the same bullets as an M-16 rifle, except M-249s can be either belt or magazine fed.

  This machine gun was designed to be used as a covering weapon for the MK-19, mounted up in the turret to give the gunner the option of launching grenades or firing the M-249 SAW. When we deployed, we did not have mounts to put the SAW up in the turrets, so we jury rigged them.

- **M-9 Beretta pistol**
  See above.

Driver

- **M-16 rifle**
  A standard-issue assault rifle has the option of firing blank rounds, allowing soldiers to train with nonlethal rounds in a simulated combat environment. The concept the military promoted was that the M-203 grenade launcher, the M-16 rifle and the squad automatic weapon would provide protection for the MK-19 grenade launcher.

- **M-9 Beretta pistol**
  See above.

Training was not appropriate to real-world scenarios. Shooting from a designated firing line on a standardized firing range taught only basic skills of how to fire the weapon. After mastering the basic skills, a soldier would need to take those basic skills and train in the environment in which the weapon would be used. Some examples would include:

- Firing from atop a vehicle.
- Firing from a moving vehicle.
- Dismounting the weapon from the vehicle and setting it up on the ground, using a tripod and the traverse and elevation mechanism to aim the weapon on other types of targets.

Although the MK-19 became our main battle weapon, a very limited amount of ammunition was allotted for training. In a combat situation, our basic load was supposed to be four canisters per gun, or a total of 180 canisters. When we deployed to Iraq, we were given ten canisters for the entire company. Very few soldiers in the company ever fired the MK-19 at all, and of those, not one of them fired it in a simulated tactical situation. Instead, the MK-19 was fired only during qualifications at Fort Drum.

Soldiers designated as MK-19 gunners were required to fire the MK-19 and the SAW for qualification. This resulted in a situation where whenever someone was promoted or replaced as an MK-19 gunner, his or her replacement would have no experience or qualifications with those weapons.

A soldier who was a driver one day might be a gunner or Team Leader the next, and would lack experience on the weapons system that went with the new position.

The same was also true for the SAW and the M-203 grenade launcher. Like the MK-19, only a limited number of soldiers were able to qualify with these weapons, which meant that most never got to use them in simulated tactical missions. Because of the limited exposure with these weapons, most of the soldiers were not comfortable with them.

With all the various weapons that we had been issued over the years, only the M-16 and M-9 were the ones that soldiers had practical applications with beyond qualifying at a range. When we were activated and sent to Fort Drum, we believed that a large part of our training would center around the squad automatic weapon, the M-203 grenade launcher, and our main battle weapon, the MK-19 grenade launcher. We were wrong.

Communication

The unit was equipped with Vietnam-era radios (VRC-46 and VRC-47 for the vehicles and backpack PRC-77s), which were not compatible with the current radios in the active-duty Army inventory. The radios themselves were good only for very short distances of no more than a couple of miles.

I was fortunate to have a very good communications chief, who was extremely thorough and had been on active-duty. Even though our radios were outdated, he knew how to keep up with the paperwork and maintain the radios to standard. Radios have very detailed requirements along with mandatory documented calibration at regular intervals.

Which was why I was surprised when the sergeant major in charge of vehicle repairs and maintenance informed me that all my radios were out of calibration, and that no maintenance had been done for years. A First Sergeant is responsible for all sections. If something as vital as radios being out of calibration (with no documentation of scheduled maintenance) were to occur, heads would roll; specifically, the First Sergeant and the Communications Chief. Unlike some presidents, a First Sergeant cannot plead ignorance.

Despite telling the sergeant major that my communications chief would never let our radios go out of whack, he implied that I was in charge, not the communications chief. He informed me that I was about to be relieved as First Sergeant for dereliction of duty.

I politely asked why the Maintenance Chief of vehicles was asking me about my radios (considering that the radios are separate inventory items and go to separate maintenance facilities). The sergeant major stated that the radios were a component of the vehicle, and because no maintenance had been done on them, all of our vehicles were deadline. If true, this would have been a major "oh shit" situation.

So we took a stroll down to the communications chief's area, where Staff Sergeant Bispham produced the correct calibrations and preventive maintenance records for all the radios, showing that they were all up to date.

At this point the sergeant major could not argue with me, and became even angrier because I had proved him wrong. He was out to have my ass hung to the wind. Remember the six vehicles that I had to pick up right away? This entire incident was supposed to be my payback for that.

I then asked him to get the hell out of my office. My response was not the brightest, since I was (1) a lesser rank then a sergeant major (2) counting on the sergeant major to repair my vehicles. I couldn't help myself, which has probably been my problem all along—I don't know when to keep my mouth shut. For the most part I always had good soldiers to take care of me, that did the job professionally, and could be counted on to do the right thing. When a person comes in and starts tearing me a new ass hole for something that didn't happen, it is hard not to take it personally. Unfortunately, I always did.

Staff

Equipment continued to come in slowly, and, over a period of years, our profile started conforming to what an active-duty Military Police Company with a battlefield circulation control mission would look like. We also continued our non-mission-specific training from 1991 through 2001, when the attacks on the Twin Towers took place.

We remained second-class soldiers under a non-MP Command, despite being repeatedly put on short notice in response to situations around the world.

Also, despite being a unit that was on short notice, for a time we were given only two of the four full-time staff the unit had been authorized. Even though we were supposed to be a combat-ready unit, (1) the full-time Readiness NCO (non-commissioned officer), who was a trained recruiter, and had not gone through the Readiness program, and (2) the full-time supply NCO was a trained readiness NCO, but had come from the Military Band and did not have experience with a Military Police Company. His experience did not involve carrying out the duties of a supply NCO; his experienced involved being responsible for scheduling performances and keeping track of band equipment.

In addition to those two positions, we were supposed to have a full-time Training NCO, which was eventually filled, and a full-time Armorer, which was never filled.

The Training NCO's job was to coordinate weekend drill activities and additional schools that soldiers had to attend to become soldiers and qualify for promotions. The coordination for annual training would be part of the Training NCO's duties, along with travel, meetings and setting up ranges or training areas. Because this position was not filled, these responsibilities fell to the untrained Readiness NCO until a qualified Training NCO was finally sent to fill it.

The Armorer's job was to maintain our weaponry, which included:

- Over forty-five MK-19 grenade launchers
- Over forty-five squad automatic weapons
- 130+ 9mm pistols
- 150+ M-16 rifles
- Two dozen shotguns
- GPS units
- Night vision equipment

We desperately needed someone to fill this position, but it remained open. These duties were handed to the supply sergeant, as the position was never filled.

Chapter Three

SEPTEMBER 11, 2001

Then I heard the voice of the Lord, saying,
"Whom shall I send, and who will go for Us?"
Then I said, "Here am I. Send me!"

Isaiah 6:8

Then came September 11, 2001, a day no one could have planned for, or ever imagined. Initially, only a few soldiers were activated, but as the days went on approximately sixty-three of the unit's MPs were activated. Around this time I began to realize that the number of soldiers we had listed on paper did not reflect the number of soldiers we could put into the field. As the activation progressed, I found I was running out of soldiers to call to active-duty, and I was only at number sixty-three.

A Military Police Company configured for our type of mission would have had approximately 144 Military Police officers. Our unit's numbers always looked very good on paper, and we were always close to the maximum number of officers and enlisted personnel. Unfortunately, in reality, many of those soldiers were ghosts who didn't exist at all, or who were training or awaiting discharge, and therefore, not deployable. Others were listed in the ranks, but they had not come to drill since enlisting, were physically unfit to ship away for training, or had legal or personal problems that prevented them from going away to train or to be called to active-duty.

One young lady had enlisted, but had not been to basic training. During a weekend drill, she observed the drill and didn't do much of a physical nature. After the evening meal, a soldier informed us that she was upstairs in her bunk having a seizure or convulsion. We called an ambulance and transported her, along with a senior non-commissioned officer (NCO) to a local hospital.

The senior NCO's duty was to remain with her and advise her family of her situation. When he contacted the soldier's mother, he found her to be neither concerned nor particularly surprised about her daughter's illness. She informed the senior NCO that her daughter had probably stopped drinking water again and had become dehydrated. She expected that if we gave her a saline IV that her daughter would be fine in a couple of hours. Surprised by this news, the senior NCO asked if this had happened to her daughter in the past, to which her mother explained that yes, it had happened several times. This information caused us to check over the soldier's medical records and history, where we discovered that she had just had hip replacement surgery.

After finding out about the soldier's repeated problems with dehydration and her recent surgery, I knew she would never be accepted into the Army once she got to the reception center. I tried to get her off of our records, but that would have made the recruiter look bad. Each recruiter had a quota of soldiers to enlist and the State had quotas as well, so this young woman stayed on the list for close to six months before being sent to Fort Leonard Wood, Missouri, for Military Police training. Four days after she arrived, she was medically discharged as unfit for military service and shipped back to Connecticut. Those four days were not reflective of her time served; she hadn't even lasted that long because the Army took four days to process her.

Another soldier who came into the unit looked like a good prospect, but had a criminal record. He should not even have been sent to the unit, as Military Police officers are not permitted to have criminal records, but again, not sending him would have made the recruiters look bad. To keep the State's numbers up, the recruiters' best interests were served by keeping this soldier, and others like him, in until the last possible moment. This particular soldier remained until he got up to the induction center where his criminal past was revealed. Despite not being able to join the Military Police, the soldier remained on our books for several months, taking up space and keeping the appearance that we actually had more soldiers than we actually did.

A third soldier, a sergeant who had been on active-duty, came to us from the Massachusetts National Guard. Everything indicated that he was a very high-speed soldier, as he had completed airborne school, air assault school and drill sergeants' school. He indicated that he had been with the airborne, had served in Korea, and had been posted to the Honor Guard in Washington, D.C.—extremely impressive credentials. No one in the unit had completed all of these intense schools.

We soon discovered that this sergeant had spent only eighteen months on active-duty, too brief a time period for him to realistically complete all of those schools and assignments. In addition, no enlistments would have permitted him to serve for eighteen months on active-duty. So I decided to check his service record, where I found no corresponding paperwork confirming that he had completed any of those courses. The full-time staff was also unable to locate the missing paperwork.

These issues came to a head when I asked the soldier to bring copies of his discharge papers and training certificates. I suspected him of being a fraud and, without directly stating it, made him aware of my suspicions. If he had completed all the training he claimed, he would have promptly brought in all the documentation and told everyone to stick it where the sun didn't shine. This solder didn't do that. After being pressed for several days, he only offered excuses about his diplomas hanging in his mother's house and being unable to retrieve them.

At this point, I knew something was very wrong, so I persisted, demanding the documentation. He threw a piece of paper with a phone number on my desk. When I asked him whose phone number this was, I was told that it was the IG's, and that he was going to call to complain about my conduct and tell him that he was being harassed. I called his bluff and handed him my phone, asking him to please make the call. He never did; instead he turned around and walked out of my office. We never received any proof of his airborne school, air assault school, drill sergeants' school, or that he had served a full tour in Korea.

Not surprising, as we discovered in the end that our sergeant—if he really was a sergeant—had been dishonorably discharged for desertion. He still claimed to have gone through airborne school, air assault school, and drill sergeant's school, and served in both an Airborne unit and with a ground unit in Korea. Only now, he was admitting that he had received a dishonorable discharge for desertion. Even the circumstances of his desertion were suspect; the soldier claimed that he deserted the Honor Guard in Washington D.C., but this was only his statement, one which no one could verify.

Somehow, even with the dishonorable discharge, the sergeant managed to get his record waived so that he could enlist in the Massachusetts National Guard as an Infantryman. Although his record was waived, the soldier could never serve in a Military Police assignment because all Military Police officers must secure a security clearance (which is not given to soldiers who have received a dishonorable discharge).

Although this solider was removed from our Military Police unit, he still managed to get a full-time assignment in the Connecticut Army National Guard—that is, until I decided to make a few phone calls. Because of privacy rights, personnel and medical records are safe-guarded by the Readiness NCO. No one can just decide to look into someone's personnel or medical records to see what's there. In this case, though, because I had genuine concern about the soldier's training, qualifications and certifications, as the soldier's supervisor and a ranking NCO, I had every right to confirm what he was telling me.

Prior to making these calls, I was told that I was not allowed to do so. I thought the reasoning was absurd; I was his supervisor and the highest ranking NCO in the company. So I ignored it. The soldier's true history was revealed, and he was finally sent packing.

Another young lady enlisted while she was still in high school. She planned to go away to training after high school graduation and expected to be home in time to start college in the fall. This strategy meant that she would serve long enough to benefit from a tuition waiver for National Guard Soldiers, guaranteeing that her college education would be paid for by the State of Connecticut. The promise of the tuition waiver was a big recruiting technique, and many of our soldiers joined the Guard because of it.

This recruit was a good student and an athlete, but unfortunately she became pregnant before she went off to training. Although pregnancy made her ineligible for basic training, the recruiters left her on the rolls to meet their quotas until her basic training ship date arrived. When she was unable to go, the recruiters finally removed her. To make matters worse, despite her being pregnant and listed on recruiting rolls, they never provided her with any medical benefits.

At the end of each year's recruiting schedule, recruiters would have a big taxpayer-sponsored party to celebrate making their personal quotas and the recruitment goals for the State. This party was also a training seminar for next year's recruiting tactics and goals. The fact that they had many people on the books who could and would never be soldiers was not important. Quotas were important, and recruiters fought hard to keep them and make their quotas in the Connecticut Army National Guard.

Chapter Four

9/11 PATRIOTS

In bygone days, commanders were taught that when in doubt, they should march their troops towards the sound of gunfire. I intend to march my troops towards the sound of gunfire.

Jo Grimond

Following the 9/11 attacks, four honorably discharged soldiers (two in their late forties) with prior service wanted back in to the National Guard, specifically into our Military Police Company. While all four had previously served in Military Police units, they had not done so in the recent past. They wanted to serve because of what had happened on 9/11, and joined the 143rd because they would likely go overseas. Sergeant Chris Sweetwood had served in Germany in various Military Police assignments and had served for over twenty years in both the active-duty Army and the Army Reserve. After being discharged, he had gone on to be a Special Investigator in the insurance industry, and his financial situation was such that he was able to retire at a very early age. Although he did not need the money or a job, he believed his duty was to serve, and so, in 2002, he returned to duty. He initially served with the 134th Military Police Company because he was told that the 143rd was full. Later, when the 143rd was activated for Iraq, and the Connecticut Army National Guard went through the State looking for MP-qualified soldiers, Chris was assigned to the company as part of Operation Iraqi Freedom. Because of his extensive investigative background and his understanding of the military justice system, Chris was assigned to lead investigations on all of our serious incidents. He was forty-three years old.

I was glad that Chris volunteered to come back, but I wished he had remembered the Army code, "don't volunteer for anything." In fact, he seemed to have never learned the code. Shortly after our arrival at Warrior Compound in Iraq, Master Sergeant Tetter came over from Battalion to see if any of our people had experience with Russian weapons, specifically the AK-47. Sergeant Sweetwood's hand shot up.

I had no idea what Tetter had in mind, but I was not excited about losing any of my people (never mind someone with Chris's experience), especially to the active-duty. Operations was already cutting as many MPs as possible, reassigning them to platoons for patrol duty. It was too late, though, because as soon as Sergeant Sweetwood's hand went up, he was temporarily reassigned to work with Battalion. He inspected confiscated weapons to access their condition, qualified Iraqi Police officers and assigned their weapons.

I gave strong consideration to handcuffing Chris's hands to his chair after this incident, but I figured I had made my point after a short conversation with him. But I was wrong; he kept right on volunteering throughout our deployment.

Sergeant Roberge was also financially comfortable, working as a state employee. A workaholic by some people's standards, Sergeant Roberge had served as an MP, both on active-duty and with the Vermont National Guard. Like Sergeant Sweetwood, he did not need the job or the money, but felt a duty to serve.

Roberge was the mother hen of the second shift, and tracked every soldier from the moment they left the wire until they were back inside the Compound. He took his responsibilities personally, and made sure that each and every soldier who he ordered outside the wire was as safe as possible, and returned. The fact that the bureaucracy actually dictated who was going where and when, did not matter to Roberge. The men and women he sent out were his soldiers; he sent them out there, and he would worry about them every minute until they returned. He was committed to each and every individual soldier.

On the radio, Sweetwood was the daytime voice of the company, and Roberge was the evening drive home voice. They made a great pair.

Figure 4.1   (Left to Right) Sergeant Sweetwood, Master Sergeant Minasian and Sergeant Roberge

The other two discharged soldiers who wanted to serve after 9/11 had retired from the Connecticut Army National Guard, both as officers. The first was Timothy Corcoran, retired with twenty years of service as an Infantry Captain. His last assignment as a Military Police officer was at the rank of Specialist E4 and, even though he had risen to the rank of Captain, the Connecticut Army National Guard would allow him to serve in an MP unit only under his old rank. As Infantry Captain, Tim would have been in charge of anywhere from 150 to 250 soldiers. The fact that the National Guard would bring him back at such a low enlisted rank was incomprehensible. Specialist Corcoran was also a sworn law enforcement officer who worked as a plainclothes detective for the MTA Police Department, so it wasn't as if he didn't have the training or experience to work at a rank and level much higher than a specialist. For whatever reason, someone higher up created a rule stating that he could not come back in to the Military Police at a rank higher than the last time he was a Military Police officer. Even with the great disparity between being a specialist and a Captain, Corcoran came back to serve.

The fourth individual was delayed and did not join the company until after we returned from Iraq. At the time of his retirement, John Salvatore had attained the rank of Major in the Connecticut Army National Guard. He was also a sworn law enforcement officer in the town of Wethersfield, Connecticut. Just like Corcoran, the State decided bring him back as a sergeant because that had been the highest rank he had held while in the Military Police. John tried very hard to return prior to our deployment, but somebody sat on his paperwork and did not push it through until we were back. We sure could have used him.

Here we had two fully-qualified officers with at least twenty years of military service trying to get back into the National Guard and into a Military Police Company, and the bureaucracy was doing everything in its power to make returning as difficult as possible. This is the same bureaucracy that gave us recruits who were never going to make it to training, yet were kept on the books for months after discovering that they had issues that would preclude them from ever becoming soldiers.

Activation

In October, 2001, the Connecticut National Guard had their annual senior Noncommissioned officer Dining In. This is a formal event where all senior enlisted soldiers above the rank of sergeant first class are invited. At this event, General Cugno, the Commanding officer of the Connecticut National Guard, announced that the 143rd Military Police Company would soon be activated for deployment overseas.

He did not mention the activation of any other unit in the Connecticut National Guard.

Needless to say, General Cugno shocked all the Military Police NCOs present, as his announcement was the first we had ever heard of definite activation with overseas deployment. We were already on active-duty in the State, providing security at the airports, nuclear facilities and other sensitive locations. The fact that we were now looking at an overseas combat deployment was somewhat overwhelming. Everyone at the table stared at each other with "holy shit" looks on their faces. Every soldier in the room went silent and stared at us.

Now that General Cugno had made his announcement, we assumed that new equipment would start to come in, that training would increase, and that our ranks would fill with deployable soldiers. That, unfortunately, was not the case. We stayed on active-duty, securing airports and other locations, until Memorial Day, 2002. Between the general's announcement and Memorial Day 2002, other units went through normal training cycles as if 9/11 hadn't happened. Those units came to us to borrow our equipment (vehicles, radios, tents, and GPS units). Not all of the equipment was returned, and some of the equipment that was returned was no longer operable. Some of the vehicles were returned in such a badly damaged condition they were never able to run again.

Even getting new, mission-oriented equipment proved to be nearly impossible. For our current active-duty security assignments, we needed ammunition for our M-16s and 9mm pistols. The activated MPs carried 9mm pistols with forty-five rounds, but before they could go on duty, they needed an additional fifty to one hundred rounds each to go through a firearms qualification course.

We totaled up the number of rounds we needed for each MP, and called to make the request from higher headquarters. We were told that because we had not forecasted the need for additional ammunition the prior year, we would not be getting any this year. However, they did inform us that, at the absolutely earliest, they would try to get the ammunition we requested by either 2002 or 2003.

At first I thought the person on the other end of the phone was joking, but he was dead serious. I explained that we had been activated for the airport security mission, that we were to be performing armed security missions, and that we had to qualify each soldier before she or he went on duty. Yet, the person in charge of ammunition requests insisted that he could do nothing for us, and no, he could not offer any suggestions on how we could possibly acquire the ammunition required to perform our job.

We had no choice but to go to a local gun store with a military credit card to purchase the necessary ammunition. We were at war, and we felt like everyone else in the Connecticut Army National Guard was still in peacetime mode.

The situation did not improve. May of 2002 found us ten months into a war nine months after General Cugno's announcement that our unit would be going overseas (albeit short on equipment and with some of the remaining equipment now damaged and unusable). Vehicles continued to be a problem, proving to be non-functional despite going through maintenance facilities in Connecticut and determined by them "operational." Later, these vehicles were turned in to the maintenance facility at Fort Drum where they were again gone over and cleared to be shipped overseas. After all this, we still had several vehicles that, only days after clearing the maintenance facility, were no longer "operational" and had to be towed onto rail cars to ship them to Texas for deployment overseas.

We came off active-duty on Memorial Day, 2002, with a warning order for potential deployment to somewhere in the Middle East (either Afghanistan or Iraq). Even with the looming possibility of deployment, our training schedule and activity did not change until December of 2002. The only preparation that took place was that we started receiving Anthrax vaccinations.

Just as we finally started getting our series of Anthrax shots, we also started losing soldiers. Three soldiers refused to accept the Anthrax shots and came off our roster. A couple of other soldiers were found medically unfit to accept either the Anthrax shot or other overseas shots, and were also dropped.

Around this time, a new officer was assigned to the company. He had an impressive education in political science from a small Ivy League college, and was a champion lacrosse player. His goal was law school, but he explained that his plans were side tracked by 9/11. He had a thick, dark mustache that was just a tad beyond military regulation. If the mustache hadn't have been so thick, he might have gotten away with it; but it stood out and he was reminded on several occasions to trim it (which of course he did).

Our roster still looked pretty good with nearly every slot filled, despite these losses—until we were called to active-duty on February 7, 2003. When that happened, soldiers began to put in for retirement, listing medical conditions, family hardships, and pending criminal cases (that we had been entirely unaware of) as reasons that would prevent them from active deployment. We also discovered that some soldiers on our list were either still in or waiting for training, and would not be available to mobilize for deployment. Then at Fort Drum (where we trained before deploying overseas) a few soldiers were unfit for deployment, and were left behind or sent home.

Following the order to activate, we were given approximately seven days to get our civilian lives in order and prepare the unit for movement up to Fort Drum for train-up. In addition, because our unit would not be returning to that armory, we also had to take time to clean the facilities. During this seven-day period, equipment was issued, vehicles were packed, and new soldiers were added to the company roster.

More than fifty new soldiers from other units were transferred into the 143rd for deployment. These soldiers were not trained Military Police officers—the largest number came from an artillery unit with no Military Police experience. While we were going through mobilization, these thirty or so soldiers also had to go through Military Police School (delaying mobilization train-up by several weeks). We also added cooks, a chemical NCO, medics and mechanics, giving us fifty-plus new soldiers. While we were glad to have them, we would have preferred to acquire them long before deployment to have the opportunity to get acquainted and learn about each others' strengths and weaknesses.

When approximately 150 people are given only seven days to get their personal lives in order, as well as the unit's equipment, and, while you're at it, clean the building, what ensues is chaos. Some of this chaos was caused by the new soldiers needing to have equipment issued through our supply, since they had turned in all of their original gear at their last unit. This last-minute restructuring and resupplying was in keeping with everything else the National Guard was doing, with no warning and no preparation.

One of the new soldiers saw what was going on and assumed that the 143rd was disorganized and creating chaos when, in fact, the State command did no planning in spite of having a year and one-half to prep.

She began commenting on how unorganized the unit was, and that she was reluctant to go into combat with this type of chaos going on. Unbeknownst to her, she was standing next to an officer's wife, who heard every word. The wife informed her husband, who then called me over to straighten out the new soldier.

The new soldier's observation of the situation was completely accurate, and her concerns were valid. The only problem was she didn't understand that the origin of the chaos was caused by full-timers from the State who had waited until the last minute to prepare us for deployment. Only the soldiers at the 143rd took General Cugno's warning order seriously and began doing what we could to prepare for deployment. Everyone else at the State seems to have just sat back and waited.

In this time of mobilization, we counted on other units to help us prepare. We had to clear several milestones before we could leave for Fort Drum, including:

- Medical screening
- Dental screening
- Pay and allowances
- Allotments
- Wills
- Various other administrative items

These tasks all had to be performed by soldiers from outside our unit because we did not have the medical, clerical or supply staff to perform these functions. In most cases, we got the distinct impression that we were imposing on other units, messing up their schedules for our benefit. They did not seem to take into consideration that we were going off to war.

Even if none of us was wounded or killed, we would still be gone for more than a year.

For example, we were advised to move down to Camp Niantic for dental screening (each soldier must successfully complete a dental screening procedure before deployment). We were given less than twenty-four hours to have our soldiers in Niantic by 1500 hours for the screening procedure. To make sure that everyone was there by 1500 hours, we told our soldiers to be in formation at 1400 hours in order to get a head count. After the head count at 1400 hours, we decided to use the remaining time to complete some of the required administrative paperwork. All soldiers arrived on time, and were standing tall in front of the dispensary by 1500 hours with all our administrative tasks completed.

But the dentist failed to arrive until 1800 hours (giving us three hours with nothing to do). When we inquired about the three-hour delay, we were told that the dentist's time at his civilian job was too valuable for him to leave early, because he would have had to reschedule his civilian appointments. No thought was given to the soldiers in the unit—no consideration to the fact that they would soon be deployed, or that they were giving up a half day of their personal time to stand in line for several hours waiting for a dentist who someone in the State must have known wasn't going to arrive until three hours after the scheduled time.

The Guard had a year and one-half to get ready, and still they waited until the last minute to prepare. Seven days later, we were on our way to Fort Drum in 38° below zero temperatures with blizzard conditions to train up for desert warfare. Only in a show like M*A*S*H could this type of irrational thinking be possible; except it was real, and we lived it.

Chapter Five

WEAPONS OF MASS DESTRUCTION

Every day Saddam remains in power with chemical weapons, biological weapons, and the development of nuclear weapons is a day of danger for the United States.

Joe Lieberman
former U.S. Senator from Connecticut

The Iraq invasion was authorized based on the belief that Saddam still had Weapons of Mass Destruction, and that he supported terrorism. Almost every elected official in the United States voted for the invasion with the belief that Saddam had the weapons and would use them. Most of the free world held the same belief.

In the past, Saddam had just about completed a nuclear reactor before the Israelis destroyed it. Stockpiles of chemical weapons were destroyed after the first Gulf War. Saddam had used chemical weapons on the Kurds, and the Shia in the south, as well as Iranians participating in that war. A large Iraqi ammunition storage facility just over the Saudi border was blown up by U.S. forces before pulling back to Saudi territory.

Unbeknownst to the U.S. forces, this facility contained chemical weapons. The massive detonation sent chemical agents high into the air, and the wind currents carried the chemical agents over U.S. troops in Iraq and in

Saudi Arabia. Debate continues as to what effects these chemical agents had on Coalition forces.

If Saddam had Weapons of Mass Destruction, chances are he would have used them again. Although Israel made sure that he was never able to get his nuclear program going again, the real possibility still remained that he would use chemical or biological weapons again.

Chemical and biological weapons are not difficult to make. Anyone who has the ability to create insecticide can make chemical weapons, mainly because the only difference between insecticide and chemical weapons is the concentration. Insecticides are created with the intent of giving a dose to kill tiny beings, such as mosquitoes or flies. To kill humans, all you need to do is up the concentration. Two commercially available insecticides available today work the same way as a nerve agent. The insecticides, Malathion and Sevin (also known as the chemical carbaryl) attack the human body much the same way as the GB nerve agent known as Sarin.

I am sure that Iraq had an insecticide facility somewhere (being a home to malaria, camel spiders, desert mantis, oriental hornets, sand spiders, fog drinking beetles, desert hairy scorpions, and desert ants). During the period of time U.S. and Coalition forces took to build up in Kuwait, more than enough time had passed for the Iraqis to modify their insecticide plants back to peaceful purposes, or dismantle them altogether.

Biological weapons are somewhat of a different case—if you can make beer, you can make biological weapons. The only hurdle is delivering the bio-agents. Germs are very susceptible to heat, cold, light, and several other factors. The current biological weapon of choice is Anthrax, because it travels in the form of a spore, which gives it a much better chance of survival in all environments. Anthrax is a naturally-occurring disease, and is studied worldwide. Medical facilities with the proper authorization can purchase Anthrax spores for research. All you would need to start a biological weapons program is to find someone to divert some Anthrax spores purchased for research.

For over ten years, Saddam insisted that he was complying with the disarmament demands from the first Gulf War—ten years! Why would complying take ten years?

In December of 2002, several scud missiles were found. The Iraqi government stated that these were short-range missiles, were not part of the agreement, and did not violate the destruction rule. Coalition forces were able to verify that these missiles did, in fact, violate the agreements made after the first Gulf War, as they were long-range missiles. Shortly thereafter, the missiles were destroyed. Having been caught in yet another lie, the Iraqis apologized for the small misunderstanding. The problem was that they had been "misunderstanding" for about ten years.

Once the war began and Coalition forces invaded Iraq, numerous politicians who had voted for the invasion were suddenly against it, deciding that they could now believe and trust Saddam Hussein…

Now, in 2015, we are again being asked to trust a Middle Eastern country, this time, Iran. We have been negotiating with Iran over their nuclear program *for years* with the single goal of keeping them from getting a nuclear weapon.

As of this writing, the deadline for compliance has just passed, and the new deadline is now three months down the road. After years of negotiating, the U.S. is giving Iran yet another three months to pursue creating weapons-grade uranium.

As Yogi Berra would say, "This is déjà vu all over again."

Saddam *agreed* to destroy of all his weapons of mass destruction, and that situation dragged on for over ten years. During that ten years, when he knew an invasion was coming, he could have moved the equipment to Syria. He could have converted it back to civilian use. He could have dismantled the equipment. As far as I know, no one really knows what happened.

Now, our government expects us to believe that the Iranians are negotiating in good faith, and that we should believe them as they insist that they are not in the process of making nuclear weapons.

I am skeptical.

Chapter Six

FORT DRUM, NEW YORK

February 7, 2003 through April 15, 2003

People sleep peaceably in their beds at night only because rough men stand ready to do violence on their behalf.

George Orwell

To this day, I have no idea who came up with the plan to send us to Fort Drum, New York in the middle of winter to train up for desert warfare in Iraq. While Fort Drum is close by, the weather conditions are nothing like what we were about to face in Iraq. Maybe Fort Drum might have been a good location to train up for Afghanistan, but even then no mountains exist anywhere near Fort Drum.

Fort Drum consists of two separate compounds: Old Fort Drum, where we would be staying, and three miles away, New Fort Drum, which looks more like a college campus. The older section of Fort Drum was originally established in 1908 when the initial property was purchased. The section was originally called Pine Camp and increased in size over the years, training up divisions during World War II, as well as being used as a prisoner of war camp for German soldiers. In 1951, the facility was renamed Camp Drum and was used extensively to train soldiers during the Korean War. In 1974, Camp Drum became Fort Drum.

New Fort Drum was originally designed for an Armored unit, but with the downsizing of active-duty Army, in 1984 the Fort became home to a light Infantry unit, the 10th Mountain Division.

The goal of our mobilization was to train the soldiers and prepare our equipment for deployment. While we were stationed in Old Fort Drum, we had to use the 10th Mountain Division's mess halls for food service. The theory for being stationed at the old fort, but using the mess hall and support services at Fort Drum, was a good one, as this arrangement was supposed to keep our soldiers in the train-up process instead of pulling KP assignments or other support activities. In practice, this theory didn't work.

For one thing, our crowded quarters in the old fort were rehabbed barracks, with no room to store equipment. Mornings in the rehabbed barracks were quite interesting. Thirty or more soldiers would be in the latrine at the same time trying to use six sinks, six shower heads, four toilets and five urinals. Modesty was out the window. By contrast, the staff tasked with getting us ready for mobilization was quartered in motel rooms off base.

For another, because Fort Drum took over our support activities, we had to rely on them for food service, vehicle maintenance and pre-deployment medical screenings. This situation left us reliant on the active-duty people to support us, and it became clear that we were little more than a nuisance to them.

We were stationed at old Fort Drum with a number of other units who were also in the process of mobilization. All of these troops, including our own, had to move from the same general barracks area to the dining facilities and back, three times a day. While buses were provided to transport the soldiers between the two facilities, the buses weren't numerous or large enough to accommodate all the soldiers. Buses could have been assigned to individual units. Instead, bus rides came on a first come, first serve basis, and walking was out of the question. We often skipped meals.

Our unit was scheduled to be at the dining facilities at the same time the 10th Mountain Division conducted their morning physical fitness activities (which involved either forced marches with full equipment or running). Quite a bit of snow was on the ground, so they had to stick to the roads, and the buses could travel no faster than about 5 mph driving past them.

Ultimately, this scheduling meant our solders had two hours to get to the dining facilities, eat and return to the barracks. Because we could not delay training and had to meet the schedules assigned to us, we often did not have time to eat breakfast. In addition, parking at the dining hall was so limited that even when our vehicles were made available so we could get a bite to eat, the parking lot was often full. Walking was out of the question (too far) and we often didn't eat.

Also, our vehicles continued to be an issue. Shortly after arrival, we turned most of them in to the maintenance facility so they could be prepped for deployment. We assumed that these vehicles were finally going to get the complete overhauls that they needed.

Instead, once again, just as in Connecticut, our vehicles were merely made to run. Starting just a couple days after getting them back from maintenance, anywhere between four and fourteen vehicles were inoperable at any given time. I want to stress that the vehicles broke down under normal driving, generally going no more than twenty miles per hour on plowed roads. I could understand vehicles breaking down if we were running them through the woods, crossing stream beds, etc., but we were never able to handle them that roughly.

What was most frustrating about the lackluster vehicle maintenance was that the facility at Fort Drum was specifically set up for pre-mobilization preparation. Preparing our vehicles for shipment overseas was their only assignment. With that time and type of focus, you might think that every vehicle completing its pre-deployment inspection would be in perfect running condition. Not so—driving the vehicles for a few hours caused many of them to break down.

The maintenance facility was able to replace our Vietnam-era radios with new SINGARS radios. SINGARS are channel-skipping encrypted radios that allowed us to speak freely without fear that the enemy is monitoring the conversation. At first, we thought SINGARS were a vast improvement, but several drawbacks emerged.

First, the radios we received were refurbished originals (about twenty years old, just like our vehicles). The SINGARS looked great, just like they came off the production line, but I am quite sure that they didn't look so great on the inside. They should have been good for eighteen to twenty miles. At most we got three or four miles between vehicles and ten or so miles from high mounted antennas. To say the least, they were unreliable.

The second problem was that we had never received training on these SINGARS. While changing frequencies and programming the radios wasn't difficult, without instructions, using them was cumbersome until we became familiar with how they worked.

We also discovered that these SINGARS had a limited range of about two to three miles, which would have been fine in most cases. The environment we would be patrolling had a range of anywhere from eighteen to twenty-five miles. In most situations, the base's radios would have been placed somewhere on a high elevation, giving them better range and line of sight—but Baghdad is extremely flat with no high terrain. During our convoy move from Kuwait to Baghdad, the lead vehicle was out of radio range of the tail-end vehicle.

When we reached Iraq, we did place the base radio antennas on top of our structures—one was about eighty feet tall—which helped to a degree. But even at that height, radio signals coming from the vehicles were still blocked by walls and buildings inside the city area. We did have marginal success with SINGARS, talking from company position to Platoon Headquarters, because these communications were from one high-fixed, mounted antenna mast to another. Even then, one of our units was always on the extreme range of the radios and communication was, at best, a "sometimes" situation. By the end of our deployment, although the radios were never misused (they were always mounted to the insides of our vehicles and were never banged around), half of all the SINGARS we had received at Fort Drum no longer worked.

And finally, training at Fort Drum was never planned more than two or three days in advance, which made planning ahead for us nearly impossible. We knew the general idea of what was expected of us during training, but not the specific time frame of when training was supposed to be completed. Some units that had mobilized months before we arrived were still at Fort Drum because of deficiencies in their training and evaluation. So we had no idea how long our unit would be there. Similarly, we had no idea when our vehicles would be returned, or when we would be issued our desert uniforms.

Patches

Because our training took place at Fort Drum in extremely cold weather, we were also supposed to be issued cold-weather boots, cold-weather gloves and other weather-related items. We received approximately half the cold-weather boots, none of the cold-weather gloves, and only some of the insulated underwear needed to outfit our unit.

At one point, a full colonel from the 10th Mountain Division arrived at our barracks accompanied by his sergeant major to see how we were doing and to determine what we needed from the powers-that-be at Fort Drum. We explained that we were short on cold-weather gear, and that our soldiers had just been forced to train several days and nights in a row, between eight to sixteen hours, in extremely cold weather. The colonel assured us that we would be issued the necessary equipment shortly. It never came.

This was yet another instance when one unit placed their own concerns and priorities over the concerns and priorities of other units. The 10th Mountain Division was getting ready for their deployment and we were not on their radar. Their attitude seemed to be that they were not responsible for us, we would be going away in very short order, and that once we were gone, the complaining would stop.

General Cugno, the commanding general of the Connecticut Army National Guard, came up to see how we were doing, along with the command sergeant major. When General Cugno asked what was needed, the First Sergeant stated that he had a list of about ten items that we needed help procuring. The General told the First Sergeant to ride in a second vehicle with the State Command Sergeant Major to go over the list.

Among the items on the list was a request for the appropriate State of Connecticut patches.

Although we had State patches for our uniforms, they were not in the muted desert colors appropriate for deployment to Iraq. Of all the items on the list, the patches seemed like the simplest one to fulfill, and one would think that the State of Connecticut would be proud and happy to approve this request.

The First Sergeant was floored when the Command Sergeant major explained that, because we were on active-duty under Title 10, he was unable to do anything to help us. While we were all surprised at the dismissal of our list, not one of us could comprehend the dismissal of such a small but important request as the State patch. At the time, we were the only unit designated to go into a combat situation from the State of Connecticut.

This same command sergeant major had recently held a position as the recruiter supervisor. His team had been responsible for accepting all those unqualified recruits knowing full well that they would never become soldiers.

General Cugno caught up with the First Sergeant after his ride with the Command Sergeant Major to see if the list was going to be fulfilled. The First Sergeant reiterated the Sergeant Major's response, saying that because we were Title 10, the Sergeant Major could do nothing for us. General Cugno thought otherwise. He made sure that we received the majority of items from the list, most importantly, the Connecticut State patches.

Military Police Training

The soldiers who came to us from the artillery had no experience in a Military Police unit and needed Military Police training. In the middle of our 63 day mobilization at Fort Drum, these soldiers were shipped off to Fort Hunter Liggett in California for a two-week crash course in basic Military Police officer procedures. While this course was enough to teach the basics, it wasn't really enough training. Additionally, staff sergeants and sergeant first class/platoon sergeants must take further courses to qualify for their positions. Ideally, their training would include basic courses for military police officers (which takes about four weeks).

Squad leaders and platoon sergeants required a further advanced NCO course (an additional four weeks). In a normal progression of promotion, a platoon sergeant would have to spend ten to fifteen years in an MP Company, serving at the various enlisted levels, making his way up the ranks, gaining experience at each level. Because we weren't given enough time before being deployed to Iraq, soldiers from the artillery never received the required training. It just didn't happen.

During our sixty-three days of mobilization, we were delayed approximately twenty-three days while soldiers from Artillery underwent Military Police training. If not for those twenty-three days, we might have been able to ship out in as little as forty days. (We were always "a first-time go" at every training station and were never recycled. Some units took three or more tries at various training stations before they could deploy; some never did deploy.)

Of course, passing each training course the first time through worked to our advantage, because the sooner we deployed to the Gulf, the sooner the clock started ticking and we could return. Some units were activated in November, 2002, but did not deploy until May, 2003, which meant that we were in Iraq and out before they were. Shortly after we left Iraq, the powers-that-be realized that the situation there was getting out of hand and required more troops, so they extended assignments beyond twelve months.

A Military Police Company such as ours operates in a more decentralized manner on a platoon and squad level than it does on a company level. At the squad level, the squad leader is the responsible party on scene. The fact that both the Squad Leaders and the Platoon Sergeant had not gone through the basic nor advanced NCO courses was very troubling. Fortunately, we were lucky enough to have NCOs who grasped both the mission concept and their responsibilities to it.

We were also fortunate that many of our NCOs had a depth of experience beyond what you might typically find in a National Guard unit, or even an active-duty unit. A number of our soldiers had been on active-duty and had served in Military Police units before joining the National Guard. While some had not served as Military Police, they had at least served on active-duty in other fields of the military and brought that experience to the unit. We were also fortunate to have a number of State Troopers, municipal and city police officers, and Department of Corrections officers, all of whom had completed time at the various training academies in the State, as well as logged real-world experience in law enforcement and corrections.

This diverse group of soldiers put us ahead of the game compared to many active-duty soldiers who, in most cases, had experience only with training scenarios and not the real world.

In general, our officers, NCOs and enlisted soldiers were older and better-educated than active-duty soldiers. At the time of our deployment, our soldiers had at least two years of college, and others had worked active-duty in supply, medical, administrative or maintenance jobs.

This education and experience helped immeasurably with the administrative side of our deployment. Paperwork associated with deployment can be a nightmare. In spite of the fact that we were moving 150+ soldiers (along with all of their equipment) halfway around the world and we had never done this before, we were able to move rather rapidly.

We Few, We Happy Few

Someone decided that we should watch the movie *Band of Brothers* as part of our development and training program. Based on a book by Stephen Ambrose, this is an excellent movie about the 101st Airborne Division in World War II.

The 101st Airborne Division was activated August 16, 1942, at

Claireborne in Louisiana. Prior to this, it had been an Army reserve division which had been disbanded one day prior to activation.

Two of the major characters in the movie were Easy Company's commander, Captain Herbert Sobel, and one of the company's platoon leaders, Lieutenant Winters. Captain Sobel, who trained the company very hard in physical fitness, lacked the true leadership qualities needed to motivate and inspire his troops, instead leading them by fear, threats, and intimidation. He often hid behind his rank when things went wrong, choosing to place the blame for his failures on the shoulders of his subordinates. Members of the company tolerated his arrogance and intimidation tactics for a long time, but eventually individuals and groups of soldiers began standing up to him. Captain Sobel took action against those soldiers.

One of these soldiers was Lieutenant Winters, whom Captain Sobel attempted to put in his place with a punitive nonjudicial action. When Winters requested a court-martial for the perceived grievance, Captain Sobel then had to explain his very weak reasoning for bringing the action against Winters to his Battalion Commander.

Captain Sobel brought the action to highlight the fact that he had complete authority and control over Lieutenant Winters, and that Winters was to obey Captain Sobel without question. This tactic backfired, alienating Sobel from the Battalion Commander. The Battalion Commander recognized Sobel's unprofessional conduct and incompetence, along with his inability to properly lead and motivate his troops. Realizing that leaving Captain Sobel in this type of leadership position was detrimental to the company and the rest of the Battalion, the Battalion Commander reassigned him to other duties away from the company.

While having us watch this movie was a great idea, the officer who chose this movie (to demonstrate Captain Sobel's lack of leadership skills and his unfortunate end) actually adopted part of Captain Sobel's persona and very same leadership skills! This officer went so far as to work Captain Sobel's lines into some of his daily dealings with the troops.

Weapons

We felt that qualifying on the various weapons systems was an important step toward successful preparation for mobilization. For those certifying us, qualifying on the various weapons systems was just one more box on a form that needed to be checked off. To them, actual training and understanding of the various weapons systems, which would give us the knowledge to employ them effectively in combat situations, was not as important as qualifying scores on the range with the least amount of ammunition in the shortest amount of time. All they wanted was to have the required number soldiers qualify to the minimum standard for deployment.

One day when I was in the mobilization center, I happened to overhear the officer in charge obsessing that the first round had to be going down range no later than 0800. He did not explain why that needed to happen, but he conveyed that it was probably the most important thing that could possibly happen during that training day.

We always tried to comply with the officers' wishes, even if they were to send just one round down range at the correct time, just so we could say that we had fired by 0800. After that, we would call a cease fire, get organized, and once everything was in order, we would be able to get back to having soldiers complete the qualification course.

The officers did not care if we were ready. They did not care if qualifying within the allotted time was realistic. The only issue that was important to them was that we met their time constraints.

While we would start that early in the morning, firing often continued throughout the day. Some units were not qualifying, no matter how much time they spent on the range. Our unit typically qualified by noon, leaving us with nothing to do other than stand around in the freezing cold (without warm clothing), doing the "Fort Drum Shuffle" to try to stay warm.

The buses would drop us off at the firing ranges, which were miles away from the barracks and the dining facilities. In almost all cases, no shelter was provided to help us keep warm. We would have to stand in sub-zero temperatures (until after dark so we could qualify at night, if that was the case). In other situations, we would complete the required course and then have to wait however long for the buses to return to transport us back to the barracks. If we completed the course in four hours, and the buses weren't scheduled to transport us back for another eight hours, we stood in the snow, and in freezing rain, for eight hours, trying to stay warm.

We also had to wait for enough darkness to do our nighttime qualification. But because we had already turned in our vehicles to be prepped for deployment (mostly because we had nothing else to do), we were at the mercy of the buses. Again, the buses had other assignments, and after dropping us off at the firing range (far from the main base or any other type of warmth or shelter), they did not return until we were scheduled to be transported back to our barracks.

Although we were always a first-time go at all the mobilization stations, we never once received positive feedback from the mobilization staff. Clearly, mobilization felt that our activation was ruining their lives and we were a burden on them. Their attitude was very disappointing.

Training was not appropriate to real-world scenarios. While shooting from a designated firing line, on a standardized firing range, taught the basic skills of how to fire the weapon, mastering the basic skills that a soldier needs is a whole different ball game. Soldiers need to train from different locations than a firing range. Some examples would include: firing from atop a parked vehicle, firing from a moving vehicle, dismounting the weapon from the vehicle and setting it up on the ground (using a tripod, as well as the traverse and elevation mechanisms to aim the weapon).

For the most part, we were training seven days a week with no real time off, even though the mobilization staff was off duty on weekends. We were ordered to remain at Fort Drum, even when we had nothing to do, no one was around to train us, and no one was there to transport us.

Time Off

After several weeks, we did begin to get some time off, usually when the Mobilization Team was also off and we had nothing scheduled. I'm not sure if the mobilization staff knew that we were taking this time, but since we had no training, we thought we might as well. We needed the break. With all the rain, snow, cold, and overcast skies, Fort Drum was very depressing during this time of the year. We needed to get away.

For our first weekend off, we received orders that no one was to travel more than a one-hour radius. Of course, we had some young hard chargers who were away from home, on their way overseas for no one knew how long. So they decided to rent a car and drive home to Connecticut. Of course they were in a traffic accident, revealing their travel beyond the one-hour radius. I understood the order and why it was given, but I also knew why the soldiers disobeyed. While some of my peers wanted me to punish them, I couldn't think of anything to do to them because, no matter what, they would soon be in Iraq. I couldn't fault individuals who were going off to war for wanting to take a last chance to go home and see family and friends. At this point, I don't recall that anything was ever done to them.

Shortly before we were slated to be deployed, we had a second weekend off while the Mobilization Team was off and no training was scheduled. With many family and friends coming up that weekend, our unit was given similar orders to stay within an hour of Fort Drum, only this time we also had to leave a phone number where we could be reached in case we were unexpectedly called back.

Keep in mind we had nothing scheduled and, by that time, we had nothing left to do except to get on the plane to Iraq, which wasn't scheduled for over a week. I don't know how or why, but the Mobilization Team found out that we had the weekend off, and the team just went ballistic. They ordered everyone back to the base and gave the direction that no one was to leave ever again. They still had nothing for us to do, but insisted we remain on base. So instead of enjoying a few days with family and friends one last time, soldiers sat around in a drizzling, miserable rain on a dingy, falling down World War II barracks, waiting to resume the training cycle when the Mobilization Team finally came back to work on Monday.

The Mobilization Team had no problem taking the weekend off and going wherever they wanted to go and doing whatever they wanted to do, but they thought our having the same privileges an egregious violation. They were staying home and we were going to war…how dare we enjoy ourselves.

Enjoying ourselves even when training was scheduled also became a problem. Most nights, small groups would gather in various rooms and have a few beers, maybe watch videos on a computer, or just talk. This became our main entertainment, and it was fine until we were given chloroquine as a preventive measure against malaria. Why we were given this drug became obvious once we reached Iraq: stagnant irrigation canals and clouds of insects trying to eat us alive. But at the time, we didn't understand why we were receiving it. Add to this lack of knowledge the fact that a common side effect of chloroquine is mood swings, and needless to say, we were not happy campers. Mood swings affected a number of our soldiers, including me. A number of different drugs were available at the time with less side effects (including doxycycline, which we began receiving several months later); regardless, the damage was done. The latter half of our time at Fort Drum was transformed into a truly miserable experience.

Shipping Out

During our last few days of mobilization, we had two final hurdles to clear:

1. Prepare all of our equipment and staff for loading and shipment overseas. We had to move the equipment in two stages: first from a railhead at Fort Drum, and then by ship from a port in Texas. Soldiers would leave on a commercial charter aircraft directly from Fort Drum, carrying a limited amount of personal equipment. Once we reached Kuwait, which we were told was our final destination, we would await further orders.

2. MRE (Military Readiness Exercise)—a four-day, three-night continuous exercise conducted in the field with soldiers living in tents. This exercise is designed to test the unit in simulated scenarios, specifically directed towards Military Police operations.

Problem was, the individuals in charge of deploying us overseas gave us a deployment date prior to the date our MRE was scheduled.

A large problem we experienced at Fort Drum was that too many commands were independently in charge of what we were to do—our unit wasn't under the command of one central authority. We had to deal with the staff at Fort Drum, the State of Connecticut, the Deployment staff arranging transportation, and the individuals conducting our MRE. Each one of these groups acted independently of one another, with no regard for one another's requirements or schedules.

Thinking that we were cleared to go because Deployment had given us a date and time, we began packing and preparing. When the Mobilization staff heard about the deadline Deployment gave us, they became upset with us. When I asked the individual from Mobilization why he hadn't coordinated with the Deployment staff, he clearly neither liked nor had an answer to my question. All he could do was tell me was to unpack everything, because we were going back to training.

Having cleaned and packed up our equipment in shipping containers so that we could unload in an orderly fashion at our destination, we had to quickly unpack it all from the containers and drag it out to the field for the four-day MRE. Our MRE took place in late March and early April with approximately three feet of snow on the ground. During the day we were subjected to freezing rain or drizzle, and at night, snow.

Our MRE gave us a glimpse into how our relationship with one officer was going to go. After being up all day completing the day's assignments in protective clothing and masks in a simulated a chemical attack, we began to settle in, making general plans for the rest of the night (including radio and security watch). Around midnight, absolutely nothing was happening, so the officer decided to turn in for the night.

Shortly after, we received word that the Controllers for the exercise needed us to send a runner to their Operations Center. The runner was dispatched and came back with four missions. My first reaction was that no one was going to get any sleep; my second reaction was that my hands were full. The First Sergeant, Lieutenant Grube, and one of the other Lieutenants were still in our Operations Center, and someone suggested that we should each read one assignment and brief the others.

My next concern was that these missions were supposed to take place immediately, but we discovered soon that they weren't scheduled to take place until the morning. This gave us several hours to plan, and soldiers who had been up for about twenty hours straight were able to get some sleep. The four of us worked on the plans for each mission and decided which Platoon would be assigned which mission. We planned to wake the Platoon Leaders who were not present about two hours before the assignment so that they had time to make their plans and brief their troops.

We got some sleep and put the plan into motion the next morning. We all felt that we had done a great job balancing rest with organization and timing. Except, the officer who had turned in before we received the missions was ripshit because we didn't wake him up immediately when the they had come in.

Keep in mind that the function of the Operation section is to do what we had just done. And with missions still two hours away, the officer had enough time to make any changes that he wanted. He was far from satisfied with this logic, even though he made no changes to our plan.

As in all previous exercises, our passing scores meant that we were first-time go at all testing stations. The new problems were that the MRE had dead-lined eight of our vehicles (some of which had to be towed to the railhead to be shipped to Texas), and the rest of our equipment was covered in mud and slush, soaked from snow and freezing rain. Our unit was now a complete mess, and we were given no extra time to get our equipment packed and loaded. Packing became simply throwing items into shipping containers.

Everything did get loaded and the train headed for Texas. We continued to reflect on the fact that every vehicle we owned had gone through a detailed inspection and upgrade at Fort Drum, and they were still falling apart (some of them had been put on the train despite being unable to start). We had nothing left to do but clean up and sit around to wait for our flight.

Chapter Seven

KUWAIT

Let's roll.

Todd Beamer, United Flight 93

Figure 7.1   Major highways allowed for fast travel, but we still had to dodge the goats and sheep

April 15, 2003 (a drizzly, rainy, miserable day with temperatures just above freezing)—We boarded a commercial airliner and flew to

Kuwait, with a short stop in the Netherlands so the crew could rest before starting the second leg of the journey.

The seat in front of me had a TV monitor, but it didn't display in-flight movies or other forms of entertainment. What they did have on screen was a GPS map of our trip, with a little airplane superimposed over it. This map showed our slow but steady progress towards the Netherlands and then onwards to Kuwait. It was almost torture sitting there, watching the plane creep across the screen, inching ever closer to the final destination. From time to time I would doze off and then wake up to be greeted by the screen showing me just how much farther I had gotten away from home.

We landed in Kuwait in the middle of a sandstorm in 105° heat. The soldiers were so used to the climate of Fort Drum that we had heat casualties just moving off the plane and unloading our duffel bags. The ground crew had us move into tents to get out of the sandstorm and gave us orders to break out the ammunition that had been stored in the belly of the plane.

Fort Drum was supposed to issue a full basic load of ammunition for each soldier. Each soldier should have gotten 210 rounds of M-16 ammunition and 45 rounds of 9mm ammunition. Each machine gunner should have received 600 rounds of ammunition.

For whatever reason, we did not have enough M-16 rounds for each soldier to have 210, nor did we have forty-five 9mm rounds for each soldier. I can't understand how the Army could deploy us without giving us what they said should be the minimum amount of ammunition, especially since this standard was the Army's and not ours.

This insufficiency would not be the last of our ammunition woes.

While at the airfield, we met up with a unit of the Massachusetts National Guard who were coordinating the movement of Military Police units going forward. Imagine my surprise when I learned that, despite years of training and mobilization, after following all kinds of protocols and completing countless assignments, no one knew we were coming to Kuwait. Since they didn't expect us, they didn't know if we were headed to Iraq, or for that matter, where we were going.

After the initial confusion, the Massachusetts Guard told us that they thought we would be staying in Kuwait, securing one of the air bases or one of the supply areas on the shore. They told us to go back to the tents and wait while they sorted everything out, and that we would be on the airfield waiting for at least several days.

A few hours later, someone changed his or her mind, and we were told to gather all our equipment and have our soldiers line up for the buses to take us to Camp Pennsylvania in the Kuwaiti desert. Everyone in the unit was in full battle uniform and loaded down with equipment and body armor. Depending on a soldier's assignment, all this equipment weighed about eighty pounds (soldiers armed with the squad automatic weapon carried even more weight). All ammunition was issued.

And as it turned out, the buses didn't have enough seats for all the soldiers in my unit. A number of us (myself included) sat on the floor, thinking that we would have only a short trip to Camp Pennsylvania. After all, at about 17,000 square miles, Kuwait is a little smaller than New Jersey.

Although Kuwaiti police officers in BMWs, Mercedes Benzes and Crown Victorias gave us escort out of the air base, they dropped back after several miles to let us continue into the desert alone. I couldn't see any landmarks or road signs on our journey, though to be fair, most of the time I couldn't see the road. We drove for several hours without the scenery changing much, and eventually the soldiers began to get a little anxious and nature began to call.

Unfortunately, we had no radio communication between the buses and the bus drivers did not speak English. In our bus, we tried sign language and hand gestures (that was interesting), but the driver didn't understand us, and the buses kept on driving. Finally, someone in the lead bus started to have the same problem and was able to communicate to the driver to stop. No sooner did the buses come to a halt than everyone charged off into the desert night, guys to the right, young ladies to left. It dawned on everyone at about the same time that we were in a war zone and a strong possibility existed that this place was mined. After quickly relieving ourselves, everyone timidly filed back onto the buses and resumed their seats.

Before we headed out, we held a quick staff meeting and determined that we were lost in the desert. The drivers were unsure of the location of Camp Pennsylvania and we had no idea of how near to the Iraqi border we were. With that good news, we decided we had no other choice but get back on the road. Our luck held, and several hours later, we arrived at Camp Pennsylvania. I am still not sure how we got there.

Camp Pennsylvania

A tent city in the middle of the desert, Camp Pennsylvania was occupied by the 101st Airborne Division before the U.S. invasion. Camp Pennsylvania is also where an American soldier of Muslim faith threw a hand grenade into the operations tent, killing several soldiers and wounding several more, with the hopes of delaying the invasion and perhaps stopping Americans from killing his Muslim brothers. Of course, it didn't work. The camp had been there for a number of months, if not years, as a training area for use prior to and during the buildup for the invasion of Iraq.

Camp Pennsylvania provided quarters for us, about twenty-five to thirty soldiers to a tent. Each soldier had space for his or her sleeping mat, enough room to store two duffle bags, and a backpack. The tents had plywood floors and no cots, leaving us with only thin backpacker foam mattresses to sleep on. The tents had been out in the desert environment for so long they were beginning to tear apart from the high winds and desert heat (the Mess and Recreational tents eventually did rip apart while we were there).

One night, a huge sandstorm blew in with such force that we were afraid our tents would blow away. Everyone huddled silently in their sleeping bags on their foam mats listening to the raging storm outside.

The storm was so loud that a sudden lull woke me.

Somewhat disoriented and wondering where I was, I switched on my flashlight but still couldn't see anything. At first I thought the batteries were dead, but I turned the flashlight to shine the light in my eyes and saw the glow of the light. But even with the flashlight, I could not see a thing. I looked around the tent where I should have seen twenty-five other soldiers and could not see the guys next to me. Fighting panic, I wondered where everyone had gone and what was going on. I thought we might have been overrun and, somehow, I was by myself.

After a few seconds, my head began to clear and I realized that I couldn't see because so much sand and dust was in the air that the flashlight beam could not penetrate more than a few inches. I covered up and went back to sleep, holding my rifle. In the morning I woke to find that everyone and everything was covered in a fine coating of desert sand.

We stayed in Camp Pennsylvania for three weeks waiting for our vehicles and heavy equipment to arrive by ship from Texas. The three weeks helped us become more accustomed to dry heat, which we sorely needed as we were rationed two 1.75 liter bottles of water a day with no reserves. These bottles were the only water we were given, though sodas and juices were available at mealtimes.

Shower time was supposed to be limited, and taking a shower with limited water just seemed to make you feel dirtier. It didn't help that the showers were overused, filthy, and covered in soap scum and dead skin. Despite being in a desert environment, the shower water never seemed to drain, leaving us standing in a few inches of water from the last hundred or so soldiers who showered before you. Even with limited shower water, a few soldiers were always around who wanted to take a shower like they were at home, and fights sometimes erupted. Most of us resorted to a daily routine of baby wipes and powder as a way to stay clean to avoid the shower situation all together.

We would make trips to Camp Virginia, where the MP Headquarters Operation was located, to try to get status updates on the delivery of our equipment, and maybe even our mission. Although Camp Virginia had a very bustling operation, they were unable to provide any useful information about where we were going, who we would be working for, when we would going, or what our job was going to be. As with everyone else we had met in Kuwait to that point, they also did not know that we were coming. I quickly became frustrated with the trips to Camp Virginia and stopped going.

There was some talk that we would be staying at Camp Pennsylvania to provide security and perform escort missions inside Kuwait. The idea was appealing, as no one was really very interested in learning what the war was really all about. Of course, there is always one exception, and we had one officer doing everything he could to get us to Iraq.

On May 1, 2003, when President Bush declared "Mission Accomplished," rumors began flying that we would soon be shipped home. These rumors proved not to be the case, and days passed after President Bush's declaration before anyone told us what we were going to be doing.

Eventually, we were given word that we would be moving to Baghdad in a two-day convoy movement; but no further information about our assignment was given. We did learn that our equipment had finally arrived, so we sent some soldiers from our unit to the port to bring our vehicles back to Camp Pennsylvania. Our soldiers got to the port just in time to stop another unit from stealing several of our vehicles.

The Dogs of War

Not long after arriving at Camp Pennsylvania, we learned that most of the combat units had already gone forward, and that as an MP Company, we were more combat-oriented than most of the other support units. The officer In Charge, who was called the Mayor, was trying to get our unit permanently assigned to Camp Pennsylvania for security and escort assignments. Our unit was assigned to perimeter security of the large sprawling outpost.

An issue came up with a large pack of roaming wild dogs. As we were miles from civilization, these animals were not pets, and they had survived on whatever they could find or kill. Deserts don't support a wide range of wildlife. Initially, the pack scavenged the dump several hundred yards from the tent area. One day, the dump was set on fire to reduce the smell. Deprived of their food source, the dogs started to edge closer to the tent area. Some soldiers, out of misplaced kindness, started giving them food, which only emboldened them to come closer (up until now, the pack had been avoiding humans). The concern was that soon the dogs would enter the tent area and inevitably attack someone.

After asking around, the Mayor learned that our Company had several expert marksmen, and one even had a scoped rifle. This soldier was directed to safely and selectively pick off dogs that got too close to the tent area, before an attack occurred.

An officer decided that he should get involved, loaded his shotgun, and headed out intent on gunning down a dog. Now, the marksman with the scoped rifle was shooting dogs from a couple of hundred yards away from the target, whereas this officer with the shotgun needed to be within fifty yards to hit a target. At night, with limited light, this officer was roaming around inside the tent area, with a loaded shotgun, searching for a dog to kill. Loaded firearms were not permitted in the tent area; only on the perimeter, and only with security personnel (with the one exception of our designated sniper).

Fortunately, the officer did not encounter any dogs.

The downside was that he was now in the tent area with a loaded shotgun, and he did not know how to safely unload it. He came into the occupied tent with the loaded shotgun, fumbling with the action, attempting to figure out how to remove the shells from the magazine.

A magazine has two tabs on the inside tube that, when pressed simultaneously, release the shells one at a time through the bottom of the shotgun. The shell in the chamber is released by racking the pump action. After fiddling with the pump action while having the procedure explained several times, the Captain simply gave up, and pumped all the shells through the action—remember, he's still inside an occupied tent. I can't count how many violations he committed in that single hour, and he never did learn how to safely unload a shotgun.

Onward to Baghdad

While we were organizing our gear to get ready for the move to Baghdad, elements of the 1st Armored Division arrived, putting a strain on the accommodations at the camp. Our soldiers were forced to squeeze into only a few tents, and the mess hall was now serving four to five times the number of soldiers that it had previously been serving. Standing in the line for chow could take two hours or more.

With our now very cramped quarters, we were looking forward to proceeding, even if we were headed into a war zone. At last, we received word that our 4th Platoon had been tasked with escorting a command element to an airbase north of Baghdad. The Americans referred to this base as "Anaconda," while the Iraqis called it "Balad."

Our heavy weapons had arrived and 4th Platoon mounted up their MK-19 grenade launchers. Each launcher was supposed to be supplied with four canisters of rounds, which held between 32 and forty-eight rounds of belted 40mm ammunition (for a company total of 180 canisters). We discovered that we had been supplied with only ten of the 180 canisters required for the entire company. Ten canisters were enough to arm one platoon (with one canister per gun) leaving the rest of the company without any ammunition for their main battle weapons. With no rounds for the MK-19 grenade launchers, they and their tripod mounts became 114-pound paperweights that we had to take everywhere and keep secure.

In addition, we were not issued smoke grenades, hand grenades or flares. To add insult to injury, squad and team leaders were not provided with rounds for their M-203 grenade launchers.

The command at Fort Drum assured us when we left that a full basic load of ammunition would be sent with our unit. When we got to Kuwait we were assured that when we got to Camp Pennsylvania a full basic load of ammunition would be sent with our unit. When we went forward into Iraq without our basic load of ammunition, the command told us not to worry—when we got to our assignment in Baghdad, we'd finally receive our ammunition. By this point, their assurances had about the same weight as "The check's in the mail," or "Of course I'll respect you in the morning."

Each platoon had a limited number of trailers in which to transport gear. While packing, we had to take into consideration the equipment we would immediately need to perform our mission, as well as items deemed "sensitive" that could not be left behind in storage. A lot of our equipment had to be left behind in storage containers.

After sorting and loading our gear, the eight foot 8' high x 8' wide x 20' long containers, made of heavy gauge steel, were arranged so the doors faced each other to ensure that they could not be broken into (the containers could be moved only by very large, specialized cargo lifters). We had no idea when or if the storage containers would ever catch up to us. In fact, months passed before command was able to have our containers moved north to our location. Even with these storage containers loaded tight, each vehicle was full of equipment with packs and duffle bags hanging from the sides and back.

4th Platoon moved out on schedule and without incident, making it all the way to Forward Operating Base Anaconda. They then pulled back to Baghdad and waited for us to arrive.

On May 9, 2003, an officer had us clear out of the tents the evening before our departure, and ordered us to sleep on the ground or in vehicles. I am not sure what his reasoning was, as we had already loaded everything onto the vehicles, and had only our weapons and sleeping gear. So that night we slept out on the ground, most of us cold and anxious. While temperatures during the day ranged from 105° to 110°, they dropped 30° or more after the sun went down. Although the tents were canvas and not insulated, they did hold our collective body heat, and kept us substantially warmer than sleeping outside. That night, none of us slept very well.

When we left Kuwait, our instructions were to proceed north to Baghdad Airport and make contact with the MP Brigade stationed there.

Before sunup, we were on the road headed for the Iraqi border, driving through what looked like trackless desert. We were given hundreds of maps, most of which did not cover the route to Baghdad (or any of the areas we would be operating in later). During the trip to Baghdad, we learned that we needed a series of a dozen maps to cover the full route, and at least four of the maps we needed were missing. We were also given several map coordinates to locate rest stops and compounds, many of which we found to be incorrect. I have no idea how the lead vehicle knew where we were going. Nevertheless, we arrived at the border crossing checkpoint several hours later and waited for our clearance to move north into Iraq. We weren't sure what we were waiting for, as the highway beyond the border crossing checkpoint was unoccupied.

While waiting, we talked about our uncertain future. We had heard rumors that Iraqi citizens would be throwing things at us as we patrolled the towns, even using hooks in attempts to rip equipment off of our vehicles. Our rules of engagement did not cover this type of scenario, and we weren't sure what to do if civilians should attack. So, one officer announced that he would open his shotgun on anyone who attempted to rip equipment off of his vehicle. I immediately had visions of a ten-year-old kid getting hit with one half dozen double 00 buckshot rounds.

At last, we were given the order to move forward, and we set off in convoy, passing through a large twenty-plus-foot-high sand berm that had been built up after Desert Storm to mark the border between Kuwait and Iraq. An Iraqi town lay immediately on the other side, and the Iraqi people met us with waves and smiles. Several children came up to us, trying to exchange Iraqi dinars for American dollars. We were greatly relieved, to say the least.

The delay at the Kuwait border meant we would be driving at night. Our destination, Talli Air Force Base, was located approximately halfway between the Kuwaiti border and Baghdad. The very early start and long delay at the border made the trip much longer and much more tiring than if we had been able to just drive straight through. The heat, sun, and desert, combined with our poor sleep the night before, left us drained and exhausted. To compensate, we rotated drivers, but even then, drivers were nodding off.

Despite our fatigue, traveling through the desert at night we were constantly on alert, expecting an attack at any moment. We traveled past destroyed Iraqi fighting positions, and observed numerous abandoned and stripped Iraqi military vehicles. The desert scenery included blown-up, burned-out Iraqi tanks and armored vehicles. We could see shell craters and pockmarks from machine gun fire on the buildings and roads—we were obviously traveling through an area that had seen a lot of fighting. Our trip, fortunately, was uneventful.

We approached the base after dark, passing lines of at least a hundred parked dump trucks on our way to the gate. The trucks were all civilian, loaded with sand slated to rebuild Talli Air Force Base. I was amazed that though the war had ended only ten days ago, the U.S. already had civilian contractors working to rebuild the base that we had just destroyed.

We entered the gate, and after a long ride down an access road, pulled into a secure area, lined up our vehicles, and had a quick staff meeting. The company commander decided to give us five hours to sleep before getting back on the road, and passed word to the troops to get settled in. The convoy turned into a jumble of noise as soldiers got out equipment and food to ready themselves for a short nap.

Like a lot of other soldiers, I walked to the tree line to take care of business. On the way out, I remember thinking that, with all the noise, no one would be able to get any sleep that night. I was wrong. By the time I got back to the vehicles, the only sound I could hear was snoring. Everybody was pretty much used up from the long day, and sleep was the only thought on their minds.

We were up bright and early the next morning and continued our journey north to Baghdad. Shortly after leaving, we discovered that we had made a wrong turn. Rather than turn back around, an officer directed us to continue onward, following a different route that no one in Command knew we were taking. This decision was very dangerous; if anything happened, no one would know where to look for us.

We made our way along the uncharted route, trying to find a refueling facility at a location called Scania—this proved difficult as Scania was located at one of the map coordinates that proved to be incorrect. We learned seven months later that Scania's incorrect grid location was still being distributed.

We were able to locate and pull into the refueling point with several of our vehicles in tow, because they had run out of fuel. After refueling, we continued on our way, reaching Baghdad at approximately 1500 hours. We found our way onto Baghdad International Airport and the Brigade Headquarters for the MPs (which was much harder than it sounds, because no one told us that only one road went to the airport—even after finding the correct road, we had difficulty locating MP Brigade Headquarters).

We finally reached the Military Police Brigade only to learn, once again, that no one knew we were coming. The concept behind the reason units in Kuwait dispatched us forward seemed simple enough: Either (1) a unit in Baghdad had requested a unit and we were selected, or (2) a higher command, such as the MP Brigade in Baghdad, had decided that one of their MP Battalions needed a company and asked for one. Neither of these situations had happened; we were just sent to Baghdad.

Seeing that we had taken the trouble to come to Baghdad, Brigade Headquarters assigned us to the 709th Military Police Battalion at Warrior Compound. That night, most of us slept next to our vehicles and were eaten alive by mosquitoes. Everyone was so tired, nobody noticed the bites until the next morning.

The very next day, we began running missions.

Chapter Eight

WARRIOR COMPOUND, WESTERN BAGHDAD

No good decision was ever made in a swivel chair.

General George S. Patton

Figure 8.1   Headquarters for the 709th Military Police Battalion

Warrior Compound had once been Baghdad's Ministry of Art and Culture. Covering several acres, the Compound was surrounded by a high wall and several guard towers. This type of design is normal in Iraq, especially for government buildings and compounds. Warrior Compound consisted of a large main building, a smaller (almost identical) building, and several other structures scattered about the Compound. While there were signs that some fighting had taken place near the Compound, most of the damage had been caused by looters from the population.

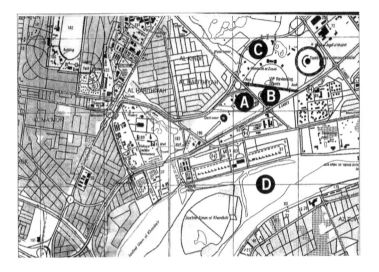

Figure 8.2   A Warrior FOB
            B Saddam's Parade Ground with the Crossed
            Swords
            C Baghdad Zoo
            D Tigris River Separating Western and Eastern
            Baghdad

We were given a fairly large room on the second floor of the main building to use as our Tactical Operations Center. We called the place a palace, but in reality, it was just an overdone government building with chandeliers, marble floors, wide staircases, and vaulted ceilings. The building was concrete and nearly impervious to any kind of available enemy fire. The roof was approximately eighty feet above ground level, giving us a good location for our radio antennas.

Northeast of Warrior Compound was the famous parade ground with the crossed-swords arches where Saddam would review his troops and fire his pistol or rifle over their heads in celebration. Farther to the east was the location that had became known as the Green Zone. Over the course of the next year, the Green Zone expanded outward until, by early 2004, Warrior Compound was inside of it.

First Assignments

One of our first assignments was to oversee the rebuilding of a jail not too far from Warrior Compound. A Battalion officer escorted an officer, along with some soldiers from our company, to the location for briefing. Shortly after returning to the FOB, an officer instructed Staff Sergeant Matus to take his Squad out to the jail and secure it. Only a few of us had been through the streets of Baghdad at this point; and although we could find the jail's location on a map, physically driving to it was another matter. So Staff Sergeant Matus requested that one of the soldiers who had already been out to the jail accompany him on this first run.

This officer was adamant, ordering Staff Sergeant Matus to get his vehicles and go out and find the jail by himself.

I empathized with the look of concern on Staff Sergeant Matus's face—I shared his concern. We didn't want a squad of our MPs wandering around the mean streets of Baghdad trying to find a building. Baghdad has no street signs, and we couldn't just swing into a 7-Eleven to ask for directions. For the safety of his men, Staff Sergeant Matus had to know where the location was and get to it quickly.

After the officer who gave the command left, Staff Sergeant Matus's apprehension became much more apparent. The last thing he wanted was to get lost in Baghdad on Day One. Fortunately, Staff Sergeant Morales, who was from a different platoon, had gone out with the first crew and knew how to get to the jail. He offered to accompany Matus.

I am forever grateful to Staff Sergeant Morales for volunteering. In times like this, when one soldier stood up for another, I felt very proud. We all knew that we would have to take risks in Iraq, but if we were capable of mitigating those risks, we could see no reason to go out and wing it.

Fortunately, the patrol went off without a hitch and everyone returned to the base safely.

Attempted Diplomacy

Because no one in theater—from Kuwait to Baghdad—had any idea we were coming, our mission continued to evolve and change, sometimes several times during the course of a single day. We did the best we could to respond to the changing requests.

Shortly after our arrival, an officer came in the Operations Center to complain about all the confusion, and how badly our efforts were progressing. He blamed Operations, telling us that we were screwing things up, and that we needed to get our act together.

I took the officer aside, and sat down with him, knee to knee. In a calm, professional tone, explained that Operations wasn't altering the unit's mission; Battalion Headquarters was, and all of the changes we were making were attempts to comply with Battalion's changing orders. I told him that the confusion was due to the constantly evolving situation in Western Baghdad. I tried to impress upon him that no one in Baghdad had extensive plans, and that we were simply responding to the situation as it presented itself to the best of our abilities.

I thought I'd been quite diplomatic, and although the conversation was admittedly one-sided, the officer didn't attempt to interrupt or contradict what I was saying.

Imagine my surprise, when, a short time later, I was approached by the First Sergeant. The officer had ordered the First Sergeant to advise me that if I ever spoke to him in that manner again, he would hit me with an Article 15, or even a court-martial, for insubordination.

This news left me speechlessness. My first thought was to find the officer and ask him what his problem was, but, on quick reflection, I realized that was a waste of time. I decided that, when possible, I would no longer include him in decision-making. Since he clearly felt that my input and insight were worthless, I would pass all decisions I could not directly handle off to him. From that point on, most interactions took place between Operations and the Platoons. To a great extent, the officer was out of the loop.

I wasn't the only soldier who this officer threatened with the military justice system.

Shortly after arriving at Warrior Compound, he assigned reading and replying to all his emails to a senior NCO in Operations.

The problem with the officer's order—and he did make it an order—was that reading and replying to someone else's emails is unprofessional at best, illegal at worst (when the email is classified). Anyone contacting this officer via email did so expecting that he or she was communicating with this officer directly, and was usually doing so to request or inform the officer about something he needed to know. I can only imagine what would have happened had the Battalion Commander or the Battalion Operations Major emailed the officer, only to discover that an NCO was reading and replying.

The NCO declined, in a less-than-military style by simply refusing the officer's request. The officer became enraged, and wrote up the NCO for insubordination and failure to obey an order. The action was referred to the Battalion Commander (a lieutenant colonel) who reviewed the charges, and dropped them with no further action.

After that, the officer read and answered his own emails.

Inter-Service Issues

We began our duties in beautiful downtown Baghdad and immediately ran into our first inter-service rivalry. Unbeknownst to us, active-duty 1st Armored Division did not particularly appreciate active-duty Military Police. Silly us…we thought we were there to help.

Our company was assigned to an active-duty MP Battalion that operated under the 18th Military Police Brigade. We learned that the battle space of our territory in Baghdad was actually controlled by the 1st Armored Division, and that we had to clear all operations with the 1st Armored Division (a requirement that the active-duty Military Police had neglected to share with us).

Stuck in the middle of somewhat of a turf war, we would get orders to patrol the city, and the 1st Armored Division would stop us to tell us to go back to our FOB. When we returned, the Battalion would send us back out, which only resulted in little contests of will to see who would go where and do what.

As I've already mentioned, we did not have a basic load of ammunition. When we asked Battalion for the ammunition needed to fill out our load just for the M-16s and the 9mm pistols (since these were our basic weapons), Battalion replied that they didn't have reserve ammunition to issue, which just seemed absurd.

After the decision was made to not supply us with a basic load, and we were able to mount only one weapon on each vehicle anyway, we all but gave up on the MK-19 ammunition. Our choice was either the SAW or the MK-19; we were not able to mount both like the active-duty. We decided that if we couldn't get M-16 or 9mm rounds, I was not going to bother asking for grenades or M-203 rounds.

I believe the general feeling was that the war was already over and we really didn't need our basic load. Of course, in reality, the conflict went on for almost seven years with daily shootings. Later impressions conveyed the idea that we were just on an extended training exercise, not a combat operation. The fact that Coalition forces in Western Baghdad were being attacked fifteen to thirty times each and every day seemed to fall on deaf ears.

Attacks became more numerous and deadly as insurgents refined their tactics. As we expended ammunition in firefights, Battalion would re-supply us with the exact number of rounds we had fired. If a soldier had fired off one round, one round was all that was issued.

Shortly after our arrival at Warrior Compound, the 3rd Brigade Combat Team of the 1st Armored Division requested a Military Police Company to be attached to them for direct support of their mission. They were assigned to relieve Infantry units that had fought their way into Baghdad and were now being withdrawn to rest and refit.

The 709th Military Police Battalion was more than happy to give up the 143rd Military Police Company, as they believed we, as a National Guard unit, could not function at the level of an active-duty unit. Our transfer to the 3rd Brigade took several weeks, and in that short time we proved to the active-duty MPs that we knew what we were doing.

The 709th had no experience in civilian law enforcement, or running police stations and correctional facilities. The 143rd, on the other hand, had a core of State Troopers, municipal law enforcement officers, and

Department of Corrections officers. Our soldiers had training and the real-world experience that the active-duty lacked. As the days led up to our transfer, the active-duty Military Police came to rely on us more and more, and they tried to stop the transfer.

At this time I decided to request rounds for the MK-19 as well as smoke grenades and rounds for the M-203. At some point, we got a few smoke grenades.

Manpower and Equipment

A Military Police Company with our designation should have 181 enlisted soldiers and five officers. On deployment from Fort Drum, we had 151 soldiers, of which five were officers. Most of our shortfall was in the ranks of Military Police officers. Each MP platoon should have thirty-two enlisted and one officer. Our four platoons averaged twenty-four enlisted and one officer. Because of our shortage of personnel, we could not fill three full squads per platoon.

Shortly after our arrival, the active-duty decided that we needed to field more squads to help establish the police stations. Because we didn't have the appropriate number of bodies to field more squads, they decided to strip down our Squads from three teams per squad to two teams per squad. This change meant that the Squad Leader was now the third person in one of two vehicles instead of the fourth person in one of three vehicles, which did give us more teams and squads in the field on a daily basis—but also put us at greater risk. The Iraqis could easily knock out and disable one vehicle, injuring or killing the occupants, leaving only one other vehicle with three soldiers to defend and recover the dead or wounded.

We began to settle in to our new routine helping establishing police stations. An MP Platoon was assigned and detailed a Squad to the station on a twelve-hours on/twelve-hours off basis. The active-duty also provided a Squad on a twelve-hour on/twelve-hour off basis, while a third Squad, supplied by the 3rd Brigade Combat Team of the 1st Armored Division, was designated to provide security at each of the police stations, backed up by a Bradley fighting vehicle (or an Abrams tank). The active-duty MPs were assigned to man the police station and provide security and perform police functions inside the police compound. Initially, our 143rd Military Police troops were assigned to patrol alone, and then later with Iraqis, throughout their patrol district in Western Baghdad.

Our troops were equipped with unarmored Humvees. While they did have bullet-resistant glass, the vehicles were fiberglass shells with no bullet-resistant material and no protection on the lower section of the doors or on the floor. The Humvees had no blast shield in the turret, leaving the gunner without protection of any kind (other than his or her helmet and body armor).

To try to improve protection, we hung old body armor in the doors and, like in World War II and Vietnam, we placed sandbags on the floor. Nine months later, we were able to bolt metal plates to the sides of the vehicle.

Photo by Master Sgt Marc Youngquist

Figure 8.3   Fully armored ASV with a 50-caliber and a MK-19 grenade launcher

This extra armor plating, which we called "hillbilly armor," was too much extra weight for our Humvees to handle and constantly caused the engines to overheat.

Active-duty units were parked at the police stations in up-armored Humvees next to ASVs. Armored cars are even more substantial and heavily armored than the up-armored Humvee. The ASVs also came equipped with a 50-caliber heavy machine gun and an MK-19 automatic grenade launcher—

heavy-duty firepower that the National Guard troops did not have. Both their up-armored Humvees and their ASVs could withstand small arms fire from AK-47s to hand grenades and provided substantial protection from mines and RPGs.

By contrast, bullets fired at one of our unarmored Humvees easily went in one side and out the other without slowing down, unless they happened to hit something inside the vehicle. On several occasions, blasts tore through the bottoms of our vehicles and exited through the roofs.

Months passed before someone, somewhere, realized the risk the National Guard troops were taking driving around in unarmored Humvees, and that the active-duty were sitting in the relative safety of police stations with their armored vehicles sitting idle. Once someone woke up to the idea that the utilization of vehicles was backwards, the mission was changed so that the National Guard troops manned the police stations while the active-duty patrolled the streets with the Iraqi Police officers. Shortly after this change, the mission changed again, so that the active-duty stopped patrolling with the Iraqis altogether, leaving the Iraqis to take full responsibility for patrolling the streets of Western Baghdad.

I don't know why no one raised the issue of why the National Guard was patrolling in unarmored vehicles, while the active-duty sat in the police stations with their armored vehicles parked out front.

Early Patrols

The 709th Military Police Battalion had us patrolling the streets of Baghdad on a twenty-four-hour basis. At the time, no civilian law enforcement was present. Our main objective was to exert influence and a military presence across Baghdad.

By the time we arrived, a curfew was in place, and Western Baghdad had little nighttime traffic (except for military vehicles). But even with the curfew, Western Baghdad was still very lawless.

Tensions were rising with the Coalition soldiers, and a lot of payback was going on between Shia and Sunni (or anyone else with a score to settle), resulting in numerous murders and attacks between Iraqis. We would receive reports each morning of bodies found in the streets, none of them related to Coalition activity.

With very little information coming out of Iraq prior to the invasion, no one knew that murders, assassinations and massacres between Sunni and Shia had been going on for years, and had been a daily occurrence long before the Coalition forces arrived.

At this point, the insurgency was in its infancy, and not yet in possession of the tactical experience it would gain in the days to come. Most attacks on Coalition forces during this time were very basic and somewhat childish.

As military vehicles passed by, an individual would pop out with an AK-47, let go all thirty rounds in a single burst, and take off running. Insurgents would not unfold their rifle stocks, and simply spray bullets at Coalition forces. Even if the first round was well-aimed, by the time the second and third rounds were fired, the rifle had jumped all over the place, making hits more of an accident than the result of accurate fire. Not wanting to get killed by return fire, insurgents might fire from several hundred yards away, making the possibility of a hit almost impossible (especially with the stock folded).

While roadside bombs were being made at this time, they were of very amateurish construction. The bomb makers didn't know how artillery shells functioned, and aimed shells point-first at the road. When those shells detonated, the blasts went sideways (parallel to the streets) instead of across the streets at the vehicles.

Insurgent bomb makers also poured concrete blocks around explosives, intending to shatter the concrete into chunks thereby causing shrapnel damage to vehicles and personnel. But because the concrete was not cured, and the explosive charges were too large, the actual effect was dust—any major injuries that occured resulted from the blast effect or concussion. Insurgents also planted single IEDs, which forced them to time the explosions just right, as the target vehicles had to be in close proximity (being off by just a second or two would mean a miss). As insurgents improved their tactics, they started daisy chaining a series of explosives, allowing them more leeway as the explosions could cover larger areas.

These early types of IEDs were simple, somewhat effective, and also very dangerous to the people planting them. A small amount of static electricity could be enough to set off a device, and accidental explosions happened all the time. Numerous triggering devices (such as garage door openers and radio-controlled cars operating on the same or similar frequencies), set off bombs before they were planted.

On one patrol, Lieutenant Grube and an MP Squad spotted a vehicle that was acting in a suspicious manner, so the lieutenant ordered his Squad to stop the vehicle and investigate. This stop turned into a chase. During the course of the pursuit, an object was thrown from the vehicle, which turned out to be an IED in a concrete block.

Once Lieutenant Grube and his Squad were able to stop the suspicious vehicle, the first questions on everyone's minds were, "Where are the other IEDs? Where is the bomb factory?" A number of interrogation ideas came to mind, most of which would not conform to the Geneva Convention. Fortunately for us, the bombers were not hard-core, stand-up guys, and spilled their guts with little prompting.

Some time later, their case was tried in court and almost thrown out. The Judge Advocate General's office did not have the evidence needed (the evidence being the IED). The only way to render the IED safe was to blow it up…attempting to dismantle it could have set it off, and transporting a live bomb into a courtroom was out of the question. Using stateside court proceedings in a war zone never stopped while we were there.

As time went on, the bomb makers became much more creative, and their bombs became much more dangerous. We also had Iranian insurgents coming in, some Palestinians, some Yemenis, and some from who-knows-where. These fighters tended to be better trained, more disciplined, and of course, deadlier.

We also had to deal with organized crime. Baghdad is a city of several million people, with all the crime that you would find in any major metropolitan city anywhere in the world. Murder, rape, robbery, kidnapping, carjacking, bank robbery, home invasion, extortion, as well as any other crime you can imagine took place on a daily basis. We were responsible for dealing with all this "typical" crime, as well as terrorists, Al Qaeda, the Republican Guard and the Baath Party.

Kidnappings, however, were much more common in Baghdad than in the United States. People who did not pay their debts were routinely kidnapped until the ransom/debt was paid. Carjacking (which I had previously thought was a more American type of crime), was also very prominent.

Because the local currency was pretty much worthless, cars had intrinsic value and were used as a form of replacement currency. Extortion is an easy crime to commit when your country has hundreds of thousands of every type of weapon imaginable available to the local population. Having your creditor walk to your home with three or four men armed with AK-47s and demanding immediate payment was not an unusual occurrence.

Iraqi Police

Police stations were hit hard during the initial attack on Iraq, particularly in Baghdad. Since each police officer was armed with an AK-47, and the stations now had radio towers and communications equipment, they were seen as armed camps. In order to reduce the effectiveness of the enemy, these fortified positions needed to be taken out.

The decision finally came down that one of our main tasks for the 709th Military Police Battalion would be to rebuild the Iraqi Police force. The command staff from Battalion came down to our company and asked us to put together an outline of what a Police Academy training curriculum should look like. Everyone in the company with law enforcement experience was asked to participate, and we would combine ideas to come up with a uniform plan.

The State Troopers in our company mapped out a twenty-six-week training schedule, which was based on the 26 weeks of training that they had gone through at the Connecticut State Police Academy. Municipal and corrections officers had a similar training schedule worked out that was about twenty-two weeks long.

As the First Sergeant and I reviewed the training recommendations, we came to the realization that in no way was the Iraqi Police Academy ever going to be able to be twenty-two or twenty-six weeks long. The one item that every person who participated put first on the list was ethics. To a man, each person felt that ethics was the single most important subject that needed to be covered with the Iraqi law enforcement trainees. We went back and eliminated certain things not germane to law enforcement in Iraq, cutting the training cycle back to approximately eight weeks. Even at eight weeks, we felt we were cutting training extremely short.

Once again, no one in real authority was listening.

The concept of rebuilding the Iraqi Police force was then made at a much higher level (probably coming down from Mr. Rumsfeld, Mr. Cheney, Mr. Bremer and Mr. Kerik). These orders insisted that two weeks of training would be more than enough time to qualify an individual to be an Iraqi Police officer, soldier, or National Guardsman—not the eight-week minimum that we had worked out. Remember, we had close to thirty people in our company who were employed in civilian law enforcement of one type or another, and all of our Military Police officers had been through Military Police schools, which all provided far more than two weeks of training.

Mr. Bremer, the ambassador to Iraq, and Mr. Kerik, who had been the Commissioner for the New York City Police Department, overrode our suggestions and made their own rules as to what needed to happen to reestablish law enforcement in Iraq. To the best of my knowledge, neither Mr. Bremer nor Mr. Kerik ever left the Green Zone to attend meetings at any of the police stations in our area of Western Baghdad. Yet they felt completely qualified to dictate what needed to happen to rebuild the Iraqi Police force, giving us a timetable for training and repairs that we could not deviate from.

Mr. Kerik's New York City police officers go through over six months of training at their Police Academy, and then are required to do field training for several weeks with an experienced officer before being sent out on their own. Soldiers entering the Army who became Military Police officers went through twenty weeks of training. How could anyone in Baghdad (which had many more problems than New York City), train police officers in two weeks?

The recruitment of police officers became nothing more than setting up a table and asking people to join. No detailed vetting of individual officers or background checks occurred; we were now just looking for warm bodies to fill the positions. Even with this lax recruitment method, we didn't have many initial takers. Most of the surviving police officers feared that our recruitment efforts were a pretext for us to round them up and take them out into the desert to execute them.

I can't really blame the Iraqis for thinking this. Just days before, we had been firing rockets and dropping bombs on their police stations, killing and wounded their friends, and overnight we were asking them to be our trusted allies—never mind that the Iraqis have been known to carry grudges for centuries. Regardless, Mr. Bremer and Mr. Kerik could not understand the Iraqis' reluctance to come rushing back to help us, "the people who had liberated them from Saddam Hussein."

Of the few Iraqis who did sign up to join, quality, dedication, commitment and professionalism were highly lacking. Many stayed only long enough to get their first checks, while others stayed until we issued new Glock 40-caliber pistols. We pointed out to command what was wrong with this situation and what needed to be done to correct it, but our objections fell on deaf ears. We had a schedule to maintain, and we had to keep this war (a.k.a. liberation) short.

As time went on, we did begin to build trust, and very slowly the police stations started coming back to life. The fact that we paid well and gave away brand-new guns certainly helped. Most the stations had been heavily damaged in the attacks and looted by both the local population and the police officers themselves as they abandoned their locations. We had to start from scratch with most of them, right down to installing doors and windows. Other than the radio towers and walls, nothing was left.

Not too long into the process, the decision was made at Battalion that each police station now required two Iraqi Police officers be formally trained in law enforcement management. This formal training was scheduled to take place in Jordan, would last approximately eight weeks, and would qualify an Iraqi officer for a supervisory/management position. We were instructed to get two of the best police officers from each station to volunteer and put them on the airplane for transport to Jordan. So we sent word to the Platoon Leaders that we needed volunteers to carry out these orders. In short order, the Platoon Leaders told us that they had no volunteers who wanted the job.

The reason that none of the Iraqi officers wanted to volunteer was that they didn't completely trust us and didn't know for sure that they would really be going to Jordan. They had already taken the dangerous job of being a police officer and didn't want to make their personal situation more dangerous by appearing to be friendlier with Americans or other Coalition forces than they absolutely had to be. As it was, Iraqi Police Chiefs, deputy chiefs and other high-ranking law enforcement officials were being assassinated by insurgents on a weekly basis. Coming back from training as a ranking officer would make an Iraqi Police officer and his family even greater targets, not to mention that being gone from his family for six to eight weeks also meant no one was around to protect his family.

This information was relayed back to Battalion, whose reply was if we could get no one to volunteer, we should just pick two officers and get them to the airport. The Platoon Leaders tried explaining that the Iraqi officers wanted to stay in Baghdad to protect their families, and the officers who had potential to become good supervisors downright refused to leave. Battalion shot back that they didn't care that the Iraqis didn't want to go, and that they didn't care how we got the officers on the plane. We were to put two Iraqi officers per station on the plane to Jordan, and that was that.

I looked at the Battalion Operations Sergeant in disbelief and asked him if this was Battalion's idea of winning the hearts and minds of the Iraqi citizens. I asked if Battalion honestly believed that dragging officers out of the stations and forcing them to get on a plane would give the Iraqi people positive feelings about Americans. Even after I expressed my perception in those terms, Battalion's response was the same—get two police officers from each station and bring them to the airport. So that's what we did, and not without some resistance. No one was handcuffed and dragged to the plane, but if he wanted to keep his job, he had to go.

Saddam Style

We began transitioning the police stations back to the Iraqi authorities, hoping that we had successfully instilled American-style justice (as opposed to Saddam Hussein-style justice). While the Iraqis seemed to embrace both the American style of justice and the American way of running a police station, they went right back to their old way of doing things once we started transitioning out. They had been under the control of Saddam Hussein and his regime since 1979; thirty years cannot be wiped clean within a six-month time span. Attempting to change the way they operated and approached situations in six months was a fool's errand. Coalition forces ran into similar problems all across Iraq.

We had been operating under mandates provided by the International Red Cross meant to ensure the safety and welfare of all of our prisoners. One situation where we followed these mandates was in feeding them. According to International Red Cross standards, all prisoners must be provided a minimum of two meals per twenty-four-hour period. We had established contracts with a catering service to provide those meals, and the service was in place when we shifted from occupying and running the police stations to just monitoring them.

Shortly after we began monitoring duties, we began receiving complaints that the prisoners were not being fed. At this time, the International Red Cross standard no longer applied to the Iraqi prisoners, because they were now under control of civilian law enforcement and not Coalition forces. We decided to look into the situation because the caterer was still accepting our money, fully assuming that he thought that he no longer had to abide by the contract because we were no longer in control of the prisons.

When officers went to the station to confirm that the caterer was no longer delivering meals, they learned that he still was making deliveries. The problem was that the Iraqi Police officers took the food. When we questioned them about this, the officers explained that they deserved the catered meals more than the prisoners, so they had no problem eating the meals. They further explained that if the prisoners wanted to eat, they needed to either have family or friends bring food every day, or do some kind of work in exchange for food.

Even when family members were able to bring food to the prisoners, they were forced to either bring extra food for the Iraqi Police officers, or find some other method of bribing them. If a family didn't have extra money or food, the officers refused to let them see their imprisoned family member.

We tried to convince the police officers to give the catered food to the prisoners, but our pleas fell on deaf ears. In their minds, prisoners were criminals, not deserving of any kindness or consideration, and they certainly had no right to be fed for free.

Another International Red Cross guideline designed for prisoner safety addressed accommodations: a prisoner held longer than twenty-four hours needed to have an individual bed. This meant that if a lockup had twenty beds, the maximum number of prisoners housed at that facility over any twenty-four-hour period was twenty. We held to these guidelines.

The Captain in charge of the unit responsible for one of our police stations discovered that one facility had far more prisoners than beds. This discovery evolved into angry family members staging demonstrations in the street outside the facility, protesting the inhumane confinement of their family members. The Captain took it upon himself to correct the situation, and promised to send excess prisoners to a larger holding facility several miles away.

The Captain thought that this solution would appease the angry family members. Instead, his announcement only incited larger and more aggressive demonstrations, with people crying, wailing and screaming in the streets in front of the police station. The Captain was truly perplexed by their response. He honestly thought that he was doing the right thing by finding space and better living conditions for the prisoners, as opposed to keeping them crowded together in one lockup.

What he didn't understand was that under Saddam's rule, any problems with prisoner overcrowding was resolved by taking the appropriate number of prisoners out into the desert and executing them—something that Coalition forces would never, ever do, and it was beyond our comprehension that they could believe that we would ever consider doing it.

The Captain tried to alleviate the family members' fears by asking some of the civil and religious leaders to accompany the prisoners to the new facility. That way, the civil and religious leaders could see for themselves and report back that the prisoners were transferred to a more comfortable and humane facility, and not taken into the desert to be executed. Assuming that he had covered all the bases, the Captain arrived on the day of transport to demonstrations that were even louder and more chaotic than before.

He quickly realized that the Iraqis now believed that U.S. forces were going to execute the prisoners and their civil and religious leaders as punishment for protesting in front of the police station. Despite screaming and wailing relatives throwing themselves in front of trucks, the transport still took place.

Several hours later, the convoy returned. The prisoners had been dropped off at the larger facility and the religious and civic leaders were unharmed and in good health. At this point, the Captain (ever the optimist) thought that he would finally get respect and perhaps gratitude from the Iraqi citizens for his act of kindness. After all, he had shown professionalism and compassion in taking care of their loved ones, even though they were criminals and prisoners.

Shockingly, not so. Apparently, treating the prisoners humanely led the Iraqis to believe that Americans were weak and lacked the guts to do what needed to be done. With that type of reasoning, no wonder we couldn't seem to do anything right. No matter what we said or did, they always found a way to turn it into a negative gesture. After thirty years of abuse from the Saddam regime, Iraqis were unable to trust that our actions were motivated by fairness, courtesy or empathy. These ideals seemed to be too far beyond their understanding.

At times, the Iraqi Police went completely against the standards of American criminal justice. During a daily check monitoring police stations, the fact that one of the stations was housing a few prisoners was noted. On the very next day, the follow-up check found the station's holding facility crammed full with prisoners, all having been picked up the previous evening. It was literally standing room only in the holding area.

When asked about the number of prisoners, the Iraqi officers proudly explained that they had learned weapons were being sold in the marketplace. Following up on this information, they made a sweep of the marketplace and picked up all of these people.

Impressed and pleased that the Iraqi Police were finally standing up and taking charge of their neighborhoods, a soldier asked the officers, "How many weapons did you seize?"

"We seized no weapons," the officers replied.

Now the soldiers were confused. "Why do you have so many prisoners if you didn't seize any weapons?"

The Iraqi Police officers didn't understand this line of questioning and said, "these were the people who were in the marketplace when we did the sweep. They were all suspects, so we brought them in."

"But if you didn't seize any weapons, how can you have prisoners?"

The Iraqis explained that witnesses would be coming to identify which prisoners had been dealing weapons. The soldiers pressed them for when this would happen, and the only reply they received was, "Very soon."

When the soldiers continued to press, the Iraqi Police became evasive.

"How long are you going to hold these people?"

"Not very long. Maybe a few hours."

This answer somewhat satisfied the soldiers until the Iraqis added, "Although maybe a day or two, or as much as a few weeks. It all depends on when we can get the witnesses here."

Although this type of law enforcement went totally against the U.S. standard of justice, we could do little about it, as the Iraqis were supposed to be operating on their own, exercising their own criminal justice system. By this point in the transition of authority, the Coalition could only offer suggestions on what courses of action to take. The final decision was ultimately up to the Iraqi Police. And when they realized that we couldn't make them do anything, they went right back to the old way of doing things. They may have hated Saddam Hussein and praised the Coalition for giving them freedom, but they only knew one system of justice.

The judicial system was also a nightmare. In one instance, an individual asked a friend to accompany him to the marketplace. His friend was reluctant to go because he had been part of the old regime and knew that there were people who wanted to get revenge on him for what he had done in the past, but his friend convinced him to go. Once there, someone recognized him as a member of the old regime, promptly walked up to him and quickly killed him before disappearing into the crowd.

The Iraqi Police responded to the scene, conducted an investigation and made an arrest shortly thereafter. The Military Police responsible for the sector were very impressed with the speed in which both the Iraqi law enforcement and court system responded to this incident... that is, until the MPs were told that the Iraqi Police arrested the murder victim's friend.

Assuming that they had misunderstood the initial report, the MPs asked the Iraqi officer if a third party had committed the murder. The officer confirmed that yes, in fact, a third individual appeared out of nowhere, fired at the victim, and disappeared again while the friend stood close by.

The MPs assumed that evidence linking the friend to the victim's death must be available (and perhaps the friend had even lured the victim to the marketplace to be killed) the MPs asked the Iraqi officer if this was the case. The Iraqi Police explained no, the friend was just a bystander. *However*, he did ask the victim to go to the marketplace; and if he hadn't, the victim would still be alive. By their reasoning, the victim's friend was complicit in the crime and arrested for murder.

This type of thinking was not isolated to this one case. It was repeated day after day, creating bizarre and ridiculous circumstances beyond our comprehension. Undoing centuries of tribal thinking in just a few short months was simply not possible. Revenge killings were common, and Iraqi Police either looked the other way or, in some cases, actively participated. According to Iraqi tradition, families would settle these problems, not law enforcement.

Gary Trudeau wrote a *Doonesbury* strip[8.1] that summed this mentality up nicely. In it, a U.S. soldier and an Iraqi Police officer are in a Humvee, preparing to raid a house,

U.S. Soldier: Okay, that's the safe house—the big white building at the end of the street.

Iraqi officer: I know this house. The owner is Sunni Scum.

U.S. Soldier: Oh, yeah? Well, Intel wants us to capture the guy alive.

Iraqi officer: This will not be possible. I am sworn to vengeance!

U.S. Soldier: Why? What'd he ever do to you?

Iraqi officer: A member of his family killed a member of mine.

U.S. Soldier: What? When did this happen?

Iraqi officer: 1387.

U.S. Soldier: What is the matter with you people?

Though the comic strip is hilarious, this type of thinking and reasoning is not. The irony was that he wasn't embellishing or editing the truth to make his Iraqi war and occupation strips funny; he just wrote down what was really happening. I often read his comics and recalled a time when what he had written actually happened to me and others in Iraq.

The Mission Continues

Our stated goal was that we would have these stations up, running, and fully manned no later than June 30, 2003, so we continued re-establishing police stations in our area of responsibility. Everyone knew that June 30th was an overly optimistic deadline as we were again starting from scratch with bombed-out buildings and no Iraqi Police officers. Nevertheless, somehow the powers-that-be thought that they could not only wrap up our mission in less than thirty days; they also planned to rebuild all of Iraq in a few months.

Figure 8.4   Confiscated Weapons

Every night, gunfire and explosions could be heard all across the city. Each day, attacks on Coalition forces became more sophisticated and deadly. Despite having an entire Armored brigade and better part of the Military Police brigade on the western side of Baghdad, we still could not control our part of the city. The situation didn't seem likely to change, even if we were able to get the Iraqi Police up and running again.

We reported every hostile contact up the chain of command. Our Battalion Commander for the MPs, and later, the Brigade Commander for the 3rd Brigade Combat Team, were out on the road on a daily basis, gathering intelligence on what was going on and briefing their higher Headquarters. For some reason, Mr. Bremer, Mr. Kerik and the President's advisors either chose not to believe the reports or simply disregarded them.

From time to time, we would catch CNN or FOX News and hear press conferences with Mr. Rumsfeld. During these press conferences, he would talk about the progress in Iraq, claiming that the insurgency was limited to only a few hundred disgruntled individuals with no local backing or support. He obviously put absolutely no stock in our reports, if he bothered to read them at all.

If Mr. Rumsfeld had been correct, and we had been up against only a few hundred insurgents, at the rate we were killing and capturing them, we should have been getting ready to go home by the end of June. Unfortunately, he wasn't correct, and he wasn't correct for the next two years.

ACTIVITY LOG
May 12–June 6, 2003

May 12, 2003

We had our first contact in Iraq. Staff Sergeant Yorski, with 2nd Squad, 3rd Platoon, confiscated the first weapon in Iraq. We thought this was a big deal, until we were directed to take it down to the storage locker and found several hundred other weapons of various types already there.

May 14, 2003

1st Platoon has a number of corrections officers in their unit, including Platoon Sergeant Roddy Porter. They were were directed to take over the construction supervision of the Al Kharkh Jail in central Baghdad. Their secondary assignment was to provide security while the facility was being built. This would be their assignment for the next several weeks.

May 19, 2003

2nd Platoon assisted in apprehending three murder suspects, confiscating two AK-47 assault rifles and one RPK light machine gun. This was more of a criminal investigation than going after insurgents.

May 20, 2003

Staff Sergeant Matus and 3rd Squad, 3rd Platoon, was sent to secure the area of a possible mass murder site. The area was later turned over to other units. On the same day, 2nd Squad, 4th Platoon was searching a building for kidnapping and carjacking suspects. They seized two AK-47 assault rifles, ammunition, and French-made military radios. They were able to arrest one carjacking suspect and return him to the FOB.

May 23, 2003

Activity continued with 3rd Squad, discovering an Iraqi male lying in the middle of the road, a victim of multiple gunshot wounds.

This was pretty much an everyday occurrence.

May 30, 2003

There was a prison riot at a facility in our area of operation. While correctional officers, who were members of our unit, initially helped construct and operate the prison, once construction was complete, another unit from outside our Battalion was assigned to the facility.

The prison held approximately one hundred inmates and, during the riot, twenty-six managed to tear down the door of their cellblock. Soldiers running the facility trained a machine gun on the opened door to keep the prisoners at bay, but had no way of securing them. After not being able to make contact with their parent company, the soldiers discovered that they had our radio frequency from our prior assignment at the prison, and had contacted us instead.

I received the call, I waited for direction from Battalion. After getting no response, I began making radio calls, trying to locate any units that were still outside the wire. I was able to reach Lieutenant Grube, who informed me that he would take two teams over to the prison. At about that time, Staff Sergeant Sullivan came up on the frequency to inform me that he would provide backup to Lieutenant Grube. I was relieved now that I knew approximately fifteen soldiers were responding to the prison's call for help.

Our Squads arrived at the facility, took the twenty-six rioting prisoners into custody, and transported them to another facility. While en route in open trucks, several of the detainees slipped off their plastic zip-tie handcuffs. They acted like it was a big joke, laughing and waving at the escorting soldiers. Our soldiers trained their machine guns on the prisoners, and had instructions to fire if any exited the vehicle. Fortunately, none of the prisoners were quite that crazy.

This was all done on the fly, without any input from Battalion. We simply reacted to the situation as it unfolded. It was the type of response you would expect from people in law enforcement back in the States; here in a military bureaucracy, getting someone to stick their necks out and make a decision was difficult.

Battalion, being structured as it was, could not respond to an unfolding situation because they weren't designed to react that way. For them, everything had to have a school solution or a book answer. When the riot occurred, no one wanted to take responsibility, and some didn't know whether or not they even had authority to order soldiers to the prison—never mind the fact that someone else's unit was over there (not one of theirs), so the concern and the idea that it might be their job to help those soldiers never crossed their mind. As this situation was unfolding, I kept asking myself, "Aren't we all on the same team?"

In another situation, we had officers on patrol outside the Compound when Battalion advised us that the police station at Abu Ghraib was under attack and needed reinforcements. Two Squads of approximately twenty soldiers from the 143rd were dispatched to the area. I contacted Battalion and asked where the insurgents were located to understand where the threat was coming from. They asked why I needed that information. I replied that I wanted to make sure that our units weren't driving into the middle of the attack or approaching from a direction that would put them in jeopardy.

The impression I got from this exchange was that they had not even considered that we could be driving into the middle of the attack. This basic tactical concept seemed to be beyond their comprehension. I kept wondering what they had been doing for the last fifteen years.

June 1, 2003

1st Squad, 4th Platoon responded to a report of shots fired, and ended up in a firefight with four individuals, one of whom was killed. The remaining three were wounded, but escaped on foot. The subjects were identified as insurgents, but by this time things were starting to blur, and we really didn't know who was attacking us.

Specialist Matt Hayes was one of the individuals to return fire. He could not see any of the attackers, and he couldn't hear the direction from which the fire was coming because of the noise of the Humvee. He could just make out winking muzzle flashes from their rifles, and fired in that direction. Fortunately, he was able to suppress the hostile fire with short accurate busts, even if he could not see a target.

We received an assignment to provide a three-team squad to escort an extremely large column of 250 fuel trucks. We were told that they were military vehicles, and that each fuel truck had a machine gun mounted on it.

In a typical convoy situation, each vehicle is allotted approximately 300 feet per vehicle—one hundred feet for the vehicle itself and a 200 foot buffer between it and other vehicles. When Lieutenant Grube arrived on the scene, he learned that seventy of the original 250 vehicles were being sent to another location by Battalion. This change meant that the convoy would be close to ten miles long. He also learned that the fuel trucks were civilian vehicles, not military, and not one of them was armed.

The idea that three MP vehicles could protect a ten-mile-long convoy was ridiculous. At best, we could have one vehicle in the lead, one vehicle in the rear, and one vehicle in the middle, each one separated from the other by a distance of five miles.

When I pointed out how dangerous this situation was, an active-duty officer countered that the vehicle convoy would not be ten miles long. Even when I did the math for them and explained that I needed the entire company to provide escort and protection, he still refused to reconsider. The officer insisted that three vehicles were more than enough coverage (an underlying fact was that their people weren't going to be in the convoy, the National Guard were).

Almost as an afterthought, he added that we would be protected by helicopter gunships flying overhead. This information helped make me feel better, but still, I knew that any help helicopters could provide would be minimal. Helicopters flying in Iraq tended to stay very low and fly very fast. Insurgents armed with RPG grenade launchers and small arms didn't have time to aim and fire. However, when helicopters fly low, their view is limited; and when they fly very fast, they do not have time to clearly assess what is going on below.

So I asked for the radio frequencies and call signs the helicopter gunships would be operating on, but the officer gave me a look of confusion. I was shocked that he didn't seem to understand why I needed this information. I explained that the helicopters would need to communicate with us if they spotted something, and if we got into trouble, we needed to be able to call for assistance. He still just did not understand why we would need this information, and said that the helicopters would be escorting us, and we wouldn't need to call them.

The more we worked with Battalion, both on this mission and in the future, the more it became apparent that they were still in training mode, could not think on their feet, and definitely could not think through a combat situation. In short, they were simply not prepared for real-life combat situations.

As no one had yet thought the destination of this convey was important enough to tell us, I asked where these vehicles were being escorted. I was told to escort the vehicles down the main road out of Baghdad, up to the city line, point them in the direction of Kuwait, and tell them to keep going.

"Who are we turning the convoy over to?" I asked.

I was told no one, that we were to simply direct the vehicles out of Baghdad.

I asked if I was just supposed to point them south and tell them that in a couple of hundred miles, they'll just run into Kuwait?

I was told that yes, that was "pretty much" what I was supposed to do.

This was one of the craziest assignments and operations orders I had ever heard, and I said so. Active-duty did not like being questioned, especially since these were officers who were all senior to me, and I was only in the National Guard.

We did, ultimately, take the mission, and Lieutenant Grube did respond to Baghdad International Airport with his detail to locate the fuel trucks. When he arrived, we discovered that not only were the fuel trucks driven by civilians, they were all Turkish civilians who did not speak English. Simply attempting to get the convoy mounted up and moving out was problematic. Although he could not get them to understand what he wanted them to do, he clearly understood that they were afraid to go.

At last, Lieutenant Grube managed to get the convoy up and moving and, to our surprise, a Marine Corps detachment was at Baghdad city limits to take over and escort them to Kuwait (which finally made complete sense). Although we were very glad they were there, we would have felt more confident going into the assignment had we known that they would be there. We did not know the Marines would be waiting until Lieutenant Grube ran into them at the city limits. We never did make contact with the helicopters, and we did not observe any throughout the assignment.

June 3, 2003

We received a call about a bank robbery. We dispatched an MP Squad but, recalling all the bank robberies from our civilian duties, we expected that our extended response time would mean that the bank robbers would be long gone by the time we got there. Apparently, they do things differently in Baghdad. Our units arrived at a hostage situation with shots fired. Two robbers escaped, but two were captured, and numerous weapons were confiscated. We needed to learn how to adjust to the Iraqi way of law enforcement, and shed our American expectations.

1st, 2nd and 4th Squads of 4th Platoon assisted the 4th Platoon of the 4/1 Field Artillery in a cordon and search mission that netted six suspected Fedayeen members.

June 4, 2003

Several attacks on Military Police units with hand grenades took place. These units belonged to our Battalion, but not our Company. One of the attackers was wounded and escaped, but eventually detained at a hospital by our officers.

June 6, 2003

We learned of a redeployment order that had come out, dated May 5, 2003, which got our hopes up. This order indicated that combat units who were part of the initial invasion would be leaving in sixty days, while all other units would be rotating out in 120 days. They indicated that the last units to come out would be the Military Police units. Interpreting the order led us to believe that the MP units would start rotating out after 120 days.

We later learned that this order was drafted not by military units, but by the ambassador and advisors to President Bush. No one on the ground saw this order as a viable option, as things were still very volatile and chaotic. A new government was not yet in place, and a criminal justice system consisting of law enforcement, courts and prisons, had not been established to the degree needed to ensure security.

The only units we did see moving south at that time were Marine Corps units. No Army units had, as yet, disengaged. In fact, several Army units that had initially been scheduled to invade Iraq through Turkey were still on their way in, because the original mission was canceled after Turkey refused to allow Coalition forces to pass through their borders. So those units were shifted through ports in Kuwait. The redeployment started taking place at the very end of May and continued through the end of June, 2003.

Chapter Nine

BULLDOG FOB, NORTHERN BAGHDAD

Do everything you ask of those you command.

General George S. Patton

On June 11, 2003, our transfer went through; and we were moved from Warrior Compound up to Bulldog, the FOB for the 3rd Brigade Combat Team, 1st Armored Division. We were collocated with Brigade Headquarters, as well as several other units in the FOB, including a Scout Platoon, Civil Affairs, and Military Intelligence.

Bulldog FOB was a great improvement over our previous location at Warrior Compound and, despite some damage from the initial invasion, was relatively intact. It had belonged to the Ministry of Oil and Technology and had been a trade school where students learned how to drill oil wells. Built much like a college in the United States, Bulldog had sufficient amenities to support training and dormitory space for several hundred people.

However, most of the electricity was off, which meant that we had to power our radios using our own generators. Somehow, people at Bulldog did manage to get the air conditioners up and running. They didn't really keep the place cool, but they did cut the outdoor summer temperatures of about 120° to about ninety to 95° indoors, which made life much more bearable.

We were in direct support of the 3rd Brigade Combat Team. One Platoon was assigned to each of the Brigade's maneuver Battalions, and three of our four Line Platoons were moved out of Bulldog to be located with the Battalions to which they had been assigned. 3rd Platoon, Headquarters, and Operations remained at Bulldog.

With the shift to direct support of the Armored Brigade and being assigned Infantry, our mission changed from manning police stations to supporting the 3rd Brigade Combat Team. Activities still took place that would be in support of law enforcement operations, and units were still supporting the police stations that they had started with, but with more emphasis towards the support of the Armored Brigade.

Even before we moved to Bulldog, the Military Police at Warrior Compound were trying to get us reassigned back to their Battalion. They realized that we were much more than weekend warriors, and that some of us had more experience than the active-duty soldiers. Our Platoons got along great with their 1st Armored Division Infantry and Armored counterparts, enjoying their assignments and their various missions. We seemed like an excellent match, and we had no desire to go back to the Military Police Battalion.

We did have a few rough spots at Bulldog with 3rd Platoon, Headquarters and Operations, mostly because of two guys whom I took to calling "the two Janitors." They were two sergeant majors from the Brigade, each of whom seemed to have only one duty to perform. One was responsible for the parking and tidiness of vehicles in the Compound, while the other was responsible for the tidiness of the inside of the building. To the best of my knowledge, the Janitors rarely, if ever, left the FOB to visit their troops. The entire time we were with the 3rd Brigade (and even today) I kept wondering what the two highest-ranking NCOs had done to rate such lofty assignments. We had two-year Specialists with more responsible assignments than these two.

Thanks to the Janitors, numerous extra duties fell to Headquarters and Operations and, because they were with us at Bulldog, 3rd Platoon. The Janitors placed top priority on "police calls" (an Army term for picking up trash in the parking areas and cleaning the building—not to be confused with law enforcement). Most of these calls were delegated to our company, which meant that our clerks and communicators, as well as other staff from Headquarters and Operations, would be doing police calls, cleaning up, or standing tower guard, instead of performing their actual duties with us. It also meant that, no matter what 3rd Platoon was doing, they still had police calls to make and had to do them on schedule and on time.

One morning, 3rd Platoon had just come off of a four-part roadblock and checkpoint mission with their Infantry counterparts. They had been going for twenty-four-hour periods involving four to six hours manning roadblocks and checkpoints, returning to the FOB for two to three hours of rest and maybe something to eat, and then going back out for another four to six hours. During each six-hour period, they had to move quickly about the city with their Infantry counterparts, setting up a roadblock or checkpoint, breaking down said roadblock/checkpoint, moving to the next location, and doing it all over again. The heat was brutal and, as you would expect, the environment was very dangerous and unpredictable.

This strenuous regimen did not stop one of the Janitors from getting in my face at 0700 the next morning, demanding to know why 3rd Platoon's police call had not been completed and why our vehicles were such a mess. I informed him that there was a war on and that my soldiers, except for a few hours of rest between missions, had been in the field for the entire previous day. He didn't think this was a reasonable excuse, and told me that there was paper blowing through the parking lot—an egregious violation that had to be addressed immediately.

To this day, I shake my head every time I think of someone who's been in the military long enough to make sergeant major and thinks that picking up paper and sweeping floors is a mission priority in a combat zone. The safety and the welfare of their troops in the face of the insurgency somehow took a backseat to the Janitors' priorities. Just to shut him up, I went out and did the police call myself, and picked up a broom once I got back inside. But even this didn't satisfy him—he wanted the troops out there doing the work. I told him that the best I could do was to give them a master sergeant.

Years later, I learned that Colonel Gold had made keeping Bulldog in a clean and orderly condition one of his top priorities. Prior to the 3rd Brigade Combat Team taking over the Compound, the unit that had been housed there took to dumping garbage and human waste in various rooms. When 3rd Brigade first moved in, the stench and health conditions were horrible.

Colonel Gold had vowed that soldiers under his command would have a safe, clean, and healthy place to live, and he directed the sergeant majors to get it done. They did, but then took Colonel Gold's command to the extreme—a few pieces of paper in the parking area, or a floor that had not been swept in twenty-four hours, became major disasters. Common sense did not prevail.

Not too long after our arrival at Bulldog, the troops noticed that the Janitors liked to use the F-word a lot. The First Sergeant went to a staff meeting of the Sergeant Majors, and brought along our Communications Chief, who had one job at that meeting—keep track of every time the Janitors used the F-word. As the meeting went on, the Communications Chief kept making tick marks on his note pad, to the point where it was getting difficult for him to keep up with the Janitors.

We found strange ways to entertain ourselves.

Ammunition and the Janitors

Our soldiers were assigned guard duty in the towers located around the perimeter of Bulldog. Soldiers assigned to each tower were expected to have their full basic load of ammunition with them. Of course, some of the soldiers were clerks, cooks and communicators who did not have their full basic load. With the limited ammunition given to us, our first priority was to make sure that the Military Police officers who were on the road had a full load. Other soldiers had only around four magazines each, as opposed to the mandatory seven.

When our soldiers responded for guard duty without their full basic load, one of the Janitors demanded to know how I could let such a thing happen. I informed him that we had issued every round of ammunition we had received, and gave Military Police officers top priority. He found the ammo situation completely unacceptable (and rightly so).

I then suggested that since he was now our higher headquarters, I would be very grateful if he could provide several thousand rounds of ammunition so we could fill our basic load for all of our soldiers. He declined, and said that was a stupid request, adding that we should just take the unused magazines from soldiers who were not in the field, and reassign them to the soldiers on tower guard.

Regardless of his indifference, we were eventually able to get a full basic load of ammunition for Platoons assigned to Infantry Battalions (albeit not through proper channels). But even after this accomplishment, our Headquarters and Operations sections were still short on ammo. With no other options, we were forced to rely on soldiers from other Infantry units who were kind enough to share ammunition they had squirreled away.

Not long after our unit returned home, several gun battles took place in which a Military Police unit, performing an escort mission, fired all seven of their magazines, and then had to return to their vehicles to retrieve extra ammo. If our units had been in one of those fire fights, we would not have had extra ammo in our vehicles to retrieve.

In spite of it all, the powers-that-be continued to insist that extra ammunition was not necessary because combat operations were over. While they were insisting that combat was over, they continued insisting that having seven full magazines with 210 rounds was absolutely mandatory for soldiers going on duty.

As of this writing the conflict is not over and with no real end in sight.

Tower Duty

One day, Sergeant Chris Sweetwood was assigned to one of the towers at the rear of the Compound. While manning the tower, his team received an urgent broadcast that the main gate had been attacked and a soldier was down. Everyone on the perimeter became hyper-watchful of everything that was happening outside the wire.

Shortly thereafter, Sergeant Sweetwood observed a number of individuals armed with AK-47 assault rifles some distance from the perimeter. Security forces, as well as the Iraqi Police and the military, carry AK-47s, so the individuals were not necessarily hostile. Even so, even *if* they were friendly, they were in the wrong place at the wrong time with the wrong weapon. Protocol required Sweetwood to engage a force if it appeared to be, or actually was, attacking.

Thankfully, Sergeant Sweetwood took the opportunity to question what action he should take, and contacted the Supervisor of the Guard Force. Only then was Sergeant Sweetwood informed that the attack on the front gate had only been a drill. Bulldog had, in fact, not taken hostile fire and no soldiers had been injured.

No one thought to inform the soldiers who were armed and ready to defend the perimeter. If Sergeant Sweetwood had blindly followed protocol and opened fire without confirmation, he would have made a deadly mistake, as he is an expert marksman.

Daily Summaries

Nearly every evening, we participated in a meeting with the MP Battalion Headquarters in the Warrior Compound auditorium. Each company or detachment would describe their current duties and discuss plans and schedules for the following day, as well as provide summaries about what had happened during the previous twenty-four-hours. The Battalion Commander and his staff addressed his units regarding activity, supply issues, weather, and other related topics.

During these meetings, an officer threw shots at other companies, making obvious attempts to one-up them. What he didn't understand was, that while he might have been able to get away with playing politics occasionally, he couldn't really get away with such games at every meeting. He also didn't understand that he was only National Guard, and that the active-duty Battalion Commanders did not care for a part-time MP who was trying to make their active-duty troops look bad.

During one such meeting, the officer announced that the 143rd had found cyanide gas (which is listed as a WMD). The Battalion Commander was shocked that no one had immediately informed either him or Battalion of this major find, and nearly jumped out of his seat, demanding to know why the officer had taken so long to share this information. After searching for over four months, finally finding a cache of Saddam's chemical weapons was a show stopper, the type of event that makes front page news, and is cause for people to be awarded promotions and medals—yet no one told the boss.

I was sitting far back in the auditorium, half-asleep, making notes when the officer made his announcement. When I heard the words "cyanide gas" my head snapped up so hard I thought I had injured myself. My two counterparts at Battalion, who were sitting in front of me, turned and stared at me. I was their contact, responsible for passing along such vitally important information. If anyone had dropped the ball, it had been me.

If I had been informed that we had found WMDs, my highest priority would have been to get that information to Battalion as soon as possible. If what the officer had said was true, and I had sat on the information, my next assignment would be cleaning latrines at high noon.

I knew the truth, and in the death glares I was receiving from my counterparts, I rolled my eyes, and slowly shook my head "no."

They looked confused, shrugging their shoulders at me. I continued to slowly shake my head from side to side, mouthing the words, "didn't happen," until I got the head nod from the Operations sergeant major to step outside.

Using several colorful adjectives, he demanded to know what was going on.

I informed him that, yes, we had found cyanide, but it was only cyanide powder, not cyanide gas. The powder had been stored in a canister with a label clearly marked "Cyanide Powder," and had been not concealed in any way. We had found the powder in an abandoned metal manufacturing facility (cyanide powder is commonly used in the fabrication of metal alloys). Yes, cyanide powder could be deadly, but not in the way that the officer had presented it.

The officer never told us what he was going to brief at these meetings, so whatever was said, we were hearing for the first time. If he had run his briefs by us before presenting them, he would have saved himself much grief in the long run.

Civil Affairs

Shortly after the start of any occupation, the country is in chaos and members of the previously established civilian government have the potential of not being very trustworthy. Civil Affairs units are dispatched to these areas to maintain order and provide support and assistance in reestablishing the civilian government. This transition needs to happen quickly so the civilian government can effectively handle the country's internal issues.

In Iraq, Civil Affairs were stymied. According to Secretary of State Colin Powell, we had liberated Iraq and not conquered it. Because of liberation, the powers-that-be decided that Civil Affairs would not be the lead element responsible for reestablishing civilian authority. Instead, that responsibility would fall to the State Department.

While the State Department did have members in Iraq, leaving the Green Zone was not safe without a heavy military presence. Due to the level of threats against them, the State Department chose to remain in the Green Zone, which meant that anyone with grievances had to travel to the Green Zone to present their issues to the State Department.

For the majority of Iraqis, visiting the Green Zone meant leaving their homes for more than a day, and they didn't want to leave the safety of their communities at all for fear of what would happen (1) to their families while they were away, and (2) on the dangerous streets of Central Baghdad (which was basically a battle zone, and the U.S. Military wasn't offering Iraqi civilians military escorts). And then there was the issue of being spotted entering the Green Zone or speaking with Coalition forces.

Civil Affairs wanted to help, but their hands were tied by the State

Department. Many Iraqis would walk into our FOB from neighboring communities to voice their concerns and ask Civil Affairs for assistance. In most cases, the only thing Civil Affairs could do was to tell them to direct their concerns and requests to the State Department.

In one instance, several Iraqi farming families came to Bulldog because their irrigation water had been shut off by a more powerful clan who lived upstream. The more powerful clan was attempting to extort water rights fees from their neighbors downstream—a clear civil rights violation that Civil Affairs personnel had successful experience handling. So, thankfully, even though it went against State Department guidelines, Civil Affairs decided to go up there and get the water turned back on.

However, because Civil Affairs was not a combat unit, they lacked the vehicles and weapon systems needed to get the job done, so Major Wishart from Civil Affairs came to us and requested a Military Police escort. This request was more than reasonable, and should have been very simple to fulfill. The problem was that we had no authorization from the combat team's Brigade Headquarters to perform this mission.

Major Wishart was adamant about helping these families and, fortunately or unfortunately, his simple logic that getting the water turned back on was beneficial and needed to be done proved to be very compelling. So I contacted Brigade Operations to request permission to escort the Major and his team. I never received a response one way or the other.

In the end, we decided to do the mission on our own, and arranged for the Operations Escort Squad normally assigned to protect our Company Commander to escort Major Wishart and his team. Then Major Wishart met with the clan leader and, in a gentlemanly way, requested that the dams be reopened so that the water could flow into the irrigation canals.

When the clan leader refused, the Major replied that if the irrigation canals weren't reopened, he would have Coalition forces blow the dams that controlled the water, ensuring that it would flow freely forever.

Retaliation and threats of force were qualities that the Iraqis were familiar with. They were not so familiar with kindness, generosity, fairness, or other concepts of a civilized nature; instead, Iraqis perceived these qualities as human weaknesses. We were confronted with this perception the entire time we were there. They seemed to understand only rule by force or threat of force.

I don't know if it was the culture of the Middle East, Saddam, or a combination of the two, but this behavior was something we had to overcome during all of our dealings with the Iraqis, whether it was with law enforcement officers or civilians. In one of his many briefings to us, Colonel Gold gave us some sound advice that was repeated by other commanders: "Be polite, be professional, and be ready to kill everyone you meet."

Brigade Staff Meetings

When the company commander was not available, I was responsible for sitting in on several Brigade staff meetings. At first, I felt very strange going into these meetings because I was the only person from the National Guard, and therefore not part of the Brigade. I was the only enlisted person in the room. Yet here I was, an MP master sergeant, sitting down with a full colonel, a half dozen lieutenant colonels, and a handful of majors.

Because I had not been briefed on my role, I had no idea what to expect from these meetings. They turned out to be much like our MP Battalion briefings back at the 709th, but at a higher level. First the Battalion Commanders briefed Colonel Gold regarding their activity in their sectors. Then the Lieutenant Colonel representing the Engineers spoke about their successes in restoring power and water to Western Baghdad (a very high priority). The Brigade Executive officer and Brigade Operations officer spoke of past successes and future operations. There was talk of equipment status and manpower availability. In the beginning, consideration was given to fixing the roads and bridges that we had destroyed. The meetings were all very cut and dried stuff, a kind of "state of the Brigade briefing."

During the first meeting, Colonel Gold turned to me and asked how the MPs were doing—a huge "oh shit" moment. As I didn't have anything planned, I didn't know where to begin. I certainly had a lot to talk about, but I didn't know what, if anything, was relevant to this meeting. I was forced to wing it.

I told Colonel Gold that our MP Platoons were having a good time with the Battalions they had been assigned to, and had no complaints about the assignments. I continued on with the fact that the Platoons and the Company would prefer to stay with the Armored Brigade than return to the MP Battalion if at all possible. I told him that I suspected the Battalion Commanders were bribing my guys to say nice things. A smile came to Colonel Gold's face as well as the rest of the officers in the room. The colonel was very pleased with my briefing. And although tongue-in-cheek, it was all true. With the exception of the two Janitors, Colonel Gold and his Battalion Commanders treated my soldiers as equals.

Colonel Gold's concept was for each of the four MP Platoons to work in one assigned area directly for the Battalion Commander who controlled that battle space. 1st Platoon went to work for the 2nd Battalion 70th Armor, initially under Lieutenant Colonel Jeff Ingram, and then under Lieutenant Colonel Lee Quintas. They were stationed in western Baghdad and operated out of Forward Operating Base Thunder.

2nd Platoon fell under 1st of the 13th Armor, and worked under Lieutenant Colonel Frank Sherman, who was referred to as "The Shermanator." That unit was located at Forward Operating Base Dakota, in the central part of Western Baghdad.

3rd Platoon was assigned to a Battalion from the 82nd Airborne, the 1st of the 325th. 3rd Platoon stayed at Bulldog with Headquarters and Operations, but took their assignments from Lieutenant Colonel Eric Nantz, better known as "Red Falcon Six." The Airborne unit was located at Red Falcon Forward Operating Base in a location we referred to as the "Dust Bowl."

4th Platoon worked for the 4th of the 1st Field Artillery, and Lieutenant Colonel Boyer. This unit was located near the Tigris River, in the central part of Baghdad. The location was known to everyone as the

"Four Heads Palace," an extravagant palace Saddam had built to honor himself, with four large heads on the roof. As a Forward Operating Base, it had the official name of "Gunner," but no one ever called it that.

Lieutenant Colonel Tony Wright was the Brigade Engineering officer. Indirectly, our Platoons supported his efforts to bring the Baghdad infrastructure back to life. For over a month, the 3rd Brigade Combat Team had been tasked with finding and destroying the Iraqi military. Now Brigade was supposed to do a complete 180^0 about-face and rebuild everything they had just destroyed.

While the 143rd Military Police Company and the rest of the MPs were rebuilding the Iraqi criminal justice system, the Engineers from the 3rd Brigade were tasked with getting the power back on, the water running, and the sewer system working, and repairing roads and bridges. To quote Colonel Gold, "These things were never covered at the War College." The military trains soldiers to find and destroy things, not put them back together.

But that was the mission.

Culture Shock

One of the concepts drilled into American soldiers is that "firing warning shots" is a fallacy, and a dangerous one at that. A warning shot is still a live round that can injure or kill, and there's no way of knowing where the bullets are going to land. Soldiers on the other end of warning shots are left to guess if the shots are being fired as a warning or are near misses from hostile fire. For American soldiers, the answer is obvious—hearing gunfire means that someone wants to kill them.

Even though we were trained to never fire warning shots, we learned, after a relatively short time that in Iraq, warning shots are necessary. No matter how much we yelled, gestured, waved, demanded, or pushed, very few Iraqis took us seriously. Only after firing off a few warning shots did people take notice.

Figure 9.1   Lieutenant Colonel Garrity addressing the 143rd after awarding the Purple Heart to Private First Class Hackett (Private First Class Hayes was awarded the Purple Heart from another engagement.) (Left to Right) Specialist Wilde, Private First Class Hayes, Lieutenant Colonel Garrity, and Private First Class Hackett

Firing into the air in Iraq didn't have the same effect as it would here. No one got excited or scared or took off running. The sound of gunfire had little affect on the locals other than making them realize that we were serious. If anything, gunfire made them curious, so much so that they tended to gravitate toward gunfire to see what was going on.

The warning shots were only one aspect of Iraqi behavior that perplexed us. Even though they had been invaded and were in the middle of a war between Coalition forces and the insurgency, Iraqis in general reacted strangely to their surroundings (by American standards). Regardless of shots being fired and explosions going off on a daily basis, Iraqis would still react in a way we found baffling, and then they would wonder why we were getting so excited about everything.

Figure 9.2   Private First Class Hackett after being awarded the Purple Heart for wounds received in combat. (Left to Right) Platoon Sergeant SFC Porter, Private First Class Hackett, and Lieutenant Grube

One example that comes to mind involves the roadblocks and checkpoints that had been set up all over Baghdad. They were not unusual, and happened all the time in search of wanted people and weapons. The areas around these roadblocks were very dangerous because our soldiers were out on a road, facing moving traffic, with large groups of people and vehicles in a constant state of motion. Early on, although we had no Iraqi Police or soldiers to assist, our soldiers generally had translators on hand.

In this case, 3rd Platoon had a translator when a speeding vehicle approached the checkpoint, showing no signs of slowing down. As the vehicle approached, one of the passengers, armed with an AK-47, climbed out the back window. Everyone at the checkpoint took cover, but no one had a good line of sight on the vehicle to open fire. When the vehicle surprisingly stopped at the checkpoint, members of the 3rd Platoon yelled for the driver and passenger to drop their weapon and put up their hands.

Imagine a group of soldiers, armed to the teeth, using every four-letter word ever created, at a decibel level that could be heard in Turkey…but these people were not getting it. The soldiers were, of course, yelling in English, which the occupants likely did not understand. But the rifles pointed at them, the yelling, and the mean-as-hell faces ought to have made some sort of impression. They did not. The vehicle occupants stayed put.

As the soldiers approached, they discovered a family of three; husband, wife and toddler. The toddler was the "person" spotted climbing out the back window; his weapon a toy replica of an AK-47. When Sergeant First Class Lawler brought the replica to us to examine, we saw that it was only slightly smaller than the real thing, but otherwise made to exacting detail. From a hundred feet away, it could (and was) easily mistaken for an AK-47.

The husband could not understand our excitement and anger. In his mind, his son was only a harmless child with a toy gun.

The impulse to smack the hell out of this father was great. No one could understand how an adult could allow his child to aim something that looked just like an assault rifle at armed American troops. Our troops were in the middle of a conflict at a dangerous checkpoint, and they could in no way determine whether what they were seeing was a joke, or a child playing. If one of the soldiers had a clean line of sight, he would have been justified in opening up on the vehicle, killing the entire family.

Understand that the Iraqi standard way of celebrating (and they did so almost daily) was to shoot guns into the air, firing off everything from small pistols to heavy machine guns. The better the celebration, the bigger the rounds. Units stationed in the vicinity of, or driving by, such shooting had to determine whether they were witnessing hostile or celebratory fire, and we could not always tell the difference. This type of attitude and behavior drove us crazy.

Colonel Gold

Colonel Russell Gold was the commanding officer of the 3rd Brigade Combat Team, and our new boss. A Citadel Graduate, the colonel stuck out for several reasons the first time I saw him, even though I had no idea who he was.

We were dining in the Brigade mess hall, and I first noticed his hair. As soon as I walked in, I saw an older person who I assumed was a soldier with, of all things, long hair. Not hippie long hair but hair longer than the rest of us. Most of us had given up on haircuts and just had a close buzz cut. But this guy had hair like a New York stock broker, neatly trimmed and well groomed.

The next oddity that I noticed was his holster, an old-style brown leather shoulder rig. I had a black leather shoulder rig that was thirty years old, but that was because I was a dinosaur. This guy was nowhere near as old as I was.

I could not help staring because he was so different, and I was trying to figure out who the heck he was. The more I stared, the more convinced I was that he had to be important. He was talking with several people at the table who were actively listening. Without hearing a word, I could see that he was conveying something important. His mannerisms and gestures reminded me of a polished college professor. Not until he stood up did I see the eagle on his collar and figure out that this was the HMFIC of the Brigade.

I was pleasantly surprised that we were now working for a no-nonsense hard-charging tanker who would shake your hand or kill you (leaving the choice up to you). He was a diplomat to the Iraqi leadership, as long as they kept their part of the bargain. If they crossed him, he would make them pay. He was more than happy to meet with the Iraqi leadership and drink the sweet tea, but playing games was not in his rule book.

In one instance, Lieutenant Grube and 4th Platoon, along with a couple of Bradley fighting vehicles and soldiers from the 3rd Brigade Combat Team of the 1st Armored Division, were going to conduct a raid on a safe house where forty Fedayeen fighters were believed to be hiding out.

Lieutenant Grube was all set to lead the assault when he learned that Colonel Gold had decided to join the mission. Lieutenant Grube was already concerned about running into too many Fedayeen and the situation becoming a real battle. With the addition of Colonel Gold, Grube's concern mounted. The last thing he wanted to do was get the colonel killed. Of course, the chance of screwing something up in front of Colonel Gold was also a concern. So Grube decided to turn the assault portion of the mission over to 4th Platoon Sergeant First Class Chris Emmerson, so Lieutenant Grube could take over coordination and security for Colonel Gold.

Lieutenant Grube didn't have to worry, as Colonel Gold showed up ready for action, toting a super cool MP-5 submachine gun. The colonel had no intentions of interfering; he just wanted to be with his soldiers while they were conducting a potentially extremely dangerous mission. He feels a leader's place is with his troops, not back in some office waiting for a report. Although the mission was a bust with no Fedayeen found, the situation did cement the bond between the 3rd Brigade and the 143rd Military Police by showing teamwork and trust in accomplishing the mission.

Although Colonel Gold's MP-5 was not an issue weapon, it somehow found its way into his possession. Not many soldiers are willing to question a full colonel's (especially a brigade commander's) choice of weapons, except maybe a general. As luck would have it, a general happened to spot the prized MP-5, and he did not take kindly to one of his senior officers toting an unauthorized, non-issued (albeit extremely good) weapon. The colonel's explanation that the MP-5 had just been confiscated from an Iraqi was met with extreme skepticism by the general. After a colorful exchange between the two, the weapon was made to disappear, along with all of the colonel's soldiers' Iraqi-confiscated AK-47 rifles. (I thought the colonel's men were just trying to be cool carrying AKs, but then I learned that their only other weapon was a 9mm pistol). While not a U.S.-issued weapon, AK-47s are accurate, reliable, and available in large quantities.

I was not there, but the term "bullshit" might have been strongly mentioned, or so I have been told. The loss of the MP-5 and AK-47s left Colonel Gold and his soldiers with nothing but 9mm pistols. I can imagine that he was not a happy camper.

At Fort Knox, tankers have a sign displaying the unofficial motto, "Death Before Dismount." The safest place for a tanker is in his tank. Tankers are armed with huge machinery, heavy machine guns, and of course, the huge cannon. Tankers were issued 9mm pistols for self-defense, but their best defense was to stay inside the tank. Getting out of the tank defeated the whole purpose of having an indestructible fighting vehicle with incredible fire power.

During the assault phase of the war, tanks were the central reason for the U.S.'s rapid advance and success—the Iraqis had nothing of significance to counter the M-1 Abrams tank. But during the occupation phase, tanks were no longer the weapon of choice. Many tanks were no longer operable because they needed repairs, and spare parts were a rarity. But even if the tanks had been running, a tanker couldn't fire a round at a sniper shooting from a hospital room window (which actually happened to our 2nd Platoon, and Lieutenant Colonel Sherman of the 3rd BCT).

Armed with only 9mm pistols, tankers were still told by generals to ignore the tankers' unofficial motto, and get out on the street to secure the city. The insurgents were firing AK-47s, RPK belt-fed light machine guns, RPGs, and in some cases, 12.7mm heavy machine guns. A 9mm pistol is no match for any of these weapons.

Colonel Gold decided to unilaterally put together a training program for his soldiers on AK-47s so they would have the official training required to effectively use these assault weapons. The colonel's program was a success, and upon completing the training course, his soldiers were allowed to carry the AKs—thanks to the Iraqis, the inventory was ample.

However, some generals and the Secretary of Defense were still not pleased with the colonel, and a serious pissing contest took place. Colonel Gold insisted that his soldiers needed the AKs to defend themselves against the weapons that the insurgents had (as the M-16s and M-4 carbines that should have been issued had not). The generals and The Secretary of Defense felt that having soldiers out on the street was priority one, but making sure that they were properly armed with standard issued American weapons was not.

The situation became ugly…very ugly—many adjectives were exchanged. Soldiers standing by began to slowly put physical distance between themselves, the general, and Colonel Gold (physical distance meant that the onlookers could claim they didn't hear anything, absolving themselves from testifying at any possible court-martials).

Once again, common sense went out the window. In the general's mind, American soldiers carrying Iraqi weapons didn't "look good." Yet he seemed to be unable to arm soldiers with the weapons they should have been issued.

As if patrolling the streets of Baghdad with 9mm pistols was not bad enough, the tankers had never been trained in urban dismounted combat. These soldiers were tankers; the tank was their home, their transportation, and their weapons system. They did not know any other way to fight a war. Their job was to drive until they found something to devastate with their big gun, blow the target to pieces, and then find another target.

MPs from the 143rd and Paratroopers from the 82nd Airborne, who were attached to the 3rd BCT, were forced to train up the tankers on Infantry and Military Police tactics: close quarters combat, instinctive shooting, building entry, foot patrol, counter-ambush tactics—all those skills that, when operating a big huge tank, you would never need.

Operations and Communications

For the next three months, Operations were somewhat slow except for the troops assigned to the company commander's team, who were on the road day and night.

In the evening we would make runs back to Warrior to pick up mail or equipment and attend staff meetings. Our Platoons were getting their missions straight from Infantry Battalions, as our Platoons were now directly supporting the Battalions. We were doing general coordination, but nothing near as time-consuming as when our Platoons were directly reporting to Company Headquarters.

Communication was difficult, even though our facility was located on the second floor of the building and our antenna masts were mounted another 20' above the roof. The 60' elevation gave us very little range with our radios. From time to time, we were able to communicate with MP Battalion Headquarters, located approximately eight miles from our location—their antenna was higher than ours, and gave us almost a line-of-sight situation, which improved chances for communication.

Communication with our vehicles was more difficult. They were on the ground with no elevation, and we were lucky if we could communicate with them for two miles before they would be out of radio range.

The farthest unit from us was located at a base in the town of Abu Ghraib. Even with their antenna on top of a building, communications was a sometimes thing. The fact that they didn't really want to talk to us also hindered communication. The liked being out on their own without being able to report back to us to follow our chain of command. The Battalion they supported was more than happy with their performance, so the coupling was a good marriage for them. Given what we all know now, I can't say that I blame them for not wanting us to interfere with their missions.

Departure Dates

We were always talking about going home, and rumors flew about our rotation dates. Since a firm date for our departure was never officially announced, this remained a hot topic right up to our departure. The powers-that-be seemed to think that our time in Iraq was only going to last a few weeks or months, not the seven years our occupation would eventually turn into.

The Brigade Commander for the 3rd Brigade Combat Team had been making inquiries about rotation dates. He explained that our rotation dates were based on several factors. While some rotations were based on the date the troops arrived in-country, others were based on the date the troops were activated. The biggest variable, as it turned out, were the needs of the military. While scheduling the first units to arrive to be the first units out makes sense, and actually did happen, sometimes it didn't. If someone decided that you were essential, there was no telling how long you'd have to stay.

Insurgents were shooting at us on a daily basis, and they did not limit themselves to one type of attack. They used a mix of small arms, IEDs, RPGs, mortars and rockets. As the situation continued to spiral out of control, the powers-that-be still talked about optimistic departure dates and how easy transitioning the country back to the Iraqis would be.

People in high places were just not listening, neither to us and our reports nor to the news broadcasts on Fox, CNN, or any other news station. From time to time, we would get a chance to see the wire service news, and what we saw was not good. With accurate reporting of the situation on the ground, the higher-ups insisted on sticking to their unrealistic timetable. The disconnect was so bad that our most accurate and timely intelligence came from Fox and CNN instead of the people in charge.

ACTIVITY LOG
June 11–August 21, 2003

June 11, 2003

4th Platoon participated in Operation Desert Scorpion, in which they detained Fedayeen suspects for further transport after interrogation. 4th Platoon set up a detention and processing facility and processed dozens of detainees.

June 15, 2003

Units continued to conduct roadblocks and checkpoints for any type of illegal activity. 2nd Platoon recovered five stolen city buses and four stolen cars. 2nd Platoon recovered an assault rifle with an infrared starlight scope, and a pair of Soviet-made night-vision goggles.

It's rare not to find contraband when our soldiers set up checkpoints. In the early days of the invasion, Iraqis took advantage of the confusion and stole whatever they could get their hands on. The

Iraqi soldiers abandoned their broken units and left their uniforms behind, but kept their rifles and any other firearms they could find.

June 16, 2003

3rd Squad, 3rd Platoon conducted a search of a library believed to have been occupied by the Iraqi secret police before the war. No items were discovered.

June 19, 2003

3rd Squad, 2nd Platoon responded to a report of shots being fired. They discovered that the shots were fired in the air during a funeral procession. This was something that happened often, and took a long time to get used to.

3rd Squad, 2nd Platoon assisted the Iraqi fire department in putting out a house fire.

June 20, 2003

1st Squad, 2nd Platoon responded to a gunfight between two individuals. No Coalition forces were involved.

At approximately the same time, 2nd Squad, 2nd Platoon responded to a report of shots being fired and discovered that, this time, they were being fired as part of a wedding celebration.

Checking on what proved to be celebratory fire not only wasted time, but helped the troops to become a bit complacent. They began to think that each time they responded to gunfire, the cause would turn out to be nothing but a celebration of some sort. Unfortunately, there were always enough incidents of deadly fire mixed in with the celebratory kind.

June 21, 2003

Mortars were fired at 1st Platoon's position, but the mortars missed. Rockets knocked out power to the west of Bulldog FOB.

Two troops were shot at close range by handguns. These troops, who were from the Infantry (not the Military Police) had left their position and the rest of their Squad to get a couple of sodas from a local store. An Iraqi insurgent, seeing that they had separated from their Squad, walked up behind them and pulled a handgun. He stuck it in the neck of one of the soldiers, fired, and killed him instantly. The second soldier turned to defend himself, but was also shot and wounded. The insurgent escaped and was never identified.

The clothing worn by the Iraqis made it easy to conceal weapons. The standard dress for an Iraqi male is a long-sleeved, cotton shirt that extends to the ankles, and is not form-fitting. This baggy garment allows for easy concealment (especially for handguns) and with enough room under the garment to even a folding stock AK-47. We later learned that men often cut the bottoms out of the side pockets, which allowed insurgents to reach inside their pockets to easily retrieve weapons concealed in their waistbands. It was impossible to search every Iraqi male, even though, with this clothing, each one potentially could have been armed.

We were also having problems with vehicles pulling up to our convoys, either opening the doors or rolling down the windows, and firing away as they rolled past. The only way to counter this type of attack was some very crazy driving on the part of our soldiers, to the point of recklessness.

Another tactic was to simply point a weapon at everyone who came anywhere near our vehicles. This maneuver was a strong deterrent, but I am sure that the locals were not thrilled with us pointing weapons at them.

Today, two of our vehicles were shot at in this type of attack, but the shots missed. One of our Squads stopped the van carrying the suspects and guns a short distance from our location.

A couple of troops, also not from the Military Police, were hit by long-range sniper fire. In one case, the round penetrated the back of the soldier's armored vest (because it did not have the extra bullet-proof plate mounted on it). The bullet traveled through the vest into the soldier, ricocheted off the plate mounted in front of the vest, and back into the soldier, instantly killing him.

An ambulance was hit by an RPG, killing the wounded soldier who it was transporting.

June 22, 2003

A patrol from 1st Platoon, consisting of two vehicles and eight soldiers, was ambushed in broad daylight as they proceeded through the marketplace in Abu Ghraib.

This marketplace was always a bustle of activity, and the streets around it are so crowded by the sheer number of people and vendors that traffic would sometimes be blocked. As the patrol travelled along the main road, pedestrians would get in between the two MP vehicles, as if intentionally trying to separate them. It felt as if Iraqis were always mutually supporting each other, whether or not they were insurgents, criminals, or civilians.

An insurgent threw a hand grenade underneath the lead vehicle. It detonated and knocked out the vehicle. One soldier was wounded and the rest were disoriented, with most of them suffering from temporary hearing loss. Between the noise and confusion, things quickly turned to chaos.

As the troops disembarked to take up defensive positions, a second grenade landed among them. Fortunately, the insurgent had forgotten to pull the pin before throwing the grenade, so it did not detonate. At about the same time, someone threw a third grenade at the second vehicle, but this grenade also failed to detonate.

If a situation like this had occurred in an American city, civilians would take off, running away from the explosion. That didn't happen. Instead, civilians rushed toward the scene, either in hopes of seeing dead Americans or for the chance to grab equipment, especially rifles or pistols. This further added to the chaos, and gave us the impression that everyone was part of the attack.

Only the discipline of the soldiers that day prevented this bad incident from turning into a complete massacre. Imagine a young soldier, eighteen to twenty-four years old, disoriented from having a grenade go off under his vehicle, surrounded by people who are screaming and running at them, with the ability to flip a switch and fire off thirty rounds in three seconds. Even in the midst of the chaos in the market place, none of the soldiers fired.

They were able to quickly restart the lead vehicle and the two vehicles exited the marketplace with only one minor wound and no civilian casualties. Professionalism and sound judgment exercised by those young part-time soldiers saved the lives of countless Iraqis.

Later that night, someone with an AK-47 opened up on one of our guys. We returned fire, but no one was hit, and the gunmen took off. We felt as if we were now in a major tennis game with the insurgents.

Lieutenant Rivera departed Iraq due to a family emergency. Sergeant First Class Lawler took over as the acting Platoon Leader and Staff Sergeant Derasamo became the acting Platoon Sergeant. We did not anticipate any replacements coming from the States.

June 23, 2003

1st Squad, 4th Platoon was attacked and exchanged gunfire with several suspects on main supply route Irish. One suspect was killed, while two were wounded and escaped.

The main roads were well-travelled by Coalition forces on a daily, sometimes hourly, basis, but attacks still took place. Some of the main roads in Baghdad were just like the interstate system in the United States, with on and off ramps, and median dividers down the center. There are the standard green signs with white letters indicating exit ramps and locations. These signs were in Arabic and English. Some variations to what would be an American highway system would include people herding goats down the grassy median or a donkey cart going down the break down lane. We always seem to have one foot in the modern world and one foot in the year 630.[9.1] Life here goes from one extreme to another at the same time.

Staff Sergeant Thompson, one of our Connecticut State Troopers, Specialist Newell, Private First Class Connor, and Private McGoldrick exchanged gunfire with suspects while responding to a home invasion. An Iraqi woman came into the police station and filed a complaint that people had invaded her home, forcing her out. The Military Police officers, assisted by Iraqi Police officers, came under attack when they went to check the location. Staff Sergeant Thompson led an assault on the house, ultimately driving the suspects from the area. No one was hit and no one was apprehended.

We later learned that we had been used as pawns in a turf war between two houses of prostitution.

June 26, 2003

3rd Squad, 3rd Platoon discovered a bunker containing numerous crates of mortar rounds and other ammunition. The Squad secured the location until Explosive Ordnance Disposal arrived to take care of the ammunition. EOD was staying busy, running all over Baghdad and Iraq to disarm bombs and dispose of ordinance that had been found. Unfortunately, the insurgents soon figured out how we responded, and would wait until EOD arrived before detonating bombs, killing EOD personnel.

June 29, 2003

We learned that we would, in all likelihood, have to remain in Iraq until April, 2004.

Members of 3rd Platoon escorted one of our soldiers to Baghdad International Airport for a class on IEDs. While en route to the airport, the Squad was hit by a command-detonated IED, which appeared to have been a rigged 60mm mortar shell. The blast injured two soldiers and heavily damaged the vehicle.

Al Kim, the machine gunner in the turret, had the blast go across the front of his face. If not for his Kevlar helmet, the explosion would have taken off the front of his head. Even with his helmet, he sustained blast injuries to his head and neck. He was a

Middletown, Connecticut, Police officer with a number of years on the force.

Private First Class Josh Clark, the driver of the vehicle, sustained several shrapnel wounds to the left side of his body. His helmet, which was recovered after the explosion, had an indentation about the size of a quarter over where Clark's left temple would have been. Again, if Clark had not had his helmet on and strapped in place, the explosion would have killed him instantly.

Individually, their shrapnel wounds were not overly serious, but together, they were numerous. Both soldiers were evacuated to the CSH and treated for their injuries. Al Kim was evacuated to Germany and then back to the United States. The teams at the CSH were able to remove Clark's shrapnel, but there was still a piece in his neck, and he still had several open wounds.

First Sergeant Jones visited Clark at the CSH; at that time, Clark's rifle, pistol, helmet, and body armor had been turned over to Jones so that it could be returned to the unit. So we assumed that we wouldn't be seeing Clark for at least a week or two, well after his wounds had healed and the hospital released him.

I was very surprised to see him come into the Operations Center only a couple of days later. I couldn't believe that the hospital had already released him, especially since he still appeared to be in pain, was walking very stiffly, and did not look all that healthy.

Incredulous, I asked him why the hospital had released him? He stated he had not been released. He had been left to his own devices and found a ride back to our unit. The hospital also thought he was healthy enough for work details, even though he still had open wounds (his bandages were stained with blood) and shrapnel lodged in his neck. Clark decided that if the CSH thought he was well enough to go on work details, then, screw it, he would come back to the unit.

I know the doctors at the CSH had been doing lifesaving work under extraordinary circumstances, putting soldiers who should have died back together again, and shipping them off to the United

States by way of Germany so they could recover. That those same doctors would put a heavily-injured soldier like Clark on work details still seems incredible.

Josh Clark never really complained about his injuries or his inability to function, but Staff Sergeant Thompson took it upon himself to get Clark evacuated after exercising with him. Seeing how much pain Clark was in, fearing possible paralysis or further injury, Thompson championed Clark's evacuation. It took several months, but we were finally able to convince higher headquarters of the seriousness of Clark's injuries, and the dangers of having him in a combat zone, and were able to get him evacuated to Germany and then onto the States.

If not for Thompson, Clark might have done the full year in Iraq with shrapnel lodged next to his spine.

Clark did recover from his wounds and went on to become a police officer in the city of Willimantic, Connecticut.

June 30, 2003

2nd Squad, 3rd Platoon had been securing a site that had numerous unexploded ordnance scattered about. Several children had to be warned away as they were going through the area picking up the unexploded ordnance. While they were in the middle of securing that site, they were attacked by a lone gunman, who fortunately missed everyone in the Squad. The Squad gave chase and returned fire, but all their weapons jammed and the suspect got away.

Weapon jams were becoming common, due to the dust in the air that got into every piece of equipment. This grit was able to jam a weapon after a single round, and was so fine that the weapons didn't look dirty at casual visual inspection. Convincing the troops to break down the weapons several times a day, do a quick wipe down to prevent jams, was difficult—they were getting complacent and considered weapons cleaning to be chicken shit. The reality of their situation would only start to set in if their weapons jammed during a fire fight.

This complacency was evident in other areas. Troops had taken to removing the doors from their vehicles, so that they would be able to exit the vehicle faster when attacked. The problem with this line of thinking was that the attackers had shifted from rifle and pistol attacks to IEDs and rockets. While the doors were only fiberglass, they did offer some protection from explosions, especially with the windows up and old body armor hanging in the doors. Unfortunately, vehicles looked cool with doors off, and looking cool overrode safety.

2nd Platoon under Lieutenant Rossi and Sergeant First Class Mongiat seemed to be catching all the heat from the insurgents, making contact every time they went out. Unfortunately, the insurgents were equal-opportunity attackers, and contacts with them were soon spread out across the entire company.

July 1, 2003

2nd Squad, 2nd Platoon was out patrolling and entered a large warehouse. Private security guards protecting the warehouse mistook the MPs for looters and opened fire. Rounds were exchanged before it was determined that these were both friendly forces. Fortunately, no one was injured.

July 3, 2003

3rd Squad, 2nd Platoon arrived on the scene of a carjacking. The suspects attempted to flee and the MP officers gave chase, trying to disable the vehicle by shooting out the tires. The suspects fired back at the Military Police officers. In response, the MP officers engaged the vehicle with automatic weapons fire, killing one of the individuals.

July 4, 2003

Today was a major American holiday, and so we were on high alert, expecting something to happen. For the most part, our day was quiet.

We did hear a loud explosion off to our west. A short time later, vehicles entered our compound with an injured soldier. The soldier had been driving one of the older two-and-a-half ton trucks when the blast went off in front of the vehicle. The helmet and the body armor probably saved the soldier's life but did not prevent flying windshield glass from going into her eyes and face.

A short time later, a MedEvac helicopter landed in the LZ to the east of our location. The soldier, her head heavily bandaged, was escorted to the chopper under her own power. I don't know how things turned out with her.

The ambush was just a few hundred meters from the front gate of our FOB on a road that Coalition forces travelled on a daily, sometimes hourly, basis. This intersection seemed to be a popular place to attack Coalition forces. It had a cloverleaf type design that forced vehicles to slow down to make various turns. Attackers took advantage of that design, and of situations similar to it, with devastating effect. Insurgents would zero in on these locations with mortars or RPGs. In the case of IEDs, slowing a vehicle made it easier to time the explosion.

July 6, 2003

Everyone was out on the road. 2nd Platoon was trying to catch a guy who had killed a lieutenant colonel, and 3rd Platoon was after some of Saddam's higher-ups known to be in the area.

First Sergeant Jones asked me to go with Staff Sergeant Milhomme to a division-wide maintenance briefing. The meeting required a staff NCO, and I was the pick of the litter. We were to meet on the east side of the Tigris River at division Headquarters. We almost never traveled to that side of the river, and the ride over took us close to Sadr City and a lot of nasty people.

We were in a canvas-sided Hummer pickup, something that I wasn't too thrilled with, but we were part of a convoy comprised of a dozen or more vehicles. Although we had adequate protection, I was still concerned because our vehicle did not have a turret-mounted gun. The insurgents had taken to dropping grenades and mortar rounds off of bridges and onto military vehicles, and without a turret-mounted gun, we were unable to engage them.

After an uneventful trip, we arrived at Division Headquarters, which was located in the Olympic Training Center. This was a fairly new, very large complex and, like a lot of the government buildings in Iraq, it was way overdone. Units from all over Baghdad were there for the maintenance presentation and briefing. There had to be over a hundred people sitting in the auditorium.

We were briefed by a general and several colonels who were in charge of maintenance and supply issues. My job was to be one of the senior representatives from our company, as I really had nothing to do with either maintenance or supply issues. Staff Sergeant Milhomme would be the one to answer any questions, if there were any, and was the one who had a handle on our vehicle maintenance and supply issues.

I was half asleep and bored out of my mind listening to the briefing, until the general hit a bottom-line figure. That's when I realized that we were in real trouble.

Fully half of all of the vehicles in the 1st Armored Division were not serviceable. The 1st Armored Division (with the exception of 3rd Brigade Combat Team) had not been part of the invasion force, and they had driven to Baghdad several weeks after we had arrived. During their trip in, they had performed no combat-type maneuvers; they just drove up the main highways in a series of convoys. During that drive, their vehicles began to fall apart.

At first, I thought that the 1st Armored Division had dead-lined their vehicles for minor maintenance issues. This could be caused by anything from broken headlights to cracked windshields. The military has various levels of serviceability and, depending on what was wrong with it, a vehicle could still be used.

We learned that the issues dead-lining the vehicles ranged from flat tires to blown transmissions, broken linkages and hydraulics, and other major problems that rendered the vehicles useless. Some of these vehicles had been towed to various locations to provide security for government buildings, police stations, and access control points, effectively turning them into armored bunkers. At least that way they still served some purpose, even though it was not the purpose for which they had originally been designed.

The 1st Armored Division was supposed to have invaded Iraq through Turkey, and their time in-country was originally to be limited. So, they did not bring the necessary parts to maintain the vehicles long term. I had not thought that the active-duty would be having the same problems that we were having, but they did. It was so bad that if they ever needed to move their vehicles in an offensive manner, they would not be able to. Of all things, spare tires were a major concern.

July 7, 2003

2nd Platoon assisted in a search mission for suspected Fedayeen terrorists and IED-makers. Approximately 40 individuals were detained and returned for processing.

Today I was thinking about home a lot. I had just finished a *Reader's Digest* article that suggested keeping a log of what I am thankful for.

In a place like this, it is easy to appreciate just how good I had at it home. There were numerous things I thought about doing when I got back. Of course, this assumed that I was going back. It was only during these slow times that the back end of seriousness crept into your thinking; other than that, you were just too busy getting things done. I wrote down several dozen things that I planned on doing once I got home. Most of them were not new— they were just things that I remembered doing: the simple pleasures, the leisurely life, the good times.

My walk down memory lane was interrupted by a huge explosion. At first, I thought it was an RPG hit, as I heard the whine of the round coming in. But we were told later that it was a controlled blast by EOD. I checked the impact after that; based on what I saw, I was sure it was an RPG round that hit us. We didn't know it just then, but we would soon discover that we had been under RPG attack several times a night since we moved to Bulldog.

There was an overgrown field and storage area for oil well pipes to our east, just beyond our parking area. Brigade was concerned that insurgents could come in through the pipe storage area and sneak through the grass to the fence line to attack us. Brigade decided to have a controlled burn of the high grass, creating an open area outside the wire and removing the insurgents' cover.

After Brigade burned off the grass, we discovered a number of pipes sticking out of the ground. These turned out to be armed RPG rockets. Some of them were training rounds that were never going to detonate, while others were live rounds, but would not detonate because the safety wires had not been removed. There were dozens of these rounds in the field that had been fired at our compound, but had landed just outside of the wire.

July 8, 2003

4th Platoon apprehended a vehicle that had run a checkpoint and roadblock they were manning. They detained the four occupants and recovered one AK-47 assault rifle and sixty rounds of ammunition. These small, but dangerous, actions would continue right on up until the time we left.

1st Platoon assisted the 2/70 Armor Battalion in conducting a cordon and search mission, arresting fifteen individuals, and confiscating over one hundred weapons of various types.

July 9, 2003

I got a bug bite on the upper part of my left leg that started out looking like a mosquito bite. Within six hours, it had turned extremely nasty.

How nasty was it?

Imagine taking a softball, cutting it in thirds, then taking one of those thirds and placing it on your leg. Now take a golf ball, cut that into thirds, and place one of those thirds on top of the softball. Once you've done that, get yourself a drill with a quarter-inch bit and drill through the golf ball, through the softball, through your leg, all the way down to your femur. That's what I had.

I could not comprehend that this bite was from some kind of insect. It was painful and the hole in it oozed pus. I thought something must have been inside the hole, so I probed around trying to clean it. Any time I tried to stand up, a black curtain would come over my eyes for a second and I would waver a bit before things came back into focus. On advice from our medic, I spent about a day or so pouring hydrogen peroxide into the hole every few hours, changed the bandages, and hoped that it would go away. When it didn't, the medic and I came to the conclusion that I had better see a doctor.

We had two doctors at our FOB. An active-duty medic examined my leg, advised the doctor that it was pretty serious, and told him that he needed to look at it. Without even examining me, the doctor told the medic to prepare my leg so that he could lance and drain the bite.

The medic tried to explain that lancing wouldn't help, as the bite was already completely wide open. This information prompted the doctor to glance at my leg and the hole in it. Without getting closer than six feet from me, and without actually examining the bite, he arrogantly spoke the word, "Disgusting," and told the staff to start me on two courses of antibiotics to "see what would happen."

I continued cleaning the wound with hydrogen peroxide and taking the two courses of antibiotics. Sometime around the sixth day I must have rolled over in my sleep and pressed my leg against the side of the cot. When I woke up the next morning I found that the bite had finally exploded and I was lying in a puddle of yellow/brown/red/green slime. The swelling had completely gone down, but I still had a quarter-inch hole in my leg. Most of the pain was gone, and I was able to stand without nearly passing out. It took another three weeks for the hole in my leg to completely close.

I later learned that the two doctors at the FOB were reservists. One was a gynecologist and the other did staff physicals for a corporation. Neither one specialized in military medicine, had knowledge about insect bites like the one I had, or had any recent emergency room experience. I also learned that bites like mine can be extremely serious and, if the infection had reached my femoral artery, I might have lost my leg.

When I spoke about my infection with medics and doctors from Connecticut, they explained that the standard course of treatment is to cut the leg open so that it would drain, and then start the patient on IV antibiotics. They also said that just having that type of open wound in that type of environment was asking for a secondary infection. Based on their information, I should have at least been evacuated to Germany, if not back to the States.

July 12, 2003

We received word that Iraqis stole between twenty to forty SA-7 anti-aircraft missiles, and that they planned to use them to shoot down a C-130 flying into Baghdad International Airport. We were told that the next few days could be really bad, and that this threat was one of many.

Tensions continued to build within the Security team. An officer hadn't been briefing his troops prior to going outside the wire; instead he had them mounting up and heading out without telling them where they would be going or what they would be doing. During these patrols, the officer directed them to stop in extremely insecure locations, where they were surrounded by crowds of people, to, in his own words, "check things out." Instead of making his plans clear, or warning his troops in any way, he just ordered the driver to pull over.

Stopping in the middle of crowds was just asking for trouble. In prior incidents, with both our unit and other units, the insurgents would look for opportunities like this to fire off a round or throw a grenade, and escape in the chaos and confusion. The officer's decision to stop in a heavily populated area handed these opportunities to the insurgents.

Figure 9.3   The author and his festering infection

To make matters worse, this officer was effectively unarmed during these patrols, carrying only a 9mm pistol (even though he was required to provide one-sixth of the patrol's firepower). Although he had been carrying a shotgun until this point, he had forgotten where he left it on multiple occasions, and had since decided to go without it. He still carried shells in his vest (I can only guess because they looked cool).

I don't know what this officer was trying to prove, but all he did was make himself a target. My biggest concern was for the other people he might have gotten killed. A lot of people, not just insurgents, wanted us dead. There were some who wanted to kill infidels, and others seeking revenge for Coalition forces killing someone back in the first Gulf War or during the current invasion.

At evening Battalion briefings, we would get reports of Iraqis taking advantage of a target of opportunity and killing or wounding an unsuspecting soldier. Like all predators, they would search for an individual who was too far out front, too far behind, or just not paying attention, and then pull a gun, fire a shot, and disappear into the crowd. Even with these continued warnings, this officer kept pulling stunts like this. Protecting him was becoming more difficult for his Security team.

July 17, 2003

2nd and 3rd Squads of 1st Platoon received small arms fire while returning to base. Specialist Tanguay and Specialist Randolph returned fire with approximately twenty rounds, suppressing the attack.

Elements from 1st, 2nd and 3rd Platoons conducted several missions involving raids and checkpoints, confiscating thirty-five hand grenades, thirty-one sticks of C-4 plastic explosives, ninety-six sticks of plastic-filled grenades, and two boxes marked as RPK machine gun ammunition during a house search. Unfortunately, this is not an isolated incident; this type of ordnance is all over the place in Iraq.

1st Platoon responded to an IED attack on the 2/70 Armor Battalion while they were in convoy.

July 21, 2003

2nd Squad, 2nd Platoon arrested Ali Waheed for attempted murder.

July 22, 2003

3rd Platoon responded to a call about an Iraqi civilian vehicle that struck an IED. The vehicle had been attempting to use a turnaround that crossed the center divider in a location that American soldiers used to enter one of the bases. The explosion killed three Iraqi males and injured a fourth. Sergeant First Class Lawler and Staff Sergeant Derasamo pulled the survivor from the burning vehicle.

While providing traffic control, Sergeant Richmond was almost run over by a civilian Iraqi vehicle. Staff Sergeant Derasamo opened fire on the vehicle, causing it to stop.

Tonight, the entire city sounded as if it had erupted into one massive gun battle. The Iraqis were firing off every kind of firearm you could think of, from small pistols to heavy antiaircraft machine guns. I couldn't believe so much ordnance was lying around the city. Hiding pistols or rifles was one thing, but they had been able to conceal antiaircraft weapons. I couldn't shake the thought of driving down a narrow street getting shot at by a 12.7mm antiaircraft gun (the Russian counterpart to the American 50-caliber machine gun). AK-47s were terrifying enough.

The night sky almost seemed like a Fourth of July fireworks celebration, with different-colored tracers flying through the air, and parachute flares floating down. We soon realized that all of those bullets going up into the air would have to come back down at some point, and that every tracer that went up was accompanied by four other rounds. We were watching from the balcony just outside our Operations Center, and decided that the best thing to do would be to move back inside, and put a concrete wall between us and the revelry. The firing went on for hours without stopping. We came to the conclusion that the weapons we had confiscated didn't amount to much.

We later learned that Uday and Quasy Hussein (Saddam Hussein's sons) had been killed by Coalition forces. The shooting in the air was in celebration of their death. During the celebration, at least 150 Iraqi civilians were wounded, and over fifty were killed (as reported by the hospitals and local authorities). Who knows how many were actually killed or wounded; in all likelihood the figures were much higher.

July 30, 2003

2nd Squad, 2nd Platoon was assigned to conduct a raid at a suspected Fedayeen militia member's residence. They recovered one AK-47 assault rifle and over 4.5 million Iraqi dinars.

July 31, 2003

3rd Squad, 2nd Platoon assisted the Iraqi Police in arresting a suspect who had fired on an Iraqi Police station. A search of the suspect's home revealed two rifles and large quantities of chloroform, potassium cyanide, and other chemicals.

August 3, 2003

Bulldog FOB has been taking small arms, RPG, and mortar fire almost every day. At approximately 2:30 a.m., our compound was hit with four rocket-propelled grenades. Two soldiers in the tower saw the flash of the RPGs being fired, and sent some rounds down range, but no one was hit.

One of the RPG rounds hit on an angle just above the windows of the Tactical Operations Center. If the RPG had come in just a little lower, it would have gone through, exploded inside the TOC, and killed or wounded everyone on duty. Luck was with us, and the grenade simply made a big black smudge on the outer wall and cut all of our antenna wires.

The three other rounds went up and over the building, impacting outside the Compound. Although we heard the explosions, an inspection of the area afterwards could not find any damage.

Sergeant First Class Lawler wanted to take his guys out and go after the attackers. My first reaction was, "go get 'em." Then I remembered that Brigade had a Quick Reaction Force that was rolling out, and that either our guys might run into them, or perimeter security might open up on them (thinking they were the attackers). I told Lawler to let the QRF handle things, as they were already out there. He wasn't happy.

Ten minutes later, a bunch of soldiers came running by us. We had moved to a safe location inside the building with no windows. I asked one of the passing soldiers who they were and where they were going. He told me they were the QRF.

They were responding somewhere in the area of twenty minutes after the RPGs had hit. At the time, I had to guess that they missed the "quick" in Quick Reaction Force.

Not until 2014 did I learn that the people running by were not QRF. Colonel Gold, who was outside the wire coordinating events, already had the QRF and a second group outside the wire looking for trouble. The people we saw running out to the vehicles were a third section heading out to assist.

In hindsight, keeping our guys inside the wire was an excellent decision. We did not have the full picture of what was going on, and could have made this situation a very dangerous one. With three sections outside the wire looking for a fight, a fourth section with no coordination would have been looking for a dangerous friendly-fire situation.

I admire Sergeant First Class Lawler's drive, but I did not want to be the one to get him, or someone from his Platoon, killed. The right decision was made by accident. Lawler is still pissed that I didn't let him go.

August 4, 2003

3rd Platoon came upon a burning eighteen-wheel truck. This vehicle was one of several involved in an ambush while carrying U.S. goods. Ten of the eleven vehicles made it to safety. These vehicles were operated by civilian contractors, and we never found out what happened to them.

August 6, 2003

We were put on standby for a major operation, in which we were to provide support for a Special Operations group. Our mission was to escort this group to and from an assault point, providing perimeter security while they conducted a raid. The purpose of this raid was to capture Muqtada Al-Sadr. We didn't know about him yet, only learning afterwards that he was a religious and political leader, and a major player in the Iranian-based Shia majority. He hated Americans and had no use for the Sunni minority. Under Saddam and the Sunni minority, his father had been murdered (his father had lead the Shia majority, opposed Saddam, and sought closer ties to Iran).

We learned about this mission when the Major in charge of Operations introduced me to one of the Special Operators. The individual was dressed in Banana Republic clothes, had a really neat MP-5 submachine gun, and wore a non-issue set of body armor. He looked like a soldier and talked like a soldier, but just looking at his equipment told me that he was something else. The Special Operator did not have any patches or insignia that indicated the branch of military he was with. I could only guess that he might have been with Army Special Forces, Navy Seals, Delta Force, or some other high-speed unit. After we had talked for a little bit, I finally asked him who he was with.

Figure 9.4   Note the slight black mark above the second arched window from the left—a little lower and the RPG would have landed in our Operations Center

He told me that he was with OGA. This confused the hell out of me, because I was sure that I knew the whole federal alphabet: FBI, CIA, NSA, DOD, DEA, etc. I asked him what OGA stood for. He replied, "Other Government Agency."

I started to chuckle, which turned into a huge belly laugh, and almost ended up on the floor. I'm not sure why I thought it was so funny, but I couldn't help myself. Of all the crazy things going on in Iraq, this one now topped the list. He looked at me like he thought I was crazy, and of course, I thought he was crazy.

This mission was cancelled, or at least put on hold. We were put on alert two more times, and both times the missions were canceled.

The first time we were put on alert, I was very impressed that they selected us for such a high-profile mission. The second time, I wondered why we got picked again. By the third time, I came to the conclusion that the reason they kept selecting us was because active-duty wanted no part of this mission.

The whole scenario that the Special Operator relayed to me sounded like the scenario in Somalia that had led up to *Black Hawk Down*. The plan, as in Somalia, was for a group of Delta Force Operators to go after key leaders (in Somalia, it was the rebel leadership, in Iraq, it was Al-Sadr). Troops mounted in vehicles would move out from the FOB and secure a perimeter, while Special Operators would hit the building, grab or kill their targets, and then return to the FOB in the vehicles used to hold the perimeter. When this plan was attempted in Somalia, it was less than a resounding success.

I felt that our mission could go one of two ways. It could be a complete disaster, just like *Black Hawk Down*. If that happened, there would be body bags all over the place, most of them ours, thanks to our unarmored vehicles and light machine guns. This would allow the 709th to blame the failure of the mission on inexperienced National Guard troops. On the other hand, we could succeed, grabbing Al-Sadr and making good our escape. Then the 709th could swoop in, take full credit for putting the mission together.

Also on August 6, 2003

After receiving information from the intelligence guys in the building that there was a counterfeiting operation going on, an officer decided to do reconnaissance to see if a raid would be possible. He told the First Sergeant and me that he was just going out with his team to do a recon of the location, and would return shortly. He did not give specifics, which was disconcerting. However, given that he had reassured us that they were just going to check things out, we left it at that.

Everybody in Baghdad who had a computer and a laser color printer could print money. The local currency kept changing, and it was hard to tell what the real money was supposed to look like, so enterprising people found ways to create their own money as fast as they could.

The officer didn't tell us that he took two intelligence people with him. These were people whose assignments and duties were so secret that they did not wear rank, name tags, or any other patches. I was never sure if they were soldiers, or if they were private contractors. A lot of their knowledge, obtained from briefings and interrogations, could become compromised if they were ever captured. This was why they were never supposed to leave the Compound.

They returned safely, but we discovered that they had spent most of their patrol outside of both radio range and our area of operation. If something had gone wrong, they would have had no one to communicate with, and would have had no where to go to seek assistance.

To make matters worse, we learned that once they located the house where the counterfeiting operation was going on, the officer decided to raid it. Fortunately, he had picked up a couple of teams from 2nd Platoon to assist him on his way out, so he had more MPs with him than we realized. Even still, they attempted the raid with only a limited number of MPs, and two Intelligence officers, receiving cover from 2nd Platoon.

The location turned out to be just a counterfeiting operation and not an insurgent hideout, or some type of base for organized crime. The subjects did not resist and the officer took them into custody, and seized their equipment.

The officer thought he had made a great score, until the Brigade and Battalion Commanders learned about the numerous procedural violations, risking the lives of the MP team, and two Intelligence officers, to round up a bunch of people printing funny money (in a place where funny money was the norm). This action almost got the officer relieved of duty, but his luck held.

August 10, 2003

4th Squad, 3rd Platoon arrested Iraqi Police officer, Captain Mohammed Mahde. The arrest was made when someone discovered that the Captain had been extorting money from civilians to return impounded property, and the selling impounded property on the black market. He was not the only one doing this, as the ranks of the Iraqi Police were rife with corruption; he was just the only one who got caught.

1st Squad, 3rd Platoon raided a house used by a bomb maker and recovered approximately fifteen pounds of TNT.

August 11, 2003

There was a large explosion inside the Compound, and one of the Scout Platoon's Humvees took a direct hit. Although we were told that this was an attack, the Humvee was parked in such a way that the surrounding vehicles would have shielded it from an outside attack.

Shortly after the explosion, Brigade came down to our operation center and asked if we had had any accidental discharges with our MK-19 grenade launchers. We informed them that we had not mounted up our MK-19 grenade launchers in months, explaining that we had the SAWs mounted in our vehicles only because we did not have enough ammunition to make the MK-19s worthwhile.

We were being accused of damaging their vehicles with an accidental MK-19 discharge. Later, we learned that one of their vehicles had fired and struck the Humvee. Fortunately, their vehicles were all inside the Compound and in close proximity to one another, so the grenade didn't have time to arm itself. The explosion that we heard was the MK-19 discharging the round. The unarmed round simply made a huge dent in the side of the Humvee.

When in doubt, blame it on the National Guard.

August 12, 2003

1st and 2nd Squads of 2nd Platoon conducted a raid on a house suspected of harboring anti-Coalition recruiters. They arrested six suspects and confiscated two computers, hard drives, and numerous CDs. This information was passed on to Intelligence.

August 13, 2003

4th Squad, 3rd Platoon discovered an abandoned Iraqi crew-served weapon in front of the local school. The 12.7mm machine gun was the Russian version of the American 50-caliber machine gun, capable of doing serious damage to people and vehicles, including aircraft.

August 15, 2003

Rumors continued to fly about when we might go home. A two star general had just announced that the National Guard would be doing a ten-month rotation, while the active-duty would be doing one year. We wanted to know if our ten-month rotation started when we were activated, when we were deployed, or when we arrived in Iraq. We received no answer. This was yet another question that was just left up in the air with no clear resolution.

Lieutenant Kerfoot from active-duty arrived from Germany and took command of our 3rd Platoon, returning Sergeant First Class Lawler to his position as Platoon Sergeant for 3rd Platoon.

August 18, 2003

Congressman Larson, one of Connecticut's representatives, came to visit us. Staff Sergeant Langlais was selected to meet with Larson, as he was from the congressman's congressional district. This visit came with some risk on our part, because we had to put Sergeant Langlais in a vehicle and escort him to the airport where he would meet the Congressman. Our security detail waited around for the Congressman while he was being briefed, and saw him only when he came out to shake hands, and then ask where the bathroom was. That was the sole contact we had with the Congressman while he was in Iraq.

We were hit again, this time with mortars. They exploded around the Compound, but no one was injured. A Porta John took a direct hit and was splattered across the parking lot. The rounds impacted extremely close to the front gate, narrowly missing the dozen or so soldiers securing the gate. This position was about 200 feet from where our Operations Center was located.

Somehow, a round exploding 200 feet away from us seemed insignificant and not a real threat. We were getting far too familiar with being targets.

August 19, 2003

A truck bomb exploded outside of UN headquarters in Baghdad, resulting in a lot of damage and casualties. Our units responded afterwards to secure the area where the breach occurred. No one is safe here, and even people that are only trying to help are subject to attack.

This attack demonstrated one of the insurgent's new tactics. Their plan was to have two truck bombs attack an area. The first would blow a hole in the wall, and the second vehicle would drive through the hole created by the first and detonate inside the Compound. This two-pronged attack allowed the attackers to bypass security at gates and entrance points.

The unintended consequence of this new tactic was that, while the first vehicle blew down the wall, it also left a huge crater in the ground that prevented the second vehicle from entering the Compound. This failure didn't stop the insurgents from trying, however.

Shots were fired at 1st Squad, 4th Platoon. A suspect pointed a weapon at Sergeant Leonard. Squad members returned fire and grazed the suspect in the calf. The suspect was later apprehended.

August 21, 2003

While conducting a joint patrol, 3rd Squad, 3rd Platoon came upon a body in the road, an apparent victim of a carjacking.

3rd Squad, 3rd Platoon assisted elements of the 325th in conducting a cordon and search for a former staff general of the Fedayeen. They recovered one pistol, five million dinar, and a general's uniform. The suspect had fled the area.

August 29, 2003

1st Platoon, 3rd Platoon, and elements of 2nd Platoon of the 527, along with 3rd Platoon of Charlie Company 1st of the 325 participated in Operation Bulldog Raptor, which involved raids on several mosques throughout the city. This is the first time that U.S. forces were permitted to enter mosques on a military operation. These raids resulted in several arrests, and in the confiscation of numerous weapons.

The Iraqis claimed that these mosques were holy places where infidel Christians and Jews were not permitted for fear of violating them (but insurgents had no problem using these places to hide weapons and train more insurgents). The Iraqis were forever using the religious card against us, always claiming violations of their sacred places by the Great Satan.

Leaving Bulldog

Leaving Bulldog was with mixed feelings. I was glad to be away from the two Janitors, but not thrilled to be back with the 709th, who had treated us so poorly in the past. Given the choice, our Platoons would have preferred to stay with the Infantry, which is not the most flattering thing for MPs to say about working for other MPs.

Before we left, Colonel Gold got the entire unit together and told us what a great job we had done and how proud he was to have had us working for him. He went on to say that he had tried everything he could to keep us, but was unable to prevent our transfer. He thanked the unit for our service before explaining, in detail, both the Coalition's overall mission in Iraq and how our accomplishments had helped that overall mission. He said that he was glad that we had helped make Iraq a safe and stable place in the midst of the Middle East turmoil, and had brought the democracy that we enjoyed at home to a country that had existed long before the United States.

Chapter Ten

RETURN TO WARRIOR

Regard your soldiers as your children, and they will follow you into the deepest valleys. Look on them as your own beloved sons, and they will stand by you even unto death!

Sun Tzu

ACTIVITY LOG
August 30–September 10, 2003

August 30, 2003

The company relocated from Bulldog back down to Warrior Compound. The 143rd was once again under the direct control of the 709th Military Police Battalion. We left the comfort of the air conditioners at Bulldog. Temperatures were in the 100° range and water consumption had increased.

September 3, 2003

The 709th MP Battalion continued trying to get all of our Platoons back inside the Compound area now that we have been detached from the Armored Brigade. The Platoons were dragging their feet coming back to Warrior, but it appears that 4th Platoon will be the only one able to stay away for now.

I received a box from home. In it was a Swiss Army knife from Jimmy Cavanaugh, my wife's former detective partner on the State Police. The Swiss Army knife had a built-in thermometer, so I could see exactly how hot it was. I would stare at this thermometer and think, "you gotta be shitting me."

Figure 10.1   The Operations Center at Warrior Compound (Left to Right) Lieutenant Rossi, Staff Sergeant Bispham, and the author, Master Sergeant Marc Youngquist

Keep in mind that when temperatures are in the 90's, pets and children left in vehicles with the windows rolled up stand a good chance of dying. In the heat of the Baghdad summer, the outside temperatures reached 120°, and the heat inside the vehicles was close to 150°. Touching metal parts inside of the vehicles would burn your hand.

One day I thought I'd roll the window down just a bit to allow a cooling breeze…a big mistake. Instead of a cooling breeze, the "breeze" actually hurt. To get an idea of how hot and painful a Baghdad breeze is, take a blow dryer, set the temperature to its highest setting, place it six inches from your face, turn it on, and hang in there are long as you can.

I don't know how we survived.

September 7, 2003

Patrols went out day and night to check on our police stations and soldiers. We wanted to make sure that they were okay and to show that we were willing to take the same risks that they took. We didn't want them to think that we were fine with sitting back in relative safety while they were out on patrol. I did not get out as much as the others. The Company Commander, Platoon Leaders, and Platoon Sergeants went out several times during the day and night, spending hours on the road.

One officer's team was increasingly on edge. They came to me with their concerns that the officer had been going out on the streets, looking for trouble, trying to get a "kill." I thought that they were exaggerating, until the officer told me himself that he was going to go out and stay out every night until he got a kill.

He was only armed with a 9mm pistol, so if he wanted a kill, he would have to have been extremely close to whoever he was shooting at.

I was disturbed. War is not nice and people often must kill or be killed, but stating that one desperately wanted to "kill" someone struck me as a sort of gang mentality—that, to be a man, you have to have been tough enough to kill someone.

The active-duty 527th Police Company has been reassigned to other duty, and control of the Al Ghazalia, Al Mumun, Al Khadra, and Abu Ghraib Police Stations in Western Baghdad has been given to the 143rd. We had already worked in these stations prior to going up to Bulldog, so our new assignment was familiar, and each Platoon would be operating in their original assigned areas.

Of the four police stations, the most dangerous one was the one at Abu Ghraib (though none were really safe). This station should not to be confused with the Abu Ghraib prison, which is located approximately seven miles west of town, and seven miles outside of our patrol area.

The location of the Abu Ghraib Police Station seemed to be a huge thorn in the side of just about everyone who hated the American presence in Iraq.

Whether they were caused by insurgents, organized crime, or local thugs, constant attacks were made at the police station and adjacent marketplace. Not a day went by without some kind of incident, whether it was small arms fire, IED blasts, mortars, or RPG attacks.

Some of these attacks were from hired guns. These part-time mercenaries would be paid a fee to shoot at Americans, or set off bombs. In some cases, they would simply spray thirty rounds from their AK-47s at the station before disappearing into the dark.

These unprofessional, unmilitary ambushes usually resulted in thirty misses. AK-47s tended to kick and buck, climbing to the right when fired on full automatic. Even if the first round was actually aimed at something, by the time the third round fired, the AK wasn't pointing anywhere near the target. Casualties from these types of attacks were usually hit by accident.

While direct attacks were common, so far, no ground assaults had been attempted.

A large reason why the police stations hadn't been overrun was because each one had automatic weapons on the roof, with either a Bradley fighting vehicle or an M-1 tank stationed outside. The insurgents had nothing to counter these armored vehicles or their firepower. They would try to inflict casualties whenever they could, but a stand and fight battle with the Coalition forces was out of the question.

Insurgents also knew that, in any prolonged engagement, we would bring in additional armored vehicles and helicopter gunships. This reality left them with nothing but the ability to chip away at us, killing one or two soldiers at a time, or possibly damaging a vehicle.

September 8, 2003

General Sanchez conducted a briefing for all units regarding how long we would be staying in Iraq. The general stated that the new policy was to have all units spending up to twelve months with "boots on the ground." This news meant that, despite the length of time that a unit had been activated, its countdown to return home would not start until it had arrived in-theater. Although this new policy counted the three weeks we had spent in Kuwait, based on the briefing, we might potentially be in Iraq for a full year, unable to go home until April, 2004.

The news was devastating. By this time, everyone, including me, just wanted to go home. Considering all the rumors flying around, no one thought that we would have to stay an entire year—the hope of returning home sooner kept us going.

Only one officer was happy with the news from the briefing. He met with everyone in company formation that evening, and changing the general's wording slightly, took great pleasure explaining that we would be in Iraq until April, 2004. While everyone sank into a depression, he seemed to revel in the fact that we would be here for a full year. He also emphasized how "lucky" we had been (a sentiment that a soldier never, ever, says in a combat situation for fear of jinxing everyone's chances for survival).

He then went out on patrol. Two hours later, he was on his way home with a bang.

While on patrol, the officer made contact with the enemy, and his vehicle was hit by an IED that had been set up on one corner of a nearby intersection. Because vehicles had to slow down to make the turn at this intersection, timing the detonation was easy.

The blast hit the passenger side of the officer's vehicle, disabling it. The officer had his right arm out the window, which exposed his right shoulder to the full effects of the blast. Several pieces of shrapnel lodged in his shoulder.

Private First Class Zampaglione, the machine gunner, suffered from blast effects, including a concussion and a ruptured eardrum. He had been facing forward, away from the direction of the blast (so he could protect his Squad from the front). The blast went off to his right rear; his body armor and helmet protected him from flying debris.

Sergeant Mike Halle was the driver in the lead vehicle. The blast was so strong that he was blown from the vehicle through the driver-side door. All that saved him from hitting the pavement was his seat belt. Pieces of shrapnel flew passed his face, shattering the windshield in front of him.

At the time, we did not think he was eligible for the Purple Heart, and at first, one was not awarded.

After our return, we learned out that active duty was issuing Purple Hearts for concussion. With all the IEDs going off during our tour, we had a large number of soldiers who, under those guidelines, were eligible for the Purple Heart.

But not all soldiers received the awards they deserved. Some soldiers completed their enlistments and simply got out, while others retired and did not follow-up on awards. Sergeant Halle received his award several years after our return home.

The concussive force of the explosion shattered the windshield of the second vehicle in the patrol. Luckily, the windshield held together, protecting the people inside. SPC Roeser, the gunner, suffered a concussion and temporary hearing loss. Like Private First Class Zampaglione, he was facing away from the blast and his body armor and helmet protected him from shrapnel.

The driver, Sergeant Melissa Richards, maneuvered her vehicle into position to cover the extraction of the wounded officer. Lieutenant Chiverton, also in the second vehicle, kicked out the windshield so that they could see and better direct the rescue effort. Once they were in position, Sergeant Jack Earley, the Squad Leader for the officer's Security team, treated the officer's wounds, started an IV, and kept the officer from going into shock. The officer was in good hands as Jack had plenty of experience treating the injured—he was a paramedic in civilian life, had previous military experience as a Navy Corpsman, and was attached to the Marine Corps.

Other units responded, taking the wounded to the CSH for treatment. The officer and Private First Class Zampaglione would soon be sent to Germany and then back to the United States.

In a twist of irony, the only person who had seemed excited to stay in Iraq for an entire year was now one of the only two who were able to return sooner.

None of us were happy about what happened, but we all saw it coming. The enemy was known for hitting targets of opportunity, and they received one.

September 9, 2003

1st Squad was on duty at the Abu Ghraib Police Station. They learned that an IED had been planted on the Abu Ghraib expressway, a major thoroughfare between Baghdad and Western Iraq. Explosive Ordnance Disposal located and removed four blocks of TNT without incident.

September 10, 2003

2nd Squad, 3rd Platoon reported hearing an explosion in the vicinity of the Ghazalia overpass. 2nd Squad stood by as an EOD Unit and Infantry elements swept the area for IEDs. They located an IED but, as soldiers from the 759th EOD unit attempted to destroy the bomb, it was command-detonated by an insurgent, killing an EOD soldier. Two Iraqi individuals, who watched the activity from a nearby vehicle, laughed and drove away when the bomb detonated. They were never located.

1st Squad reported gunfire in the vicinity of the Abu Ghraib market. A child had apparently thrown a hand grenade onto a tank, which caused several locals to panic and open fire. Indiscriminate fire killed three civilians.

Supply and Maintenance issues had begun to get out of hand.

None of the shipping containers left behind in Kuwait by our Battalion have been moved forward. These containers held excess clothing, spare parts, and other important equipment that we could not cram in our vehicles when we moved from Kuwait to Baghdad. We could live without some of it, but the rest was becoming a necessity.

Battalion organized a convoy to head south to Kuwait, so each unit could retrieve the needed equipment and return it to Warrior Compound. We sent down a Sergeant with several soldiers, a couple of Humvees with trailers, and a 2.5 ton truck. Several days later, the convoy returned with some supplies and equipment Maintenance needed, but the Sergeant, one of our other soldiers, and the 2.5 ton truck were conspicuously absent.

Not until several days later did the NCO and soldier return with a completely empty truck. When questioned, the NCO stated that the soldier accompanying him had gotten sick, and they remained in Kuwait until he was able to travel; he explained that they had returned with an empty truck because all the necessary equipment had already returned with the other soldiers. But, this was not the case; as numerous items were still in Kuwait that we needed in Baghdad.

A few weeks later, we organized a smaller convoy, led by First Sergeant Jones, to go back down to Kuwait to retrieve as much of the equipment as possible. When First Sergeant Jones got to our storage containers, he discovered that they had been broken into. All kinds of equipment had been stolen, and what was left had been pulled out and strewn about the desert sand.

The thieves took numerous personal items, along with our old night-vision equipment, which had been left behind because it was not compatible with the equipment we were using. But the old equipment still had extreme value as a sensitive military item, especially on the black market.

We learned that, during the initial convoy, the NCO had the supply people move the shipping containers apart so they could be accessed; yet he had neglected to have the containers put back into their original positions, which left them vulnerable to anyone with a pair of bolt cutters.

Chapter Eleven

LIEUTENANT GRUBE ASSUMES COMMAND

Never tell people how to do things. Tell them what to do and they will surprise you with their ingenuity.

General George Patton Jr.

ACTIVITY LOG
June 11–August 21, 2003

September 11, 2003

Today, Lieutenant Grube was appointed as our Company Commander. No one (except possibly Lieutenant Grube) knew he was next in line for command. I think he was chosen because he had done a great job with 4th Platoon, who had gotten things under control during his leadership. I knew that he was probably not looking forward to his new assignment, but he had no choice.

Lieutenant Grube was a Commander with whom I could speak freely, and have discussions. I knew that he respected issues brought up by all his men, and that we had honest give-and-takes about how things should be done. While we did not always agree, we always managed to conduct ourselves professionally.

1st Squad, 2nd Platoon fielded an intelligence report from an Iraqi civilian about the whereabouts of a wanted person. The civilian stated that he knew the location of #14 on our most wanted list. The informant believed that #14 was using a vehicle to transport weapons to the Fedayeen for a possible attack on the Baghdad airport.

Figure 11.1   Staff from the 143rd inspect an Iraqi Police Station with General Hertling from the 1st Armored Division (Left to Right) Lieutenant Grube, Lieutenant Chiverton, General Hertling

September 19, 2003

1st Squad, 4th Platoon was struck by an IED while on patrol. Private First Class Hayes was treated for a shrapnel wound. Sergeant Morales, Sergeant Leonard, Specialist Bettini, Private First Class Montoya, Private First Class Pesta, and Private First Class Hayes were all treated for concussion and hearing loss.

The attack appeared to have been set up by the Iraqi Police patrolling with the Squad. The Iraqi Police had made a lot of demands, directing the Squad on where to go and where to stop, leading them to the location of the ambush. Just before the Squad was ambushed, the Iraqi Police unit disappeared, leaving 1st Squad, 4th Platoon out in the open.

September 20, 2003

Now that we had a return date, as bad as it was, the bitching about finding out when we were going home had stopped. People were still in shock, but reality had set in, allowing them to focus on the task at hand.

The troops decided to not report all incidents and attacks taking place around the city unless they were hit or fired back. While I understood that they were getting tired of filling out paperwork, their decision left me in the dark with no idea how many actual engagements we had been in. If I didn't have a clear idea of how many times we had been engaged, I didn't know how the people scheduling turning control back to the Iraqi government could make successful decisions.

September 21, 2003

The Abu Ghraib Police Station was across the street from a very large complex referred to as the Milk Factory. In the past, insurgents had launched attacks at the police station from the Milk Factory, using the many buildings for cover as they took shots. Insurgents were also fond of planting roadside bombs in front of the Milk Factory.

The Iraqi Police covered the checkpoint that granted access to the police compound, but the Military Police maintained a presence on the roof with a squad automatic weapon to cover the approaches. This was backed up by several additional soldiers on the roof who were armed with M-16 rifles.

The police station was attacked late at night by insurgents hiding out in the Milk Factory, who opened fire with AK-47 assault rifles. Specialist Escobales returned fire with a squad automatic assault weapon. Escobales' rounds struck an insurgent who was attempting to fire an RPG, killing him. The rounds' impact also caused the rocket to fire into the air, missing the police station.

Once the RPG gunner was killed, the rest of the insurgents broke off the attack and slipped away into the back buildings of the

Milk Factory. A sweep of the area located the body of the gunner, three un-fired RPGs, and the grenade launcher.

RPGs originated with the German Panzer Faust in World War II. As the name implies, they are rocket-propelled weapons where the rocket keeps burning for the entire flight time. The rocket is somewhat slow, so when these weapons are fired from a great distance, the target might be able to see smoke from the launch, hear the missile, and have a second or two to react.

The RPGs used in Iraq were of Russian manufacture, and had been in use all the way back to Vietnam. They are easy to use, single-shot, reusable shoulder-fired weapons that come with various types of sighting systems, a launch tube, and the missile itself.

These weapons were extremely accurate at fifty-meters, allowing a trained gunner to put a rocket through a window. At one hundred-meters, they were still accurate enough to hit a good-sized vehicle or small building. At over one hundred-meters and beyond (a maximum range of 920 meters), their accuracy drops off rapidly. But, if your goal is to launch an RPG from a great distance and hope that you hit something, they'll still work for you.

These RPGs were effective against our unarmored vehicles and could heavily damage or destroy even the up-armored Humvee (depending on where their rounds impacted). M-1 tanks, on the other hand, had nothing to fear.

September 23, 2003

An Iraqi national, Ehsaw Nijem, began negotiations with the 143rd Military Police Company to sell surface-to-air missiles back to the Coalition. Lieutenant Grube met with the informant at Al Ghazalia police station to begin the negotiations.

Coalition forces had always been willing to purchase enemy weapons or ordnance, but this was the first time we were aware of surface-to-air missiles being part of the negotiation. Getting these weapons off the street would have a significant impact on our aviation assets, so we hoped that the negotiations would succeed.

Being in Iraq, nothing ever went easily, and these negotiations were no exception. They dragged on for days. In the end, we did not recover surface-to-air missiles, but we did find antitank rockets. Recovering the rockets was still extremely important, but not as important as getting the surface-to-air missiles we knew were out there. These missiles are capable of shooting down Coalition aircraft, and could be easily smuggled out of Iraq to shoot down civilian airliners.

September 26, 2003

We began construction on a new Abu Ghraib Police Station, located some distance away from both the original station and the Milk Factory. Ten men armed with AK-47s and rocket propelled grenade launchers overpowered the guards at the site and set off bombs that destroyed the rear wall of the facility. None of the guards were injured.

It was evident that the insurgents didn't like the new location of the Abu Ghraib Police Station any better than they liked the original location. So, we began to look for a third location that was both defendable and within the Abu Ghraib area.

Chapter Twelve

OFFICER AND SENIOR NCO TRAINING

Learn from other peoples mistakes; you will not live long enough to make them all yourself.

Author Unknown

We Were Soldiers Once...and Young

The battalion commander at the 709th Military Police Battalion had several mandatory meetings with various officers and senior noncommissioned officers of the companies assigned to the 709th. During one of these mandatory meetings, we viewed *We Were Soldiers Once...and Young.*

Based on a book written by Lieutenant General Harold G. Moore and Joseph L. Galloway, the movie tells the story of the Battle of the la Drang Valley. The battle took place in Vietnam in November of 1965 and was situated in two locations, LZ X-Ray and LZ Albany. While the book discusses the battles at both locations, the film ends after the battle at LZ X-Ray and does not cover the disastrous confrontation at LZ Albany.

Both the book and movie begin in the United States, with the unit forming up and training for deployment to Vietnam. The unit was to become the forerunner of the modern day Air Cavalry as these soldiers would fly into battle on helicopters, relying on them for close air support, resupply, MedEvac, and ultimately, extrication from the battlefield. Using helicopters during warfare was a new and innovative concept—no matter what the distance or the terrain, soldiers could be quickly and efficiently moved across the battlefield to affect the outcome of an engagement.

The book and movie then follow General Moore's unit to Vietnam and the battle of LZ X-Ray; however, both overlook a couple of mistakes and the overconfidence of the American forces.

General Moore, who at the time was a lieutenant colonel, had his battalion out on a sweep in one general area for five days before a decision to move the Battalion to a location called LZ X-Ray. At the time, Lieutenant Colonel Moore had very little intelligence on the new location, but was aware that a least three NVA battalions were known to be operating in the area. His reconnaissance was limited to a quick helicopter fly over of the area where he wanted to insert his battalion. He didn't have the luxury of on-the-ground assets reporting on the activity in either the general vicinity or the specific area of LZ X-Ray.

A mountain called the Chu Pong Massif, which was suspected of being an NVA stronghold, overlooked LZ X-RAY. Rumors proved to be true, and the NVA had full view of the landing zone below. In moving his battalion to the landing zone, Lieutenant Colonel Moore faced two major problems: (1) The landing zone could accommodate only a limited number of Huey helicopters at one time, and (2) he had a limited number of helicopters for each lift (which meant that several lifts were required to get the entire battalion into the landing zone). Even with helicopters, getting his entire battalion on the ground would take several hours.

The area was prepped with artillery, aerial rocket and machine gun fire prior to landing the first transport helicopters. Lieutenant Colonel Moore was on the first lift and the soldiers who were with him fired into the tree line as they went in. According to both the book and the movie, neither the preparatory fire nor the assault fire had much effect on the NVA.

Shortly after landing, the first lift started taking fire. Colonel Moore was able to establish the perimeter, and subsequent lifts began arriving as they took fire. Troops on the ground quickly became fully engaged prior to the last helicopter bringing in the last soldier. The battle, which raged on for several days, was bloody and vicious, at times descending into hand-to-hand combat, with high casualties on both sides.

At this point the movie diverges from the book, leading the viewer to believe that Lieutenant Colonel Moore hit upon a brilliant strategy that destroyed the NVA. He leads his unit on an assault against the massif, an attack that draws out the NVA, which, according to the movie, were hammered by the Battalion's artillery and aviation assets.

The book (the true account of what happened) states that the NVA were never defeated in a final glorious battle at LZ X-Ray, but instead melted away into the brush. The NVA did take very heavy casualties, but were never defeated, and remained an effective and dangerous fighting force. Out of the approximately 411 men in Lieutenant Colonel Moore's unit, seventy-nine were killed in battle, 121 were wounded. The NVA suffered between 634 and 1,200 casualties, though the exact number cannot be confirmed because bodies were either taken off the battlefield or left in the brush. Why the Brigade Commander thought he should send a single battalion to engage three battalions remains a mystery (especially after learning that actually, a full NVA division was in the area).

Lieutenant Colonel Moore's unit was relieved by two other battalions and his battalion was helicoptered out of LZ X-Ray. The two battalions chose to leave from two other locations, making their way towards LZ Columbus and LZ Albany. The 2/5th Cavalry would continue onward to LZ Columbus, while the 2/7th Cavalry traveled to LZ Albany.

According to the book, the 2/7th Cavalry, tired and used up from a prior engagement, made their way toward LZ Albany in a somewhat elongated column, with a distance between the point and the last man of about 550 yards. Two NVA soldiers were captured as the lead elements reached Albany, and the Battalion Commander halted the column so that he could personally interrogate the prisoners. During the interrogation, the Battalion Commander requested that his company commanders move forward to his location. The company commanders complied, most of them accompanied by their radio operators and one or more senior NCOs.

The exhausted American soldiers had not set up much of a defensive perimeter, simply stopping in place to take off their packs, drink water, eat C-rations and, in some cases, fall asleep. Flank security had not been set out and machine guns had not been placed to cover the column. At that point, no one knew what the Battalion Commander had in mind and no one knew how long the column would remain halted.

At about the time the last company commander arrived to meet with the Battalion Commander, the NVA opened up with devastating fire. The NVA had no way of knowing what was going on in the American ranks, but their attack could not have been better timed. The initial effects of the assault were devastating, as there was virtually no cover for the soldiers other than tall grass. Fire from the Americans and the NVA crisscrossed the area, striking friend and foe alike. With all the command staff at the head of the column, no one was in place to give orders or coordinate any type of defense. Ranking officers attempting to make their way back to their companies were cut down by the NVA fire.

The battle raged on until the predawn hours. In that time, 155 American soldiers had been killed and 124 had been wounded. Though they did slip away again, the NVA also sustained heavy casualties. The movie makes no mention of this second battle and of the American forces' major defeat.

When the movie was over, our battalion commander opened up the floor for questions or comments. I doubted that any of the soldiers in the room had ever served in Vietnam; none of them had been in the military in 1965. I doubted if any of them had ever read the book, but I did expect quite a few comments regarding the movie, including the fact that it covered only half the battle and did not accurately portray the final outcome.

No one raised a hand. I was about to raise mine right before I realized that I was outranked by just about everyone in the audience and that I was only a part-timer in the military.

While I fully understand that Lieutenant Colonel Moore was a hero to most people in the modern day Army for defeating the NVA in a major battle, I do not see it that way. The lieutenant colonel, knowing that he was probably outnumbered, with no idea of the NVA's location, moved his battalion into what was, ultimately, a trap that he picked for himself. He took the chance that the first elements would be cut off from reinforcement by an NVA attack, trusting that U.S. artillery and air assets would be able to support him. In this case, he was partially right, but as the NVA moved in as close to the U.S. forces as possible, the artillery and air strikes were of limited value.

The lieutenant colonel did stay with his unit even after being ordered out, as the U.S. high command did not want to lose a battalion commander if LZ X-Ray had been overrun, and he stuck with them all through the battle. He took his chances with his men and did not leave until all of his men had left the landing zone.

The fact that the remaining two battalions would hike out to two separate landing zones after being exhausted by battle is something I do not understand. I also don't understand why the Battalion Commander both halted the column short of LZ Albany in order to interrogate two prisoners, and ordered his command staff forward to his location prior to a defensive perimeter being established. His confidence that the battle was over and that they were relatively safe was sorely misplaced and led to the slaughter and wounding of many American soldiers.

I saw this same overconfidence in our Battalion. Staff rides were set up to bring the entire Battalion Command staff to locations where Battalion had been assaulted and seriously injured over the past year! Every senior person in a battalion was required to participate in these staff rides, from the Battalion Commander and his staff to the company commanders and First Sergeants to the platoon leaders and platoon sergeants.

I sat there after watching this movie, not raising my hand, wondering if anyone had ever read a history book, or if everyone had just decided to learn how to fight a war all over again from day one, remaking the same mistakes that other humans have made again and again so we can learn for ourselves what not to do.

The honor, bravery and sheer determination of Lieutenant Colonel Moore and his soldiers once they were attacked cannot be ignored. Despite a bad location and overwhelming odds, Lieutenant Colonel Moore and his troops refused to give in. With individual courage, they survived the battle. I was proud to be serving with eighteen- to twenty-two-year-old soldiers of our units, who were just as determined as those in Lieutenant Colonel Moore's.

We Were Soldiers Once...and Young (the book, not the movie) should be mandatory reading for every NCO and officer.

Chapter Thirteen

BACK TO THE PRESENT

I know God will not give me anything I can't handle. I just wish that He didn't trust me so much.

Mother Teresa

ACTIVITY LOG
September 28–October 18, 2003

September 28, 2003

Sergeant Matthews, Specialist Rogers, and Private First Class Ethier participated in the war fighter competition. Out of twenty-two teams, theirs placed eighth overall, and came in first among National Guard teams. This qualified them to be issued a state-of-the-art combat vehicle that was just starting to be issued to MP units.

The new system was termed the XM-101 CROWS, an entire vehicle-weapons system. It was an up-armored Humvee with a 50-caliber machine gun and an MK-19 automatic grenade launcher.

The beauty of the system is that the gunner is able to remotely operate the weapons system from inside the vehicle instead of being exposed in the turret. The gunner has a computer screen that behaves as his gun sight but, unlike a normal gun sight, this system can zoom in or out, and has low-light capability. In addition, the sight is equipped with an FLR for night firing, as well as a laser range finder for daytime targets. Thermal imaging allows the gunner to locate warm bodies in the cold background of the night at distances farther then the eye can see. Once the guns are locked onto a target, they follow that target regardless of whether the target, the XM-101, or both, are moving, ensuring a first-round-burst hit every time.

We anticipated getting this vehicle and using it as the scout unit for every mission. The firepower, accuracy, mobility and protection would give us a big edge on the battlefield. There was only one problem: Powers-that-be would not release the vehicle because, I can only assume, they were afraid that we might damage or destroy it. The military had no problem sending three soldiers out in an unarmored vehicle with a light machine gun, but they were not willing to risk the possibility of a $200,000 vehicle being damaged. So, the vehicle sat parked at Falcon FOB, displaying our unit and bumper number, waiting for someone to come to their senses and release it to the combat role it was designed for. That never happened.

About this time, the Iraqi Police arrested Mohammed Aubada Afin, a security guard suspected of direct involvement in the bombing of the new Abu Ghraib Police Station. We learned that Afin had ensured that security would not interfere with the insurgents.

September 30, 2003

1st Platoon and Iraqi Police officer Colonel Kareem of the Abu Ghraib Police Station got into a confrontation with members of the Iraqi Civil Defense Corps (the Iraqi version of the National Guard).

The Iraqi Civil Defense Corps stopped an Iraqi civilian driving a van not far from the police station. They surrounded the vehicle, with various members of the Civil Defense Corps shouting different and conflicting orders at the driver. During the confusion, one of the Defense Corps members accidentally discharged his firearm. This triggered a full response from the Civil Defense

Corps members on the opposite side of the vehicle who thought the driver, or someone else in the vehicle, had shot at them. Civil Defense fired dozens of rounds into the vehicle, killing the driver.

1st Platoon members, Staff Sergeant Rosatti, and Colonel Kareem of the Iraqi Police attempted to intervene, but were forced away at gunpoint. This type of confusion and reckless firing was sadly quite frequent. It was not uncommon to see an Iraqi Police officer or soldier walking around with a loaded weapon set on full auto, his finger on the trigger.

Attacks continued to take place on almost a daily basis in the vicinity of the Abu Ghraib Police Station and nearby marketplace. Part of the reason might have been the area's proximity to the Abu Ghraib prison. The prison once housed the worst of Baghdad's criminal element, who were released by Saddam Hussein just prior to the Coalition's invasion.

While political prisoners remained incarcerated, murderers, rapists, thieves, kidnappers, and other dangerous criminals were now free. Without money or transportation, they headed east to the first major population center in relation to the prison, the area around the police station. Some probably earned a few dollars for every bomb set or rocket fired on Coalition forces.

Between insurgents willing to die for Allah, and others who were willing to kill for pay, we had our work cut out for us.

October 1, 2003

A female Iraqi civilian called the Al Khadra Police Station, informing 3rd Squad, 2nd Platoon that she was treating two wounded U.S. soldiers at a residence. A patrol dispatched from the 527th discovered that the two soldiers, who were from Alpha Company 1/13 Armor unit, had sustained gunshot wounds. The soldiers were evacuated to the combat surgical hospital, and one of them later died from his injuries.

October 3, 2000

4th Squad, 3rd Platoon dispatched an Iraqi Police patrol to

investigate a report of a possible IED near the Jordanian Embassy. They found a bag of TNT. No detonators were found.

Once again, active-duty seemed to be in training mode. They informed us that everyone would be going through rifle qualification. The standard qualification course required approximately sixty rounds of ammunition for each soldier. I asked the active-duty Operations people where we would be getting this ammunition and was informed that we would shoot 20% of our basic load and get resupplied.

I told them that we had repeatedly tried and failed to get enough ammunition to bring us up to our basic load. We had been in-theater for six months under several different commands, and each time we had asked for additional ammunition, we had been told that none was available. I stated that there was no way we could fire 20% of our basic load when we did not have 100% of the required basic load, and asked for the ammunition up front to balance the unit's combat load. I was told that was impossible.

This made no sense. If they wanted to qualify 750 soldiers on the M-16 rifle, those soldiers would have to fire at least 45,000 rounds of ammunition. I wanted 100% of the required rounds in case our soldiers should find themselves in a prolonged gun battle (which did happen).

After all the units in the Battalion passed their qualification, I requested that our ammunition be resupplied. Battalion issued only enough rounds to replace the ones expended during qualification. When I again asked for rounds to bring us up to 100%, I was told they were not available. This situation put soldiers in the National Guard at risk. The active-duty had their full combat load, plus rounds for their MK-19 grenade launchers and their 50-caliber machine guns. It seemed as if having ammunition for qualification had a higher priority than ensuring National Guard units on combat patrol were properly armed.

The qualification course also cut into time we needed to perform our combat mission in Baghdad. Our company had been working seven days a week nonstop, and all of our Squads and Teams had daily assignments. By comparison, active-duty got at least one day off each week, to maintain their vehicles and weapons, and also to relax. Our seven-days-a-week assignment had gone on for weeks, and Battalion rescheduled us every time it appeared that we might get a day off to rest and perform maintenance. But we were now taking off a full day for rifle qualification.

Getting rifle qualification, along with several other qualifications, out of the way was important to active-duty before they returned to Germany, because they would have to return to peacetime training standards once they were back in garrison.

I later learned that there was another motive for the rifle qualification course which was more important than winning the insurgency…

October 4, 2003

An IED detonated prematurely in the area of the Al Ghazalia police station. The blast killed the insurgent setting the device. Unfortunately, we cannot always be so lucky.

October 6, 2003

Our fears are coming back to haunt us…we just heard that the officer wounded on September 8th is trying to get back to Iraq.

October 7, 2003

While walking alongside the road, an unknown Iraqi male detonated explosives that were in a bag he was carrying, killing himself. According to eyewitnesses, the detonation appeared to be accidental, as no one was near the subject, and no vehicles were passing when the bomb detonated.

October 8, 2003

Sergeant Jack Earley came up to me after hearing that the officer wounded on September 8th would be coming back. He wanted to discuss the officer's cowboy attitude (his statements to "get a kill;" his penchant for carrying a shotgun, flipping a knife open and closed; his habit of unsafely unloading a shotgun by running the shells through the chamber while in an occupied tent, etc.). If this officer came back and went on the road, Earley and I were both very concerned that the officer might be injured or killed.

After hearing his concerns, Chaun and I talked about meeting with our Battalion Sergeant Major, but I could see the futility of trying to explain the situation. In response, he would probably have said that the officer was just being aggressive, taking the fight to the enemy, something a good soldier would do.

October 15, 2003

We felt like we had more control over what we were doing. Lieutenant Grube and I had been going out to check on all the police stations almost daily. For various reasons, some days, we went out more than once.

Today we went out to Abu Ghraib Prison, hoping to resolve some transport problems we had with the staff out there who were picking up prisoners that we had in lockup. Units from the prison were supposed to pick up our prisoners from our police stations and transport them to the prison. If the transport unit decided to take the day off, they told the Specialist working the phones. The Specialist would then call us to say the run was canceled. When we called back to find out why the run had been canceled, we would get the same Specialist, who always gave us the run around.

We found that the lower enlisted were running the prison, taking care of their friends, and that the place was in complete chaos. At the time, we didn't know that there were grave concerns about how the prison was being run, an issue that later became a major scandal.

Construction started on the third Abu Ghraib Police Station, which we located on the west end of the Baghdad International Airport compound. The new police station would be closer to the center of the city and, as a result, Coalition forces. The area also eventually became a gate for the west end of the Baghdad Airport, and consequently handled a lot of Coalition traffic.

We became stuck in traffic on the way out to the old Abu Ghraib Police Station. Insurgents had attacked a Coalition tank belonging to the Estonians in the center of the marketplace. Traffic had backed up on either end of the marketplace, and the area became very crowded. Lieutenant Grube and I were concerned about being trapped in this position, surrounded by both military and civilians, and we decided that we needed to get moving.

Figure 13.1   Lieutenant Grube inspecting the construction of the third Abu Ghraib Police Station

Lieutenant Grube knew the area much better than I, so he led us down a side street. I was concerned about being attacked in these narrow confines, but I realized that no one would have ever expected us to go down that way. A large puddle, with a black, yellow, and green color to it, covered the entire street. I didn't know what it was until we hit it, and when we did, the stench was overwhelming.

We continued onward through the puddle and out on the far side of the marketplace, our vehicle now plastered with all kinds of fecal matter. Traffic had been stopped here as well, and our Squad had to stop. Those of us who were passengers piled out of the vehicles to provide security from the crowd that was just an arm's length away.

The look of hatred on the faces of the civilians was somewhat unnerving, but we had overwhelming firepower on our side and could easily respond to any threat. Our protective posture prevented anything from happening, and no one took advantage of us while we were dismounted.

We continued onward at a very slow pace through the west end of the marketplace toward the old Abu Ghraib Police Station, which was now several hundred yards away. As we left the area near the marketplace, the traffic picked up speed. Initially, we kept pace, but now we were trotting along, trying to keep up.

My vehicle was the last in line, and I was trotting to the rear on the driver's side, screening the left and the back of the vehicle. I kept my eye on the crowd, which meant that I was facing to the rear and trotting backwards so that my back would not be towards the crowd.

As the Humvee started to pull away, I heard the machine gunner yelling for me to catch up. With the machine gunner covering the rear, I turned and began running for the vehicle. It crossed my mind that, at fifty-two years old, I was getting a little too old for this. Fortunately, the day turned out to be uneventful, and we completed our tours of the police stations without incident.

We received word that the 709th would be rotating out of the country between February 3rd and March 26th, and that their Battalion would not be replaced. We crossed our fingers that we would be pulling out with them, but no news about us came down. We had rotated into theater after they had, so we assumed that we might be staying longer.

Around 8:00 p.m. (almost dark) Warrior Compound was hit with mortars. This direct attack was the first that I can recall. Numerous attacks had taken place around us, with rockets and mortars flying over our position to the Green Zone; but nothing had ever been directed at the Compound.

It may sound funny, but when the rockets and mortars flew over our compound, no one gave it much thought. No one became scared, or even concerned because everyone knew these attacks were not directed at us…they were someone else's problem.

In the wake of the attack, the Battalion Commander put the Compound on a full alert. Soldiers in Battalion Headquarters, who did not normally go on the road or go out at night, were sent to designated fighting positions (which were really secondary positions, most of which consisted of a series of drained concrete fountains).

Warrior's primary defensive positions were the high walls and guard towers that surrounded the Compound. These positions were manned twenty-four hours a day, and each position was armed with at least one machine gun. The idea that anyone would attack the Compound facing machine gun fire from several positions was ludicrous. Knowing our level of security on the walls, I felt extremely safe inside Warrior, and my only concern was being attacked by mortars or rockets fired over the walls.

Battalion Headquarters, on the other hand, was not only scared to death, but fully armed, locked and loaded. A few of us exited the main building while the alert was going, intending to cross the Compound and return to our sleeping area. We left the building without concern, because we knew the attack was over. Any time the insurgents fired mortars at Coalition forces, the attack ended almost as soon as it began, because they knew that helicopter gunships or AC-130A Spectre gunships would respond to a prolonged attack, raining fire upon them.

As we made our way from the main building, crossing through the fountain area, Headquarters (who was still hunkered down behind the concrete walls) began challenging us. It would have been amusing, except these soldiers had rifles locked and loaded. In the midst of this, I heard soldiers crying, including one female soldier who was screaming and just wigging out.

I am not sure where those soldiers' NCOs and officers were that night. I would have expected them to be out there taking charge, reassuring the troops, and calming the situation. I did not hear anyone out there, either talking to the troops or taking charge. It crossed my mind that I should say something, but these soldiers were not my troops, and they did not know my voice. If I spoke up, I might have triggered a response that would have gotten me killed.

Imagine how unnerving stepping outside the building, and finding a group of terrified soldiers pointing twenty or more loaded rifles at us was. They were on such high alert, the fact that we wore the same uniforms, stood in full view, and made no threat did not put them at ease.

We looked at one another, and realized that we stood a very good chance of getting shot. Moving across the darkened compound, even in a secure environment, was a dangerous proposition with inexperienced soldiers aiming weapons at us. We quickly retreated to the main building, and waited for Battalion to call off the alert.

A day or so later, I ran into the Battalion Commander. He was a super hard charger, out there day and night seeing to his troops. He made sure they were doing their duty while staying as safe as they possibly could. I had a lot of respect for him, because both he and his Battalion Sergeant Major shared the dangers of the streets of Iraq with their soldiers. He was easy to talk to, so I had no problem discussing the events the night of the alert.

I told him it must have been a real wake-up experience for those soldiers who rarely, if ever, went outside the wire. While almost no place in Iraq was truly safe, Warrior Compound did have an air of security that had never been challenged until that night (not that we were ever in danger of being overrun, but try and explain that to someone who has never had to fear for their life).

Half in jest, I asked the Commander to refrain from putting those people back out there again, because it was just too dangerous. The fact that no one got shot that night was a miracle.

October 16, 2003

An unknown male fired at Iraqi Police officers who were guarding the Spanish Embassy. The attacker fled on foot and was not located. Why anyone would have a problem with the Spanish Embassy is beyond me…unless the attacker just wanted to kill someone, attacking the Embassy made no sense.

October 18, 2003

Ten people met with Congressman Rob Simmons.

Staff Sergeant Brian Young was scheduled to leave on October 20th so that he could go home to be with his grandfather, who was eighty-eight years old and very sick. I gave him copies of the awards I had typed up for our soldiers, that were getting turned down by Battalion. I asked him to give these to higher-ups back in Connecticut, so they would know what our soldiers were doing (even if those soldiers didn't get the awards they were being put in for).

Battalion had been making moves to get us out of the country. While it was only October, plans to move us back to the United States were already in the works. April was still a long way off, but we held mobilization meetings, made equipment lists, discussed space required on boats, and determined the number of boots on ground that would be rotating home. Battalion wanted to move out somewhere around February 1st, and they were scheduled to be the last unit of the Brigade to depart. Brigade Headquarters would be replaced, but not specifically the 709th Military Police Battalion. Warrior Compound was going to be turned over to someone else. I heard some talk that, when we redeployed, we would drive south from Baghdad to Kuwait.

The 18th Military Police Brigade had also made plans to rotate out. Colonel David Philips was slated to command the 89th Military Police Brigade, which would take over from the 18th. To help prepare his troops for deployment from Fort Hood, Colonel Philips came to Iraq for a firsthand assessment of the situation.

He had been stationed at the Pentagon in a prior command, and his office had been on the side of the Pentagon struck by American Airlines Flight 77. Although the Colonel had not been in his office at the time of the attack, he made his way back to assist with rescue and recovery of injured and dead soldiers. He suffered respiratory problems from breathing the toxic air from the ensuing fire, which caused him difficulty when speaking for long periods of time. Even with this affliction, he refused to stay out of the war zone. I believe he felt going to Iraq was his duty as a soldier.

The Colonel was not a Green Zone soldier, and made his way out to the Battalions and Companies in the area. He sat down with several members of our company to get an assessment of how things were going, and he was very interested in what we had to say. We told him that the transition was moving too fast; the Iraqi Police forces were improving, but they had a long way to go.

There were some positives to report, however. Although the Iraqi dinar was almost worthless, somehow Iraq was still functioning. Fresh food was available at the markets, including butchered lambs and goats hung up for sale. These items would have rotted quickly in the desert heat, so someone had money to buy them. All sorts of vehicles were on the roads, and new satellite TV antennas were being installed all over the city (a marked difference from Iraq under Saddam's rule, when only a select few were allowed to have satellite).

After hearing our take on the local situation, Colonel Philips, being a good soldier, decided that he had to see Baghdad for himself. Lieutenant Colonel Garrity escorted Colonel Philips through the streets, day and night. These escorts are chronicled in the book, *Warrior Police*, which describes how surprised Colonel Philips was at the level and frequency of violence in Baghdad. Apparently, none of this information was getting back to the States—Colonel Philips had been under the impression that the situation was under control and getting better all the time.

He was discovering that this assessment was completely wrong. Along with insurgents, thousands of criminals roamed the streets. During a nighttime ride through the Abu Ghraib district, the Colonel's patrol repeatedly came under small arms fire and narrowly missed being struck by an RPG. None of this type of activity had been briefed to higher-ups when the 89th was ordered to deploy. Somewhere along the line, those fifteen to thirty attacks a day in Baghdad were being buried—Command was not being told that the liberation of Iraq was turning to shit.

When a full colonel in charge of an MP brigade is tasked with a year-long assignment in Baghdad, and is not briefed on the unfolding situation, you have to wonder. If Colonel Philips had only gone to Brigade, and not met with the Companies or driven through Baghdad, he would had never been aware of what was really going on until after he took command.

Every day, units filed reports that were going up the chain of command. These were not paper reports, but computerized reports emailed up the chain that were available real-time, just waiting to be read. They detailed both the daily attacks and the rise of various types of insurgent groups who had come from all over the Middle East to kill Americans and other Coalition forces. Somehow, the reports were not getting back to the States. While Mr. Rumsfeld was painting an optimistic picture of the occupation, Colonel Philips and the 89th Military Police Brigade found themselves walking into a shit storm.

Being in somewhat of an informational vacuum, we were not aware of a number of situations that had occurred or were occurring while we were in Iraq. We did not know that the Army Chief of Staff, General Shinseki, had disagreed with Secretary of Defense Donald Rumsfeld and his Deputy Paul Wolfowitz. General Shinseki told them that he would need several hundred thousand soldiers to secure Iraq in the postwar period. General Shinseki's plan was strongly rejected and the results are now obvious to anyone who can read a newspaper.

The other situation that we were not aware of was that Iraq was not under the same level of control that we had in Baghdad. We had more than ten thousand soldiers from the 3rd Brigade Combat Team of the 1st Armored Division, the 18th Military Police Brigade, and other Coalition forces patrolling Western Baghdad. We had no knowledge of the outright lawlessness of Fallujah or Ramadi, which were just a short drive northwest of Baghdad.

Other parts of the country were also not under tight control. Groups hid out in Fallujah or Ramadi to make their plans. They would hit Baghdad and then slip back out to the safety of these towns that were not heavily patrolled. Not until April 2004 did Coalition forces try to take full control of Fallujah. By that time, the 143rd was already on our way home.

General Shinseki had warned Rumsfeld and Wolfowitz what was going to happen. We tried telling them what was happening, and still they insisted that they had the right plan, even when it was obvious that the plan was not working. Even today, when I hear Secretary Rumsfeld speak about Iraq, he does not admit to this major mistake. I am no fan of news reporter Robert Woodward, but this time he got it right in his book, *State of Denial*. Several other writers and reporters brought up the same mistakes being made by the administration, and in particular, Secretary of Defense Rumsfeld.

Chapter Fourteen

THE REPLACEMENT SYNDROME

Send lawyers, guns and money.

Warren Zevon

In October, we received four replacement soldiers from Connecticut. All four had been in the Guard with us prior to deployment, but they had not completed training. When they completed training, they volunteered to join us in the big sandbox, with all the eagerness and enthusiasm of college sophomores desperately wanting to be on the varsity squad. Since we had been deployed with less than our full complement and then had soldiers sent State-side for various reasons, any additional soldiers were greatly appreciated. Thirty soldiers and two officers would have been better, but if all we could get was four, then we would make that work.

The four replacements wanted to hit the ground running and be out on the road the day they arrived. While their "can do" spirit was admirable, it scared the hell out of most of us. First of all, the four were not acclimated to the weather in beautiful downtown Baghdad.

We knew, after being in Baghdad for six months, that we had a lot to teach them about Iraq. During World War II, the Korean War, and Vietnam, replacement soldiers stood a good chance of getting killed within their first few days. Those soldiers were not trained, not given time to acclimate to the climates, and not given opportunities to bond with unit members. We did not want to see any of the newbies killed, so we collectively decided that a train-up period was needed.

Collectively, leadership put together a list of "must learn tasks" that each soldier had to read and fully understand. Each Platoon Leader and Platoon Sergeant added items specific to the soldier's assignment, as well as information on how each Platoon functioned. The core of our training was to ensure that each replacement:

- Had several days, if not weeks, to get acclimated to the weather.
- Clearly understood his/her job and responsibility.
- Knew how his/her respective Team, Squad, and Platoon functioned.
- Had an understanding of the combat environment.
- Was capable of fully contributing to the success of his/her unit and his/her own personal survival.

Leadership was also clear that none of the four replacements was to patrol the road until each had mastered his/her assigned tasks. Then he/she could go patrol, but not as a team member; only as an observer, to watch and learn.

We sent the soldiers to Platoons that need beefing up. Private First Class Marissa Foglia went to 1st Platoon. Private Nathan Vaichus and Specialist Thadeous Hutchinson went to 2nd Platoon, and Specialist Brian Ohler went to 3rd Platoon.

Our plan worked. The four replacements became outstanding soldiers.

But even with all our precautions and training, we weren't the only one's voting—the enemy always has a vote.

After finishing a turkey dinner on Thanksgiving Day, Specialist Ohler was acting as a gunner in the lead vehicle in a two-vehicle patrol. En route to a police station, the patrol was hit by an IED; Specialist Ohler was hit in the head by a flying piece of concrete. If he had not been wearing his helmet with the chin strap in place, he might have literally lost his head. Because he was prepared, he suffered only blast effects and a concussion. Specialist Ohler was awarded the Purple Heart for his injuries.

We overcame the replacement syndrome.

Figure 14.1   The author standing in front of an ASV holding the Flag of New England, designed by World War II Veteran Albert Ebinger of Ipswich, MA, who was wounded in action at Anzio and hospitalized for eighteen months

Chapter Fifteen

ABU GHRAIB POLICE STATION

The Loss of Specialist Rachel Bosveld

From this day to the ending of the world,
But we in it shall be remembered—
We few, we happy few, we band of brothers;
For he to-day that sheds his blood with me
Shall be my brother.

William Shakespeare
King Henry V

ACTIVITY LOG
October 26, 2003

October 26, 2003

Tonight has to be one of the most difficult for the 143rd. We were out on an inspection tour and had stopped at the Abu Ghraib Police Station. We parked our vehicles so that they were backed up against the north wall of the Compound, several hundred feet from the roadway. This location offered protection by being up against the wall, and not out in the middle of the Compound.

Unfortunately, if by chance just one individual in the Abu Ghraib Police force was working for the other side, they would know where we parked our vehicles every night when we went to the station. That information would have pinpointed the locations of any number of our soldiers, and grenades or other explosive devices could be lobbed over the wall directly onto our vehicles, or whatever else was parked there.

Tonight, several of us made our way through the police station, checked in with the desk officer, and made our way to the security post on the roof, which consisted of at least one machine gun and several soldiers.

Our group and a Squad from the active-duty 527th arrived at the station at approximately the same time. After checking on the troops and seeing how things were going, I made my way to the north side of the roof. This position overlooked the Compound's courtyard where our vehicles were parked. The roof was somewhat crowded with the number of soldiers up there. They included normal security detachment, soldiers from the 527th that had gone up to check on their troops, plus several soldiers that had accompanied Lieutenant Grube and me.

This was all fairly standard, as Platoon Leaders and Platoon Sergeants made daily and nightly checks on their people, ensuring that things were getting done and that everyone was all right. On top of that, our Battalion Commander and his Sergeant Major made the same tour. Add to that, an Infantry unit was also located in the same compound, so chances were good that their Platoon Leader, Company Commander, Battalion Commander or Brigade Commander might make a swing by. All in all, numerous military patrols were out crisscrossing the city day and night.

In an almost John Wayne moment, everything got deadly quiet. The proverbial, "This is way too quiet, something is about to happen," definitely applied—no conversation. Somewhere off in the distance, east of our location, the only sound we could hear was a car engine. We could hear its progress westward through the marketplace. The engine would stop for a short period of time, and then it would start up again, only to stop and start up a short while later, all the while slowing travelling west toward our location.

Direct view of the major portion of the marketplace was blocked by buildings to our east. We could see only about a mile of the very western end of the marketplace.

I don't know about everybody else, but I readied my rifle. Vehicles passing through the marketplace down the main drag normally traveled at a high speed. Nobody wanted to drive slowly through the marketplace because of the danger it presented. Nobody anywhere in Iraq drove slowly. Whether military or local, nobody wanted to remain exposed for an extended period of time.

As the seconds ticked by, everyone became increasingly on edge. At last, we observed the vehicle heading from the east, traveling westward on the road passing directly in front of the police compound. This section was a roadway divided by a median barrier. The vehicle stopped as it came into view of the police station, only to start again and resume its westward travel. It stopped again, this time directly in front of the gate to the police compound.

Although it could not turn into the Compound (because of the barrier), the fact that it stopped in front of the Compound's entrance concerned us. All eyes were on the vehicle as it started up again, moved a short distance to the west, and stopped. This time, the doors flew open, and the explosions began. We were being hit.

The first explosion hit inside the Compound, in the middle of where our vehicles were parked against the north wall. Six more explosions detonated in rapid succession, and in between them we could hear screams coming from the area of the parked vehicles.

I'm not sure how long this went on; I felt like time was standing still. The explosions left a rain of something that looked like sparkling glitter—the kind you see in a fireworks display. Someone was screaming for a medic, and in the darkness following the explosions, soldiers from the 143rd raced to assist the wounded individuals.

The vehicle we had been watching restarted its engine a few seconds after the last explosion, moving west again with its lights turned off. I raised my rifle, yelling to engage the vehicle. We opened up with several rifles and one machine gun, spraying the area. By this time, the vehicle had vanished into a darkened area and we could only shoot in its general direction. A soldier from the 527th, who was standing next to me, fired a M-203 grenade round, which detonated in the area where we thought the vehicle was.

By this time, six soldiers from the 143rd had moved three wounded soldiers out of their damaged vehicles into the safety of the police station. Examination found that two of the soldiers had severe injuries to their lower legs and were bleeding profusely. Tourniquets were applied and IV fluids started.

The third soldier, Specialist Rachel Bosveld, was unconscious, not breathing, and medics could not detect a pulse. Unlike the other two soldiers, there was no indication of any kind of wound. It was first thought that she might have been knocked unconscious by the concussion from the blast, but that would not explain why she had no respiration or heartbeat. CPR was started as medics continued to check for signs of a wound. The detailed check revealed a tiny hole in the underside of her upper left arm. There was no bleeding from this wound and no other injury could be found.

An armored ambulance from the Infantry arrived and evacuated the first two soldiers to the CSH. A second ambulance, actually an unarmored civilian vehicle converted into an ambulance, transported Specialist Bosveld to the CSH. Two soldiers from the 143rd, Specialists Escobales and Colon, went with the second ambulance, continuing to perform CPR all the way to the CSH.

Specialist Bosveld was pronounced dead upon arrival. The small hole in the underside of her upper left arm was later determined to be caused by a piece of shrapnel that had entered and traveled across her body, damaging her lungs and heart, causing near instantaneous death.

Our gunner, Specialist Melissa Roberts, had slipped out of the turret and down into the seat behind the driver's seat to take a quick break and relax from the uncomfortable position in the turret. The door where she was sitting was secured and the window was closed when attack happened, and they both absorbed the force of the blast. If either had been open, Specialist Roberts would have been wounded or even possibly killed.

A check was made of the rest of the soldiers and no one was found to be injured. One of the active-duty vehicles had been severely damaged and no longer operable. The vehicle I had arrived in had sustained some shrapnel damage.

There was no follow up ground attack, which would become a standard tactic for the insurgency later in the conflict. Following this attack, several of us maintained security on the roof, and I positioned a few soldiers to cover the rear. Lieutenant Grube made his way down to the wounded and coordinated the transport for the injured. Ten minutes after the attack, things seemed to have settled down, and no further activity was noted.

With security on high alert, I made my way down stairs after the three soldiers had been evacuated. As I approached the room where the casualties had been treated, I found several soldiers cleaning up the room. There was blood all over the place—the soldiers dumped buckets of water on the cement floor and pushed the blood out the door with a mop. It was a very sobering sight. The Lieutenant and I moved through the Compound, checking on everyone.

As I made my way through the Compound, there was another explosion, which I felt more than heard. I had no idea how close or how far away the blast was from my position (concussive force can travel a good distance through the air). The concussion rolled over me, forcing my helmet back causing the chin strap to dig in.

I didn't wait to see if there was a second round coming and made a quick dash back to the protection of the concrete walls of the police station. No one knew a fat old guy could move that fast.

Six of the soldiers from the 143rd risked their lives under fire to retrieve those three injured soldiers and move them into the safety of the police station. Quick action and first aid by Specialist Wilde and several others saved the lives of the two other soldiers. Both were evacuated to Germany and then back to the United States. While both survived their wounds, I am uncertain whether either one lost a limb. Sergeants First Class Lawler and Porter, Specialist Corcoran, Roberts, and Colon, and Staff Sergeant Cloutier were awarded the Army Commendation Medal with V for Valor for rescuing the injured soldiers. It was one of the few times that the active-duty honored our request for awards for valor. Specialist Wilde received the Army Commendation Medal for performing life-saving first aid.

We rounded up the soldiers from the 527th whose vehicle had been damaged and returned to Warrior Compound. Damage done to my vehicle caused its left rear tire to go flat en route to the Compound. We stopped to assess the situation and decided to head to the nearest base, leave the vehicle there, and return the next morning with a spare tire to fix it.

Back at Warrior Compound, the tension of the day overwhelmed us. The soldiers who had performed first aid and CPR were devastated. Two soldiers' lives had been saved by quick action, but nobody was willing to accept the death of Rachel Bosveld. Her observable injury seemed so minor that it was inconceivable that such a tiny little hole could have killed her. Swift action had been taken to try and save her life, but we later learned that it would not have mattered—her internal injuries were too devastating. This was still unacceptable to the soldiers who had tried to save her.

We were told that the explosions were caused by mortar rounds, but the absence of any sound typically made by mortars made me wonder. If the explosions had been 81 or 82mm mortars, they would have been detected by radar. Radar detected nothing.

If the mortars had been smaller of the 60mm variety, they might have gone undetected by radar; but they would have had to have been fired in relative close proximity to the police station. At that close proximity, we would have heard the audible thump a mortar round would make as it exited the tube. In addition, falling mortars should have made an audible sound, caused by air moving over the round and through the holes in the tail fins. While this would not have been a very loud noise, it still would have been an audible whoosh of air.

I asked numerous people who were there that night if they had heard anything that sounded like a mortar attack, but no one heard a sound until the first explosion.

While it was possible that no one heard the incoming mortar rounds, it was also possible that this wasn't a mortar attack, but hand grenades thrown over the wall by passengers in the vehicle (who could have also simply thrown mortar shells over the wall).

In the past, insurgents had attacked Coalition vehicles by dropping mortar shells from overpasses. It's possible that, with all of the ordnance lying around, insurgents used this tactic against the police station that night. Most of the rounds landed in close proximity to one another in very rapid succession, which is not normal when rounds are fired from a small mortar. The launching of each round from a mortar tube shakes the tube, moving the base plate and bipod mount, changing the trajectory of the next round. When a mortar is fired using aiming sights, the sights are removed prior to each firing and reinstalled before the next round is launched, so that the mortar can be realigned for accurate fire. The rounds came in so fast that using aiming sights would not have been possible. The accuracy was too precise to have been launched from a mortar tube. The bottom line is that we will never know.

Not long after, a memorial service honoring Specialist Rachel Bosveld was held at Warrior Compound. All the soldiers in the Battalion were requested to attend, and only the few who were on duty were absent. I chose to stay behind in our Operation Center manning the radios and the telephone. The last thing that the Company and Battalion needed was to see the oldest noncommissioned officer break down in tears. Rachel's loss was devastating, with some taking it harder than others. The sadness and frustration of our inability to do anything to save her weighs heavy on all of us.

Years later, I found some of the details about that night on internet postings. The two soldiers wounded with Rachel were Sergeant Shawn Monroe, and Adam Busby.[15.1] Sergeant Monroe lost a leg that night; the other leg was severely injured, and he suffered other wounds as well. Busby had both legs broken as well as other injuries.

One of the posts mentions that Rachel liked the song *Ironic*.[15.2] How ironic that Rachel was supposed be off duty that night. She swapped out so another soldier could go on a video conference with his young daughter back in Germany.

Chapter Sixteen

CAR BOMB ATTACK ON KHADRA

It is not the critic who counts: not the man who points out how the strong man stumbles or where the doer of deeds could have done better. The credit belongs to the man who is actually in the arena...who, at the best, knows, in the end, the triumph of high achievement, and who, at the worst, if he fails, at least he fails while daring greatly, so that his place shall never be with those cold and timid souls who knew neither victory nor defeat.

Theodore Roosevelt

Some weeks before, the police stations were put under Iraqi control and the company's duties shifted from manning police stations to monitoring status. Monitoring duties included reviewing prisoner logs, checking weapons inventories, reviewing assigned officers, seeing to the needs of the prisoners, and generally just checking in to see how things were going. With the MPs out of the stations, the Infantry and their M-1 tanks and Bradley fighting vehicles had also been removed.

When the assignment shifted from manning the stations to just monitoring them, the Iraqi Police staff of the Al Khadra station decided to take down the vehicle barriers surrounding the station, using bulldozers to remove the wire mesh, sand-filled barriers. These had been placed in such a way so that, while a vehicle could maneuver around them, it could not do so with enough speed to ram through the building. The Iraqi Police believed that because Coalition forces were no longer actively in the station; the threat to them from the insurgents had magically disappeared.

Both Lieutenant Grube, who was acting company commander, and Lieutenant Kerfoot, 3rd Platoon Leader (who had also been in charge of the police station overall), saw the security deficiency and the potential threat posed by the insurgents. So they decided to reestablish a security barrier in spite of the Iraqis' optimism. The lieutenants located large concrete planters inside Warrior Compound and arranged for them to be moved out to the police station, two at a time, using one of our 2.5 ton trucks and a very large tow truck. Moving these planters took several days, and each move was dangerous because our vehicles were moving very slowly through the back streets of Western Baghdad. Even so, the assignment was completed, and as of October 27th, large, concrete planters ringed the station.

This proved to be fortunate. On October 27th, a suicide bomber approached the Al Khadra Police Station in an SUV while Staff Sergeant Cloutier and her Squad were performing a monitoring inspection.

When a squad conducts a monitoring inspection of a police station, one machine gunner is dispatched to the roof to cover the facility, while a second individual remains in a Humvee maintaining communication with the company's Tactical Operations Center. With these precautions in place, the rest of the soldiers in the squad go about their duty conducting the inspection.

The police station was on a dead-end street with the road ending several hundred feet past the station, with civilian businesses and apartments lining the opposite side of the street. Private First Class Levi Saucier, the machine gunner from Staff Sergeant Cloutier's Squad, went up to the roof to monitor the street. He observed the SUV approaching and watched it pass the station. He noted that the driver had a keen interest in the station, including the gunner on the roof who was watching.

Figure 16.1   Specialist Timothy Corcoran

Figure 16.2   The massive crater left by the vehicle bomb

Figure 16.3   The heavily-damaged Khadra Police Station; Staff Sergeant Cloutier exits the building with Sergeant First Class Lawler and Lieutenant Kerfoot

Figure 16.4   The view from Private First Class Saucier's position on the roof of the Khadra Police Station

The driver did not pull into any of the business establishments or residences, but instead continued down to the end of the road before making a U-turn. Private First Class Saucier feared that this activity might be a prelude to an attack. So he repositioned his machine gun from one side of the fighting position to another so he could point his weapon in the direction of the SUV.

The driver of the SUV saw Private First Class Saucier shift his weapon, and hit the gas, attempting to ram the SUV through the barrier of planters. The SUV struck the planters and became disabled atop one of them. Then the driver detonated the vehicle, leaving a seven-foot-deep crater in the road.

The blast knocked Private First Class Saucier back, but did not injure him. Inside the police station, Staff Sergeant Cloutier had fortunately just stepped into a hallway, shielding herself from the blast that came through the front doors and windows of the police station. Sergeant Staron and Specialist Kenyon, who were sitting at the station's front desk, were wounded by flying glass. Specialist Corcoran, who was manning the radio in a position behind the police station, was shielded from the blast.

Specialist Corcoran contacted the company's Operations Center to request medical assistance and reinforcements, as well as provide details of the attack. Staff Sergeant Cloutier, fearing a follow-up attack, reorganized the defense of the police station, provided first aid, and held the position until other units of 3rd Platoon and Lieutenant Grube, the acting company commander, arrived.

In the midst of all of this chaos, an individual charged toward the police station from the crowd that had gathered on the opposite side of the street. When the individual refused orders to halt, he was shot and wounded by members of 3rd Platoon.

The police station was heavily damaged by the explosion. All the doors and windows had been blown out (as well as all the doors and windows on the opposite side of the street), and the structural integrity of the two-story building was in question. There were no Coalition deaths, but one Iraqi Police officer died and several more were wounded. We did not know how many Iraqi civilians were killed or wounded in the blast, but they were numerous.

If Lieutenant Grube and Lieutenant Kerfoot had not taken it upon themselves to use those concrete planters as a barrier, the SUV would have gotten closer to, if not inside, the police station. Had it detonated inside, it would have killed all six of the soldiers from the 143rd 3rd Platoon along with all the Iraqi Police officers. The bomb itself was large enough to level the entire police station.

This assault was Staff Sergeant Cloutier's and Specialist Corcoran's second major attack in less than twenty-four hours.

ACTIVITY LOG
October 30–November 29, 2003

October 30, 2003

2nd Squad, received a report of three males observing the site of the new Abu Ghraib Police Station with binoculars.

October 31, 2003

Colonel Gold became frustrated by the volume of attacks made from the marketplace against Coalition targets near the Abu Ghraib Police Station. The area around the marketplace was the second most dangerous location for Coalition troops, second only to Sadr City (east of the Tigris River, outside of our normal patrol area, and entirely controlled by the Shia militia).

Attacks had gone on day and night for months. During this time, the Colonel had been directing construction of stalls within the marketplace, with the hope that stalls would help organize the marketplace and facilitate vehicle traffic. The Brigade Commander also met with local leaders to try to come to an understanding about the marketplace. After each meeting, the Colonel's requests for cooperation fell on deaf ears, and the marketplace attacks continued.

Colonel Gold considered Abu Ghraib's marketplace the center of gravity for western Baghdad. Most of the hostile activity either originated in the market, or came through the market from the west, such as Fallujah (only a short drive away on a major highway). Gaining control of the market was one of Colonel Gold's highest priorities if hostile activity was to be controlled in western Baghdad.

Plans were made to eliminate the problem once and for all. Intelligence reports coming in from Iraqis recruited from the east side of the Tigris River identified several individuals who were leading the attacks. These operatives would identify the insurgents, and when the opportunity was right, round them up and turn them over to the 3rd Brigade. Unfortunately, two of the five intelligence sources were compromised and killed. Still, their impact had done serious damage to insurgent activity. The insurgents who compromised intelligence sources were identified and eliminated.

If three Iraqis, who were not from the area—but instead were from out of town—could move in and identify troublemakers, local leaders had to know who the bad guys were.

Still, tribal leaders were not cooperating with Colonel Gold. He and his Battalion Commanders began brainstorming. The plan they came up with was simple in detail, but dangerous to execute.

The marketplace needed to be sealed off so no one could escape, and insurgent reinforcements could not get in. Once the marketplace was isolated, Armored and Infantry units could make a determined sweep, rooting out insurgents. The units would be supported by helicopter gunships.

Although the plan was being worked on and fine-tuned, it did not have the luxury of a rehearsal or practice run. Another downside was that no one had any experience with this type of operation. The most dangerous aspect of the plan was that Coalition forces would be in a 360° perimeter, which opened up the real possibility of fratricide and the shooting of civilians.

The dismounted Infantry would be conducting the sweep, backed by helicopters. The perimeter was to be held by armored vehicles. Coordination between the 2/70th Armor Battalion, 1/13 Tank Battalion, the 1/325th Airborne Infantry, the 143rd Military Police Company, along with the helicopter gunships had to be precise and executed on the fly.

Following an ambush on Coalition forces who were traveling through the marketplace, a crowd of more than a thousand people began rioting near the marketplace (a short distance from the still-manned old Abu Ghraib Police Station). The rioting took place east of the station, out of the line of sight of the building. As the disturbance continued, the police station came under attack from small arms, mortars, and RPGs.

Colonel Gold decided that today was the day that the Brigade was to put an end to the attacks and regain full control of the marketplace. The insurgents wanted the fight and thought they could intimidate the Coalition forces.

These insurgents could never imagine the hell that was coming down the road and out of the sky. Colonel Gold put Operation Rat Trap into motion.

While the rioting escalated, the 709th was preparing to conduct a scheduled staff ride with the entire Military Police Battalion leadership. Everyone from the Battalion Commander to the Platoon Leaders and Platoon Sergeants were supposed to be in attendance. From my point of view, having Battalion's leadership in one place was not the smartest idea.

To make matters worse, the purpose of these staff rides (of which this was to be the first) was to review previous engagements and each company's worst encounters with insurgents. I could not understand taking the entire Battalion leadership out for a ride to known dangerous locations where we had had our asses handed to us, only to have them stand around in the open chatting about what went wrong.

While Battalion leadership was getting organized for their ride, we were giving Battalion Headquarters minute by minute updates on the fighting in Abu Ghraib (which was rapidly deteriorating). For whatever reason, Battalion Headquarters failed to notify the Battalion Commander that we were in a full-fledged and protracted fight. While most engagements in Iraq lasted only from a few seconds to several minutes, this one had been going on for two hours.

I was finally able to get through to Lieutenant Grube, who was just about to leave on the staff ride. He broke away, taking his Squad and others from 1st Platoon, to reinforce the police station. As word of the battle continued to spread, elements from the Armored Brigade, along with reinforcements from the 143rd Military Police Company, and later, the 709th Military Police Battalion, also began to respond.

This is when First Sergeant Jones informed Lieutenant Grube that he would be going along with them to the police station. Lieutenant Grube did not want his First Sergeant out in the middle of the battle. A few nights prior, when we had lost Private First Class Bosveld, a large number of the company's senior leadership had been in a single location. One lucky mortar strike could have devastated our company's leadership. We had already lost one officer to an IED, and at that time, First Sergeant Jones was the highest-ranking person in the Company who was still in his original position (two of our Platoon Leaders had rotated home, one for a family emergency and the other for a non-combat injury). Lieutenant Grube insisted that he did not want to keep unnecessarily exposing company leadership. But First Sergeant Jones prevailed and responded to the police station.

The Platoon Sergeant for 1st Platoon, Sergeant First Class Porter, took half of one Squad (consisting of Sergeant Arrojado, Sergeant Potts and Staff Sergeant Smith) outside the Compound to where the armored vehicles were forming. For a while they stood watching and screening the armored vehicles for insurgents who might pop up and fire an RPG at them. The Squad engaged some insurgents with small arms as the cordon was formed around the marketplace.

Lieutenant Grube and First Sergeant Jones arrived at the Abu Ghraib Police Station just ahead of Colonel Garrity and Command Sergeant Major Paff. First Sergeant Jones immediately observed two M1A1 Abrams tanks on the main road just east of the police station.

When Lieutenant Grube and First Sergeant Jones realized that the Military Police officers were acting as dismounted Infantry, Grube and Jones had them turn over their duties to the Infantry soldiers who accompanied the armored vehicles, and got the MPs back inside the police compound. As Military Police and the Infantry units set up a perimeter adjacent to the police station, Lieutenant Grube and First Sergeant Jones made their way to the roof of the police station to get a better view of the situation.

Upon gaining access to the roof, they discovered that approximately twenty soldiers from various units were already there. An Infantry officer came up to them, briefing them on the unfolding situation. He said that two armored personnel carriers and an Abrams tank were blocking the east side of the marketplace. The two tanks in front of the police station were awaiting additional armored vehicles to make their way into the marketplace.

While waiting for the additional armored vehicles to arrive, our side watched the mob continue to grow. Rocks were being thrown at tanks, and the soldiers providing security for them. The ages of people in the mob ranged from small children to older adults. First Sergeant Jones expressed sadness when he recognized several individuals in the mob, many of them children, who had frequently hung out with MPs at the police station over the past several months.

Two attack helicopters came into the neighborhood, darting up and down the street, stopping to hover over the marketplace. The activity stabilized for approximately forty-five minutes as the Armored unit waited for additional Armored personnel carriers and soldiers. The noose was tightening as more units began to arrive.

Colonel Gold directed Hawk Troop, the reconnaissance troop from 3rd Brigade, to lead the way, and assigned helicopter gunships to spot insurgents from above. The execution was not going to be a wild charge down the street. Insurgents would be located, isolated, and eliminated in a slow, deliberate, advance through the marketplace. Because gunships had both telescopic sights and thermal imaging sights, they could spot people hiding behind dumpsters and direct the ground forces to them while alerting the troops to dangerous locations. Lieutenant Colonel Quintus with 2/70th Armored was the first to engage the insurgents. Based on his reports, additional units were activated.

Soldiers from the 143rd Military Police Company laid down protective cover fire for the Bradley fighting vehicles as they maneuvered through the marketplace. Bradleys don't need much in the way of protection, but the MPs were concerned that someone might pop up and let an RPG round loose from close range. We were also using suppressive fire to keep attackers away from the walls of the police station compound, only a short distance away.

While all this chaos was taking place, two loud explosions shook the station, and small puffs of smoke were visible in the street between the station and the Milk Factory. After a moment's pause, a third explosion close enough to really shake the station caused First Sergeant Jones to notice the soldiers on the roof. They had been very calm throughout the attack, merely took a knee,[16.1] and were scanning the area for the location from which the mortars had originated. Maybe they were calm because insurgents were not very technically proficient with the use of the mortars, and their aim was not very good. Unfortunately, sometimes they did get lucky.

Shortly after the third explosion, Sergeant First Class Porter made his way onto the roof, laughing as he approached. He informed the First Sergeant and everyone else on the roof that the Iraqi Police had taken possession of a brand new white pickup truck a few days earlier, and had parked it next to the wall surrounding the police station. They didn't want anything bad happening to it. Still laughing, Sergeant First Class Porter explained that one of the last mortar rounds hit the truck square in the hood, demolishing it. Everyone, including the Battalion Commander and Command Sergeant Major Paff, burst out laughing. First Sergeant Jones, however, was nervous despite their laughter, because the ruins of the vehicle were about ten feet away from where they had just parked.

Events continued to spiral out of control, and the helicopters returned, this time patrolling more aggressively. The size of the mob continued to increase, and more random gunfire could be heard.

Finally, the tanks and armored personnel carriers moved out into the marketplace, returned the insurgents' fire and cleared the mob from merchant stalls. For months, command staff from Brigade had been warning the local leaders that if the attacks continued, Coalition forces would eventually have to clean out the marketplace. That day had arrived.

After the attack, I was told that Lieutenant Colonel Garrity had heard about the fight going on at the marketplace only when Lieutenant Grube broke off from the staff ride. When Lieutenant Colonel Garrity realized what was happening, he was royally pissed that no one had bothered to tell him.

He demanded to know who had kept him in the dark, and naturally, Battalion Headquarters quickly looked around for someone to blame. They decided to pin the lack of communication on the incompetence of the National Guard…more succinctly, on me. I had no trouble countering the accusation, as I had radio logs and several witnesses to testify that we had been relaying information to Battalion from the very start.

Battalion had sat on this information for two hours while the staff ride was forming. During that time, I kept wondering what the hell Battalion was doing. How could the Lieutenant Colonel take everyone for a staff ride when we had a major engagement— the biggest one since our arrival in Iraq—going on? In the end, I realized that Lieutenant Colonel Garrity had not failed to make a decision; his staff had failed to inform him. In particular, three people in the Battalion Headquarters always seemed be a road block.

In the end, the insurgents were driven off with no casualties to Coalition forces reported. According to reports by hospitals and Iraqi Police, forty-seven insurgents were killed, but estimates on the total casualties were much higher. Numerous weapons were seized, and we heard no reports of civilian casualties.

With the insurgents eliminated, the time had arrived for Colonel Gold to keep the promise he had made to local tribal leaders. The Coalition forces had spent time and money fixing up the marketplace to make it livable and a place where business could be conducted. Numerous Iraqis were able to make money rebuilding the marketplace. In return, all Colonel Gold asked for was a little cooperation and safety. He had given the tribal leaders many second chances over the past months, and now the marketplace was coming down. Not one wall, one table or one roof was left standing. When we were done, all that was left was a pile of rubble. While the Iraqis could not understand generosity and kindness, they did understand complete destruction.

Armored, Airborne Infantry, and Military Police, all covered by the helicopter gunships, came together to pull off a devastatingly coordinated assault on the insurgents, and regained control of the marketplace. We still had problems in Abu Ghraib, but not to the extent that we had had before the assault. Because tanks destroyed all of the stalls that the U.S. forces had built, merchants now had to take their business elsewhere, which meant that the insurgents had to move on as well.

Although a shame, we knew that the tribal leaders had full control over the marketplace if they wanted to exercise it. I knew this was true because of one road that came into Abu Ghraib from the north, off the White Gold Expressway. My first time on this road made me very nervous. The road went through a farm area, with fences and buildings close to the narrow road—a perfect place for an ambush or IED. After my first trip, I commented on the potential danger to Sergeant First Class Porter. He told me an attack on that road would never happen because the Wahhabi tribal leaders controlled that area, and they did not want U.S. forces tearing the place apart. I was skeptical at first, but during our entire year, I never heard of one report about an attack on that road.

During the debriefing back at Warrior, the subject came up about how many rounds had been fired. Sergeant First Class Porter stated that Sergeant Potts had fired some single shots, and then had put his rifle on "three shot burst fire." Sergeant Potts replied that on automatic, the rifle bucks a bit. We all chuckled, and then I realized: This incident was the first in Sergeant Potts' military career where he had had a chance to fire his weapon on automatic. Potts had been serving for several years, and this was the very first time he had fired his main battle weapon on automatic!

So much for preparing us for war.

November 2, 2003

Estonian forces in the Abu Ghraib marketplace came under fire. Three Estonian soldiers were wounded. The resulting cordon and search of the market led to the shooting of one Iraqi male and the seizure of twenty-four AK-47s, four SKS assault rifles, one handgun, and one computer. This all occurred within walking distance of the police station.

November 11, 2003
Veterans Day

The Battalion Command Sergeant Major asked if I would say a few words about being a veteran at the up coming Veterans Day ceremony. He told me that the Battalion Commander had asked for me, as I was the oldest member of the Battalion, and probably the oldest member of the Brigade. When a battalion commander asks you to do something, he really isn't asking you; he is very politely and professionally letting you know what you are about to do.

I told him that I would be honored, and set about trying to figure out what to say. I made some notes, none of which I can recall, went into the auditorium and waited my turn. The Battalion Commander got up and said a few words that got me to re-thinking what I would say.

Then the Battalion Command Sergeant Major got up, and he spoke about his time as a young soldier arriving in Korea in the '80s or '90s, and seeing one of the National Cemeteries from the Korean War. His words struck a chord and got me to thinking about the National Cemeteries that I had visited: Arlington, the National Memorial Cemetery of the Pacific at Punchbowl Crater in Hawaii, and the Manilla American Cemetery. These are all beautiful and serene places, meticulously maintained. I began remembering the first time I'd sailed into the Philippines, and was struck by the fact that I could be in deep trouble for deciding to become a Marine. I put my notes in my pocket, and got up to speak about an incident that, forty-four years later, still gets to me.

We had been on a landing ship tank of Korean War vintage for about two weeks, sailing from Okinawa down to Subic Bay in the Philippines. The distance doesn't require two weeks, but we sat off the coast of Vietnam for a while as a floating reserve battalion landing team. One morning, we pulled into Subic Bay to re-supply and conduct some training just outside the Naval Base. But before we could pull into the main harbor, we had to go to the Ammo Supply Point (ASP) dock to unload our ammunition and artillery shells.

As we moved very slowly through the water towards the ASP dock, we were taken in by an intense glow. The sun was reflecting off an area on the dock, and we could not see anything specific— just a huge, intense, white light shining back at us. The light was so intense that we could not look directly at it; even with sunglasses we had to squint with one eye, and only for a short period of time.

Everyone was drawn to the intense light. We all stood quietly, staring. As our ship inched closer, the angle of the reflection began to change, and ever so slowly, began to take a different shape. Then, as though someone was pulling back a curtain, the object began to become *objects* that were coming into focus ever so slowly. At this point, I stopped breathing, and am sure that my mouth dropped open as I realized that we were staring at rows and stacks of silver military shipping coffins.

Several hundred, maybe a thousand, were stacked several high, a few hundred feet long, with row upon row behind them. These coffins didn't contain remains. They were simply ready, neatly stacked in uniform military style, patiently waiting. The thought occurred to me that they were waiting for us. This is when I realized what I had gotten myself into.

I pointed out to the soldiers in the audience that few jobs exist where you sign up with the expectation that, in all likelihood, you will get hurt, possibly even killed, doing your job. One of those jobs is being a police officer, the other is being a soldier. We were both.

I shared how old I was, and how young most in the audience were—a good portion of them had not even been born when I had pulled into Subic Bay in 1970…I acknowledged that my senior NCOs and officers were Korean War veterans, having started their service when I was born. My most senior NCOs and officers, the Command Sergeant Majors and the Battalion Commander, had served in World War II.

I explained that each soldier in the audience had a connection through me and others going back to World War II, and each one had joined a never-ending line of veterans defending our country.

Every soldier in the audience, like all service personnel worldwide, are now volunteers. Each one of us made the decision to join the military.

I told the young men and women in the audience that their generation would carry on the long line of service of going into harm's way to defend our country. They are the professional Army of the new millennium. Though much smaller than past armies, their generation would shoulder the same responsibility of defending our nation as past generations had. I wanted them to know that they are part of something much larger than a company, battalion, or brigade, something that has spanned decades and generations of men and women.

I hope the young men and women in the audience heard me, but I'll never know. Maybe someday one of those soldiers will think about doing something unprofessional, and will change his or her mind remembering that he or she might be breaking the trust of that long line of veterans.

General MacArthur made a speech at West Point that has come to be known as the "Duty, Honor and Country" speech. He spoke for about forty-five minutes and used lofty terms and glowing words to describe what those three words mean. I had them explained to me in a much more abbreviated form.

DUTY is my job. HONOR is my promise to do my job to the best of my ability, no matter what. COUNTRY is every person standing with me, counting on me to keep my promise to do my job, no matter what, *in spite of it all.*

November 15, 2003

1st Squad, 1st Platoon, while manning the new Abu Ghraib Police Station, reported that ten mortars had exploded in the vicinity of the old police station. Later, they reported that additional rounds had impacted near the airport, farther to the east of the old police station.

November 20, 2003

An interpreter working for Titan Corporation was shot three times in the leg by an unknown assailant. The assailant had gone to the interpreter's residence, and it was believed that the attack was in retaliation for working with U.S. forces.

While working rooftop security at the new Abu Ghraib Police Station, Specialist Uccello fired on an individual who had twice targeted him with a laser beam coming from the general direction of the Agricultural College. There is no indication that anyone was hit. The subject was never located.

I went out with Lieutenant Grube to check on the police stations. We were up on the roof of the Abu Ghraib Police Station when Colonel Garrity pulled in. It was late at night and everything was dimly lit, most of the illumination coming from streetlights on the road and the windows of the adjoining buildings. Faces were not recognizable at distances of only a few feet.

I noticed that Colonel Garrity had an unusually large number of vehicles with him. Normally, he traveled in an escort of three or four vehicles, but he had almost twice that with him. I watched as people exited the vehicles, made their way across the Compound, into a building and onto the roof.

Something kept running through my mind…I had seen these types of actions before. It took me a while, probably because we were in a desert, but I realized that what I was seeing reminded me of a bunch of people who were going skiing for the first time, walking out of the ski shop with their brand new skiing equipment. Until they got used to all that equipment (poles, skis, boots, gloves, goggles, and bulky clothing), it all worked against them. Until they had experience handling that equipment, and learned how to use and organize it, they looked like skiers who didn't know how to manage with their equipment very well.

Their helmets were askew, their rifles banged into things, and the rest of their equipment did not hang from them in a uniform and consistent pattern.

Colonel Garrity was the first one onto the roof, and it wasn't until we were a few inches away from each another that I realized who he was. Because identifying him as a person in a leadership position was something you don't do in a combat zone (unless you want to get him killed), I initially addressed him as "Boss" and asked him how his night was going. He took no offense and replied that they were making the rounds to the police stations and, so far, had noted no incidents.

I asked him who all the extra people were, and he advised that this was the Battalion staff. These were the majors, captains, lieutenants, and senior non-commissioned officers who manned the Battalion Headquarters. As I looked around, it dawned on me that this might have been the first time any of these people had been outside Warrior Compound in the past six or seven months, which explained why they appeared so disorganized wearing their full battle rattle.

Not that I had spent a whole lot of time outside the Compound either, but after just a few trips of getting into and out of the Humvee, climbing stairs, and walking through buildings, I learned to adjust my equipment comfortably.

We heard a couple of explosions off in the distance, and everyone's attention was drawn in that direction. We compared notes, trying to determine where in the city the explosions had originated so Lieutenant Colonel Garrity could take his group in that direction.

For the soldiers on the roof who had been manning that post, and for Lieutenant Colonel Garrity, this was business as usual and no big deal. Battalion staff, however, was greatly concerned.

November 27, 2003

President Bush made a surprise visit to Baghdad International Airport to have Thanksgiving dinner with the troops. We had been asked to send two soldiers to the airport, but were not told the reason until after. We chose Staff Sergeant Andrea Cloutier and Private First Class Tanya Simmons. To their surprise, they were able to meet, shake hands, and have their picture taken with the President of the United States. It was certainly a high point for them. Staff Sergeant Cloutier had certainly earned the honor after her prior engagements. Private First Class Simmons was one of our top mechanics, keeping enough vehicles running through sheer determination so that we were able to remain…100% combat ready.

4th Squad, 3rd Platoon was hit by an IED in the area of the Al Ghazalia Main Street. Minor shrapnel damage was inflicted on the vehicle. Private First Class Ethier took impacts to his body armor, but was not injured.

November 29, 2003

Abd Al Amer Hurafesh and Ali Al Sada, members of the Supreme Council of the Islamic Revolution, came to Al Huriya Police Station claiming they had direct knowledge of Saddam Hussein's location. These people were turned over to Coalition Intelligence contacts at Baghdad International Airport. We never learned if their information was any good.

Chapter Seventeen

THE ONLY TREE IN BAGHDAD

Things are never so bad they can't be made worse.

C. S. Forester
The African Queen

The National Guard continued to be second-class citizens in the eyes of the active-duty, and the Command Sergeant Major kept finding work details for us to do. This make-work was not limited to the Connecticut National Guard—units from Tennessee and Ohio were also subjected to it, as were all Guard units.

Battalion had funds for work projects to employ local citizens to improve the Compound, which would pump money into the Iraqi economy and help to improve our relations. Despite having these funds and a ready labor force, the active-duty still created make-work details for the National Guard. I cannot recall active-duty being sent to the Compound to do this type of work.

One of our make-work details was to spread gravel in the area where we parked our vehicles. This task was no small feat, as the area was the size of half of a football field and the Command Sergeant Major had thirty tons (or more) of stone delivered. Prior to our arrival, the Compound had been planted with date trees in a fashion similar to the way we planted apple trees, trimmed so they would grow wide and not tall. The Command

Sergeant Major directed us to spread the gravel underneath the trees.

Our units were still performing patrols and escort missions seven days a week. When they returned, they desperately needed downtime to sleep and relax. Regardless, they did occasionally find time to spread gravel when they felt like it, which was slow going. I never pushed them on this issue, knowing that their downtime was more important than any make-work project.

Seeing that we were giving our soldiers a pass, the Sergeant Major took exception to our tardiness and demanded that our senior noncommissioned officers get out there and spread the gravel ourselves. So we assembled down in the date grove and began to spread the stone by hand with shovels.

I remembered that there was still a full-sized farm tractor on the Compound with a grading bar that the Iraqis had used to spread gravel. So, I decided to retrieve the tractor, as it was a far more efficient tool than shovels for spreading stone. I reasoned that once we got the stone leveled, the Command Sergeant Major would be off our backs, at least for this situation.

So I brought the tractor back to the parking area and began to slowly drag the stone out and spread it between the trees, while the troops broke down piles of stone. The tractor had a roll bar, but instead of coming completely down and over the front to make a cage, it ended in a U-shape just forward of the driver and about two feet over my head. Regardless, I made several passes and everybody was very happy that the tractor was doing the heavy work for us.

As I was concentrating on the grading bar and not paying attention to where I was going, I didn't notice that the roll bar had hooked a tree limb. The tractor kept moving forward at a very slow pace, pulling the limb to the rear and increasing tension as the tractor continued past. Finally, the limb reached the end of the roll cage just above my head, released all that tension and slammed down on my head and into my left shoulder, scraping across my chest and forearms before finally breaking off.

I was almost knocked unconscious, but managed to stop the tractor before it rammed into the perimeter wall. I was dazed, with numerous cuts and scrapes on my head, arms and chest, and my left shoulder was dislocated, not to mention pinned into the seat by this very long, heavy tree limb that was now sitting on my lap. The troops came running to get me out from underneath the branch, but unfortunately, some pulled from the front and some pulled from the back. The effect was that the limb sawed back and forth across my body.

I yelled out for everybody to stop (which they abruptly did) and told Sergeant First Class Porter to take charge in getting the limb off of me in one direction, please. With just a slight amount of coordination, they were able to unpin me from the limb.

Now the only problem was getting me off the tractor. My feet were about five feet off the ground, and I was having trouble moving due to great pain. Everyone was making all kinds of suggestions, but everything they proposed would have caused stress on my dislocated shoulder. I finally took charge again and directed the three biggest guys to come to the side of the tractor and reach up to grab me by the belt. Once they had me, I carefully stepped off the tractor and, in one coordinated move, they lowered me down to the ground. It worked like a charm—I came down as if I were on an elevator.

The medics showed up and they knew just from looking at me that they had to get me to the hospital. I clearly needed x-rays and they were concerned that I had broken my shoulder and not dislocated it. To prepare for the potentially dangerous trip to the hospital, the medics put on my helmet and then attempted to put my body armor on, which proved to be impossible because my shoulder was now out of joint. Then they piled me into a Humvee and we headed off for the CSH. That's when the real fun began.

When I arrived, the first person I met was a nurse who reminded me of Nurse Ratched from *One Flew Over the Cuckoo's Nest*. Her hair was neatly pinned up and she wore a perfectly white nurse's outfit as if she was working at a stateside hospital, even though everyone else was wearing battle dress uniforms. She was very officious, directing me to a litter that sat on a pair of raised-up sawhorses. It had a back that tilted up, but I was unable to rest my back against the tilted part because I needed to keep the pressure off my shoulder.

I climbed into it as well as I could, hunching forward, my legs hanging over the end. The litter's bar began cutting into my legs, stopping the circulation to my feet. I asked if I could sit in a chair, but was told to stay in the litter because it was easier for them to treat me up there.

They decided to start an IV to replace my fluids and give me medication. They called in a young, female Specialist, who did not have much experience in starting IVs and was going to practice on me. I understood that the best and brightest were obviously busy caring for the more seriously injured soldiers, but I wasn't looking forward to being someone's training dummy.

Hands shaking, the Specialist attempted to start the IV several times. I wasn't sure if she was more rattled by the fact that I was a senior noncommissioned officer, because she had very little experience starting IVs, or some combination of the two. Either way, she kept missing the vein and had to start over after digging around inside my arm with the needle.

She became so nervous that Nurse Ratched finally decided to start the IV herself, rolling my arm over to expose the veins on the underside of my forearm. The Specialist, who had been trying to insert the IV on either the opposite side of my arm or the top of my hand, saw Nurse Ratched roll my arm over and got some of her confidence back. She told the nurse that she could hit the vein and Nurse Ratched backed away to let her try again.

While this was going on, I was talking with the orthopedic surgeon who would be taking x-rays to determine if my shoulder was broken. I hate needles, IVs in particular, so anything that distracted me from the situation with Nurse Ratched and the Specialist was very welcome. As I was talking to the surgeon, I felt the needle go into my arm, and a second later, all conversations stopped. Everyone was looking down at my arm with their mouths open. I knew something had gone wrong, but I was too afraid look.

My leg started to feel wet and I told myself that whatever it was, looking to see what was happening was not a good idea. After what felt like a lifetime, but was actually only about ten to fifteen seconds, the Specialist corrected her mistake, and I could see by the huge sighs and looks of relief on everyone's face that the IV was now running properly. The orthopedic surgeon and I went on with our conversation as if nothing had happened. I still didn't look down, even though it felt like I had peed down my own leg.

As I got up off the litter to get the x-rays done, I slipped in a puddle of my own blood that had pooled on the floor from the bad IV stick, almost falling on my face. I had no idea I had lost that much blood. I wasn't going to die, but it was not an insignificant amount of blood.

I told them that they would have to tilt the x-ray bed up so I could stand against it because there was no way I could lie on the table and roll my shoulder down without causing a whole lot of pain. They told me that would not be a problem and arranged the bed so that it was vertical. Then they told me that they were going to take several shots of my shoulder, one of which involved me extending my arm up over my head.

I was sure that they were kidding. They weren't.

"You do understand that my shoulder is dislocated, right? It's out of its joint. It's not going to move."

They assured me that they would move it for me. I replied that I still had one good arm and, if they tried to touch me to move my dislocated shoulder, I would break their faces. They didn't feel I was being very cooperative.

They summoned Nurse Ratched, who was not very happy with my attitude. She commented that I didn't seem particularly docile for someone who was on medication. I informed her that the only thing in my IV so far was saline solution; no one had given me medication of any kind. For some reason, this information just made her madder than she already was, and she acted like it was my fault that I hadn't gotten any medication.

She injected me with something that didn't knock me out, but did make me feel cranky and listless. They took my x-rays, thankfully, without attempting to move my shoulder. After the x-rays were complete, they wheeled me back to the treatment area, where Nurse Ratched informed the orthopedic surgeon that I was ready to have my shoulder relocated.

I think my head must have snapped up when I heard that, because the surgeon took one look at me and said, "He doesn't look like he's out."

Nurse Ratched told him that I was very much out, having received my medication.

Then the surgeon turned to me and asked me if I was out.

"I don't think so," I said. "How will I know when I'm out?"

He gave Nurse Ratched a dirty look.

This made Nurse Ratched even madder. Not only did I bleed all over the place, not get my medication, and refuse to move my dislocated shoulder; now I was making her look bad by not being unconscious when she thought I should be. In her mind, I had been screwing up left and right ever since I had come in. She didn't apologize, and instead just left and came back with another dose of medication. This time, I was off to Neverland but was still able to talk and look around.

I was told afterward that my shoulder popped in with no trouble, and as soon as it did, I raised the injured arm and scratched my nose.

A short time later the medication started wearing off. I was groggy and cranky again, and I noticed two large, dark stains on my right leg. In my stupor, I thought they were part of the coloring of my camouflage uniform. It was only later, after the medication had worn off, that I realized that the dark stains were blood from my bad IV stick.

While I was in a daze, Nurse Ratched returned and asked the Specialist if she was going to clean me up, in a very condescending way, implying that the Specialist wasn't performing her duties properly. Admittedly, I was pretty messy, covered in dust and sweat with cuts and scrapes all over my head, chest and forearms. I was also covered in quite a bit of blood, some of it from the bad IV sticks, some of it from lacerations.

I watched in a stupor as the Specialist tore open a small white packet and took out a wipe. Before I could manage to find the wherewithal to ask if the wipe was an alcohol wipe, the Specialist swabbed the deep cuts and scrapes on my forearm. Even drugged up as I was, I felt like I had plunged my arm into a bucket of boiling water. Alcohol on an open cut is quite painful.

Imagining what other help they were going to give me, I hopped off the litter and told the First Sergeant to get my helmet. I had received enough help for one day and was getting out of the CSH. So far, I hadn't hurt anyone or used any four-letter words, but it was only a matter of time. I figured I'd better get out while the getting was good.

They tried to stop me, but I was determined to get out the door before any more help came my way. I did make it out the door with one medic running behind to schedule a follow-up appointment in three days.

They gave me a month's supply of painkillers, anti-inflammatory drugs and antibiotics. I wondered why they gave me the antibiotics, and then remembered how filthy the environment was and all of the open cuts on my head, chest and forearms. I looked at the month-worth of painkillers, wondering just how long my pain was going to last.

After quickly realizing that I could handle the pain, but not the side-effects of the painkillers, I stopped taking them the next day. The anti-inflammatory meds worked very well, and I stayed on the antibiotics.

Three days later, I returned to the CSH for follow-up and found that Nurse Ratched was, thankfully, nowhere in sight. The orthopedic surgeon told me that everything looked fine and referred me to a physical therapist, who met with me to check my range of movement. He also thought I was doing fine, but recommended that I return every two to three days for therapy. I balked at this, not wanting to risk having a team drive through Baghdad every couple of days just so I could go to physical therapy for an hour. So I asked what the physical therapy involved, which was basically some stretching exercises with oversized rubber bands in an isometric training regime. The therapist went over the exercises with me and gave me some rubber bands so I could do the exercises on my own. I was sure that I could handle this and assured him that I would have our own medics check on me if I ran into any trouble.

He then asked me if I needed any more medication, specifically medication for pain. I told him that I absolutely did not. He then gave me a note indicating that I should not do push-ups for the next thirty days. I could not believe that I was getting a limited duty form to excuse me from doing push-ups in a combat zone.

"I'm a master sergeant," I said. "I don't do push-ups unless I feel like it. Do I really need this?" The therapist didn't respond.

I went on to ask about any combat operations that my injury might prevent me from performing. He replied that he couldn't answer that question, but he did know that I should not do push-ups for the next thirty days. This was one of the more insane contradictions I experienced in the military—that they could excuse an injured soldier from doing push-ups, but could not assess his ability to go out on combat patrols. He explained that after thirty days he could give me a second note, just in case.

This was a medical unit who had done unbelievable work saving the lives of soldiers who had sustained some of the most horrific injuries imaginable. Yet they were worried about a fifty-two-year old Master Sergeant doing push-ups.

Somewhere along the line there was a disconnect between those who were saving lives and those who were providing continuing care. As in the case of Private First Class Josh Clark, who had been put on work details when he was covered with open wounds and still had shrapnel lodged in his body.

To be fair, the note that the physical therapist gave me did help. One officer took exception to the fact that I wouldn't do push-ups (unless I felt I could) even though I had told him about going to the CSH and that I had a note excusing me from push-ups. He gave me a condescending look, and was about to order me to do push-ups, until I told him that I still had my note from the CSH.

I had hoped that my injury might put an end to the make-work details, but I was wrong. A day or so after my injury, a senior NCO from Battalion and First Sergeant Jones inspected Company areas. They visited 3rd Platoon, and the NCO found a very large limb blocking part of the parking area. He complained to First Sergeant Jones that the limb had been there for weeks, and no one had removed it. First Sergeant Jones explained that the limb had just come down and was, in fact, the tree limb that had dislocated my shoulder. The NCO was not impressed. He continued to create make-work assignments for our Company and other National Guard units.

ACTIVITY LOG
December 2–December 4, 2003

December 2, 2003

Members of the Company had dinner at Baghdad International Airport with State Senator Christopher Dodd.

December 4, 2003

Some of the following information comes from a news article written by Joseph L. Galloway, a combat correspondent since the beginning of the Vietnam War, and author of the book *We Were Soldiers Once... and Young.*

For months, Coalition forces had been receiving fire from an apartment complex, or watching as insurgents disappeared into the complex following hit-and-run attacks. At this point, Colonel Gold had had enough and received permission to start the necessary planning and operations to stop this problem permanently. The raid netted forty-three detainees and resulted in the confiscation of over 260 weapons. The raid was so large, and hit the complex so fast, almost no active resistance resulted.

Joe Galloway was documenting a series of raids in western Baghdad. He refused to wear a helmet or body armor and was riding with the Brigade Commander in an unarmored Humvee (the Brigade Commander wore a helmet and body armor).

Members of 1st and 2nd Platoons, along with Lieutenant Grube and his Security team, participated in Operation Bulldog Mammoth, a raid on a massive 2,400 unit apartment complex in western Baghdad. Operation Bulldog Mammoth included both the Military Police and large numbers from the 3rd Brigade Combat Team.

The complex was a slum in close proximity to the Abu Ghraib Prison, and many of the former inmates had relocated there. Numerous attacks, both by ground forces and mortars, had originated from this complex. Colonel Gold led 1,450 soldiers from the 3rd Brigade Combat Team in isolating the complex and sweeping through the entire area. Utilizing

Bradley fighting vehicles, M1A tanks, and attack helicopters that provided overhead cover and observation, Military Police Platoons in Humvees cordoned off the area and blocked anyone from escaping. Colonel Gold proceeded into the complex with other Bradley Fighting Vehicles, Abrams Tanks, and dismounted Infantry from 1st of the 325th Airborne Infantry. Twenty-four weapons were taken from one apartment alone. The raiding units met little resistance, but at the same time, also received no cooperation. This area had been an insurgent strong hold from the beginning.

In another raid, MPs detained three Iraqis who had been identified as responsible for the death of Rachel Bosveld, as well as wounding two other soldiers.

In a 3:00 a.m. raid, a Bradley fighting vehicle was used to ram down the gates of the home of a suspected bomb manufacturer. Once the Bradley crashed through the gates, soldiers from the 1st Platoon, 1st Squadron, 1st Cavalry Regiment quickly moved in and rounded up several female residents without incident.

Talib Abbas Ahmed Faiad Hamadani was taken into custody. This individual was a former member of Saddam's Secret Police and had made IEDs that had been used against Coalition forces. The house was swept by a bomb-sniffing dog, followed by MPs testing surfaces for explosive residue. Nothing was found, but no one was giving up. A team of four FBI Agents went through the house and recovered two AK-47 assault rifles as well as the sight for a mortar.

A mortar consists of several parts and is easily disassembled. Parts include the sight, the launch tube, the base plate, and the bipod. Breaking down the weapon allows for faster transport by several individuals.

Attacks in this part of Baghdad had been a daily occurrence. Colonel Kirk Fuller, Commanding officer of the 2nd Brigade 325th Airborne Regiment of the 82nd Airborne, stated that this area of Baghdad had generated 118 attacks from homemade bombs, thirty-one from mortars, twenty-six from rocket propelled grenades, sixty with small arms, seven with large rockets, and three with grenades.

Chapter Eighteen

NO OTHER OPTIONS

I ask not for a lighter burden, but for broader shoulders.

Jewish Proverb

When we received word that the officer wounded on September 8th would be returning, a wave of depression settled over the unit. After his evacuation, everyone had realized how much danger he had put all of us in—not only his Security team, but the rest of the Company as well. Without him around to put everyone on edge, soldiers were relaxing and getting along. With the news of the officer's return, everyone was already back on edge. I was beside myself.

I went to the chaplain, of all people. This was not your run-of-the-mill Pastor, but a man of God and a high-speed troop. He was airborne and air assault qualified, and had done a tour in Afghanistan before being assigned to Iraq. If you missed the cross on his collar, you would think he was an Infantry Company Commander on his way to becoming a Major. He had the GI haircut and looked like he hit the gym every day, but he was easy to talk to.

I explained the situation, trying to communicate the level of unnecessary danger the officer represented. I told the chaplain that I understood war and understood that soldiers would be hurt, and sometimes killed, as a result of fighting a war. What I could not understand was being reckless with the lives of the soldiers and exposing them to unnecessary risks. I described some of the officer's previous actions and my concerns for what he might do in the future.

I expected that the chaplain would either put me off or defer my questioning, but he turned out to be very understanding. After listening to me, he made a swift recommendation that I should sit down one-on-one with the Battalion Sergeant major and ask for "some professional counseling." I thanked him for the advice, but didn't think this would be a good course of action. I wasn't sure how the Command Sergeant Major would react to hearing a staff NCO speak badly about one of his officers.

But I also realized that I didn't have any other options, so I took the chaplain's advice and went to see the Sergeant Major. Without hesitation, the Sergeant Major invited me in, and we had a long, frank discussion (though I did most of the talking). He thanked me for coming in, and though he made no promises, he did say that he would see what he could do. I had been afraid that I would be labeled a troublemaker or a coward, but the serious look on his face and deep concern gave me a completely different impression.

After leaving his office, I reflected back on the reception I had received with the chaplain and his quick advice to meet with the Sergeant Major. Even with my apprehension, I had gone straight to see the Sergeant Major after speaking with the chaplain, so the chaplain had no opportunity to give the Sergeant Major a heads up. Despite that, the Sergeant Major seemed to know what I was going to tell him and maybe even shared my concerns. I had the distinct impression that someone else, possibly even more than one person, had shared similar discussions with the Sergeant Major.

ACTIVITY LOG
December 6–December 12, 2003

December 6, 2003

3rd Platoon participated in Operation Choke Out. The operation involved a large-scale series of highway checkpoints designed to apprehend individuals on the Most Wanted list and to seize weapons. The operation was considered a success, even though no individuals from the Most Wanted list were apprehended.

December 10, 2003

The 135th Military Police Company from the Ohio National Guard was assigned to patrol the Tigris River with Iraqi forces. When this assignment first came out, it was offered to us. I almost accepted. We had a Platoon Sergeant who had been small boat qualified while in the Navy and had extensive experience, as well as several people in the unit who owned small boats. It sounded like a good assignment until I remembered that the Tigris is a wide river with very high banks on both sides offering no place to hide. The river was also a stinking cesspool of human waste and garbage, as it served as a convenient dumping ground for the city. I declined the assignment.

Patrols were conducted in small boats with outboard motors. The Iraqi Police provided one officer to pilot each boat, as well as a second officer for each boat.

One of the soldiers from Ohio accidentally fell into the Tigris River, and a second soldier, seeing the first one in distress, entered the water to assist. Both soldiers went under and never surfaced, and it was a good guess that they had drowned (they were in full combat gear weighing over eighty pounds). Immediately, an extensive search began. Divers from an engineer unit responded and joined the search, which lasted for several days. The bodies were finally recovered about a mile down river from where they had gone under.

During this time, our Company took over the assignments that the 135th Military Police Company from Ohio had been doing, to free them up so they could search for their friends. They were scheduled to rotate out of Iraq within the next two weeks when this tragedy struck.

Figure 18.1   The Tigris River, where we lost Bates and Reese from the Ohio National Guard

December 12, 2003

The 269th MP Company received a warning order that they were being reassigned to the 168th Military Police Battalion of the Tennessee National Guard at Graceland FOB. This location is inside Falcon FOB and is on the south side of Baghdad on the main highway leading south to Kuwait. We had worked closely with one of their companies for several months prior to this move. All of the units assigned to the 168th were either National Guard or Army Reserve. The active-duty from the 18th Military Police Brigade were heading home.

The days were cool, sometimes even cold, and temperatures were getting down to almost freezing. A constant cold, wet drizzle came down. After not seeing a cloud since we got here, the rain caused some very miserable conditions. It mixed with the dust and oil in the air, turning into an oily, slimy mud that coated everything. The troops who had it the worst were the poor gunners, in their exposed turret positions, the lead vehicle gunner facing forward into the rain, mud, and slime. We were starting to have issues with colds, and troops were reporting to sick call. With everyone living so close together, colds were spreading throughout the Unit and Battalion.

Chapter Nineteen

ANOTHER BODY RECOVERED

When the Lamb opened the fourth seal, I heard the voice of the fourth living creature say, "Come and see!" I looked and there before me was a pale horse! Its rider was named Death, and Hell was following close behind him.

Revelation 6:7–8

ACTIVITY LOG
December 12–December 31, 2003

December 12, 2003

The officer wounded on September 8th returned from medical leave. He called from Baghdad International Airport to request transport back to our base, speaking with Sergeant McWhorter (one of our medics at the aid station). Sergeant McWhorter had been with us during our entire deployment (close to eleven months by this point) but the officer didn't recognize him, and asked him his name three times.

Arrangements were made to get a detail down to Baghdad International Airport to pick the officer up; but, this being Baghdad, things did not happen very fast. The officer called twice to ask where his transport was.

I don't know how the officer managed to get a medical clearance to return to Iraq. The nerve damage caused by the shrapnel in his right shoulder had rendered his right arm useless. On patrols, he sat in the right front passenger seat, with the door handle and the window lever on his right side. This positioning made getting in and out of the vehicle using only his left hand extremely difficult.

In a squad of six soldiers, he made up one-fourth of the Squad's available firepower. The drivers of the two Squad vehicles had to remain behind the wheel so that they could maneuver in dangerous situations, leaving protection to the vehicle's two machine gunners and two passengers, one of whom was the officer. If his Squad was attacked, the officer was responsible for protective fire to the right side of his vehicle.

If you remember, before the officer had been injured, he had taken to carrying only a 9mm pistol (which gave him the ability to fire only thirteen- to fourteen- rounds before reloading). With his injury, reloading the 9mm was very difficult. He would have to drop the magazine with his left hand, then put the weapon down so he could use his left hand to retrieve a second magazine, wedge the weapon so it wouldn't move, reload the second magazine, then operate the slide to charge a new round.

Considering the big picture, his injury put his Team and Squad in extreme jeopardy.

Beside the combat challenges the officer faced, the challenge of loading/unloading his weapon every time he went in or outside the wire was also difficult. Most of the time, someone did these tasks for him.

December 13, 2003

Iraqi citizens fired their guns into the air in celebration again. There were even more of them firing than the last time a celebration like this occurred (when Saddam's sons had been killed). This time, we learned that they were celebrating Saddam's capture by

U.S. forces. Like everyone else, we learned about Saddam's capture from watching news coverage on CNN.

The shooting went on for hours, and bullets flew all over the city. There had to be thousands of Iraqis firing millions of rounds into the air, with no letup. Even with all the weapons that we had confiscated, the Iraqis still had more rifles and machine guns than we did. No one was permitted outside of the Compound once they had returned from patrol, as it was too dangerous with all the shooting. One soldier was struck in the butt by a round, but luckily the bullet didn't break his skin.

Wearing my helmet and body armor like everyone else, I went to chow for the evening meal, sat on a bench near the mess hall, and waited for the First Sergeant to catch up to me. I happened to notice a shiny object on the ground between my feet which I didn't think had been there when I had sat down. When I reached down to pick it up, I discovered that it was an AK-47 bullet. It was still warm and had a little bend in it, indicating that it had ricocheted from somewhere. This gave me pause. I'd thought I was safe inside the Compound, but all of those rounds flying up into the air had to come down somewhere, and the Compound's walls offered no defense against them.

We never did find out how many people were killed by stray rounds during the celebration, but I suspect that it was at least a few hundred or so. We were mystified that all of the Iraqis seemed to be celebrating Saddam's capture, yet so many continued to oppose Coalition forces being in Iraq. Even after Saddam's capture, insurgent attacks continued without letup.

We had shared a section of the second floor with a company from the Tennessee National Guard, getting along with them very well and sharing assignments in Baghdad. They were reassigned to Graceland FOB and came under the command of a battalion that was also from the Tennessee National Guard. Their unit was not replaced at Warrior FOB, so we were allowed to take over the space that they had vacated.

We divided up the space with some tables and maps, using it to split up Headquarters and Operations, with Headquarters on the left and Operations on the right. We set aside a portion of the left side of the room for an officer's and First Sergeants' desks, along with an area for briefings.

Before the officer's return, everyone who came up to Operations would congregate over on the left side, drinking coffee and sharing information. With his return, no one went over to the left side.

At Battalion up-briefs, all officers traditionally tried to have a "good news" story to report. One officer's good news story was that he was back.

December 14, 2003

I'm not sure why, but I was just told that I have been fired from Operations. Master Sergeant Minasian, who was my counterpart, is now in charge.

Nevertheless, my Operations duties continued, and an officer assigned me to present a full briefing at noon to cover our replacement of the 135th Military Police Company in the police stations that they were currently monitoring. Monitoring stations wasn't a big deal for us, as we had already been monitoring several stations for the past few weeks. All we needed to do was adjust our schedule to add the new stations.

We took over the detail that issued firearms to the new Iraqi Police officers, and qualified them on the range. For this purpose, were given a container that held thousands of brand-new Glock 40-caliber pistols to issue (which disappeared almost faster than we could issue them).

Our inspections of the police stations included a check of the names of officers against the serial numbers of weapons issued. More often than not, we would find Iraqi officers, who had just been issued brand-new Glocks, carrying rusted old antiques. When questioned about the location of their new pistols, the Iraqi officers would answer that they were being serviced, or explain that the guns were at home because the officers were afraid the guns would be damaged, or something else equally absurd. Most of the Glocks had been sold on the black market.

We passed this information to Battalion and learned that other Companies were having the same experience. Despite the fact that we all knew the Iraqi officers were obviously selling the weapons that we had issued to them, we were told to continue issuing weapons to Iraqi officers.

During tonight's briefing, the Battalion Commander encouraged everyone to stay safe and to engage the enemy if threatened. He indicated that, far too often, soldiers took fire and did not return it, which only encouraged the enemy to keep attacking.

If an insurgent fired on U.S. forces and we did not return fire, the insurgent was more likely to make another attempt because he had nothing to fear. On the other hand, if he fired thirty rounds at U.S. forces and one-hundred rounds came flying in his direction, he would reconsider his course of action and think twice before shooting at American soldiers.

The Battalion Commander also stated that appropriate force should be used when engaging hostile forces. If the enemy's firing location could be specifically identified, then we should engage that specific location.

Unfortunately, there were a lot of conditions to engaging the enemy. If we received enemy fire from an apartment complex and we could not identify a specific window as the source, then we should not engage the complex. On the other hand, if we took fire from a house, we should consider the entire house hostile and engage. Not all Platoons agreed with these rules of engagement, and many soldiers were reluctant to fire because they feared that they would get in trouble.

December 15, 2003

Attacks were increasing. The insurgents had started to use larger explosive devices and VBIEDs (vehicle-borne improvised explosive devices). They made VBIEDs by packing vehicles with whatever explosive materials they had on hand. These devices, similar to the car bomb used at Khadra, were capable of inflicting massive damage and creating huge craters.

Because VBIEDs were mobile, one minute, everything was fine, and in the next minute, a massive bomb could be rolling toward us at sixty miles per hour.

As Christmas and New Year's approached, the threat level kept increasing. There were indications that insurgents could stage a ground attack on our bases at any time. We manned more positions on the guard towers and were instructed to plan for a wall breach, followed by a ground assault into the perimeter. I didn't think such an attack was likely, but I didn't want to take any chances, either. Our soldiers, on the other hand, didn't seem at all concerned by this threat.

We were issued AT-4 antitank rounds, at least one for each Squad. These weapons are handheld, shoulder-fired rockets designed to knock out light tanks and armored vehicles. They could also be used against bunkers, buildings, and other protected structures. They are designed to penetrate before detonating, delivering damage inside the target area. They are simple to use, reasonably accurate, and very effective.

I knew that most of the troops had been writing home, but I doubted that they had mentioned the dangerous details of our job or what they, as individuals, had been doing to ensure our success. I decided to write home on the behalf of our soldiers who were in law enforcement or corrections in their civilian lives. I wanted to let their department heads and Chiefs of Police know just what their employees were doing here in Iraq. I informed them that we counted on their employees to be our core of information and professionalism. I mentioned that I was uncertain if these soldiers had shared any of this information with their families, and asked that they not bring this information up with them.

We discussed an interesting incident at the evening briefing which, fortunately, did not include anyone from the 143rd. A unit securing the Baghdad International Airport had decided to conduct a training exercise, where they would dispatch the QRF from the airport to the main access road, which was located outside of their compound. Unfortunately, no one informed the security detail at the main gate that a training exercise had been scheduled, or that the QRF would be involved.

The soldiers on the gate had to follow a number of rules regarding approaching vehicles. They were supposed to check any vehicle coming into and leaving the Compound, and were also supposed to stop any vehicle that attempted to run through their security checkpoint.

At the beginning of the exercise, the QRF deployed an M1A1 Abrams tank and several Bradley fighting vehicles, which came roaring down the road from inside the Compound to respond to the incident outside the main gate. Security at the gate did not know that a training exercise was going down, and began waving frantically at the tank to stop. When the tank did not stop, security fired warning shots into the air. No one inside of the tank was able to hear the warning shots and, chances are, none of them were even aware that security was firing into the air.

When the soldiers manning the gate realized that the vehicles weren't going to stop, the soldiers engaged the vehicles with their M-16 rifles, spraying the tank and the Bradleys with small arms fire. This was ridiculous for two reasons: In the first place, M-16 rounds wouldn't do much more than chip the paint on an Abrams tank. In the second place, it was obvious that they were firing on American vehicles. Even in the unlikely circumstances that insurgents had managed to enter the Compound to steal an M1A1 Abrams tank, engaging such a vehicle with an M-16 rifle, despite following the letter of the security detail's rules of engagement, was futile. But this was the Army, and thinking out of the box was not in the rule book. Fortunately, no one was hurt.

With this instance, as with so many other instances, it was clear that the active-duty could not separate themselves from their training mind-set, even though they were in the midst of fighting a war. Why no one would think to get everyone on board with the exercise, especially considering it involved soldiers armed with live ammunition in the middle of a combat zone, was beyond me. If those vehicles had been Humvees instead of tanks and fighting vehicles, we would have sustained numerous casualties from friendly fire.

December 23, 2003

Despite the fact that exiting the vehicle was extremely difficult for him, the officer whose shoulder was injured on September 8th insisted on going out on patrol.

The body of the second soldier from the 135th Military Police Company of the Ohio National Guard was recovered from the Tigris River. Specialist Bates was found approximately one mile down river from where he had gone under. Everyone had been taking on extra duty time to search for Specialist Bates, as well as doing extra duties to free up other units for the search. While we were relieved when we finally found him, we were also sad at this tragic event.

The 135th Military Police Company had left Baghdad only six hours before Bates was located. They had not wanted to return home without him. Everyone knew he was dead, but they did not want to leave his body behind in the stinking city. After so many combat operations, the loss of two soldiers from this type of accident, this close to returning home, must have been unbearable.

December 24, 2003

Christmas Eve—Brigade had given an order that all MP units had to be inside before dark, as there was great concern about attacks, and no one wanted a lightly-armed MP Squad out in the dark. But, one officer went outside the wire with his team, keeping them out long after they were scheduled to be inside the Compound. No one inside of the Compound knew where he had taken his team, as no one dared to ask.

We had no available teams outside the wire to send to search for the officer and his team, and no one was available to go to their assistance if they had been hit. None of our units inside the wire were mounted up, and QRF typically needed between fifteen to twenty minutes to get outside the gate. If there was an engagement with the officer and his team, the fighting would likely be over before QRF would even be ready to leave the Compound.

Fortunately nothing happened, and the officer was never disciplined for this late run. Only Battalion had the authority to discipline him—but to my knowledge, they never learned about it. No one was checking in teams when they returned.

The fact that no one was hurt on this excursion didn't stop us from being deeply concerned about the safety of the officer's team—but we simply didn't have the authority to do anything about it.

At the evening briefing, we were informed that insurgents had hit over one hundred locations across Baghdad. To make matters worse, our QRF forces were ambushed when they responded to the attack locations. Things had become much more like Vietnam, with insurgents using consistently improved tactics, and hitting us with coordinated attacks.

We were told that, from now on, no MP units were to leave the base until after 9:00 a.m. when the roads had been cleared by Infantry in their armored fighting vehicles. AC-130 Spectre gunships had hit ten separate targets in Baghdad. With the escalation in attacks, we assumed that the plan to turn over Iraq would change. We were wrong. The fact that the situation was getting worse was just ignored.

December 25-December 28, 2003

Several rockets passed over the Compound, but didn't hit anything in the Compound. We weren't sure if they had been fired by insurgents or Coalition forces.

A lot of shooting was going on, and it was difficult to tell if these were attacks on or by Coalition forces, or if they were just more local payback and crime. Forces from Iran have been infiltrating

Iraq to help support the Shia, and forces from Saudi Arabia were sending help to the Sunnis.

The rear tower on the south side of the Compound, manned by 1st Platoon, took and returned fire. Insurgents set up a fake IED outside the wall to lure our people outside. Once the MPs were outside of the Compound attempting to locate the IED, insurgents ambushed them, opening up with small arms fire.

Our tower security engaged the insurgents, and they fled the scene. This engagement was one of numerous small skirmishes we had with the insurgents on a daily basis. The engagements never lasted long, but they could always be deadly.

December 29, 2003

Operations had become a very tense and lonely place to work. No one wanted to be there when the officer wounded on September 8th was around. He had been difficult to work with before his injuries and his disposition did not improve during his recuperation.

He was aware that he was not popular, and seemed to attack us when he could. If anyone told him something in confidence, he ratted them out in a second. He also had the unfortunate habit of taking everything said to him in the worst possible way.

One day, he walked into Operations while I was engrossed in a project, to tell me that he was heading out. He didn't describe his mission to me, he just said that he was "heading out."

"Oh, okay," I replied.

He replied that he wasn't asking for my permission.

"I wasn't giving you permission, merely acknowledging your statement."

As long as our Company did its job, Battalion never had the need to discipline him.

When he did screw up badly enough to come to the attention of the current Battalion or the Brigade Commander, his past antics were unknown because the Commander was always a different person.

December 31, 2003

New Year's Eve—We were on high alert, but there had been no shooting anywhere near us and everything seemed quiet. Temperatures were cooler, and even with the sun, we were quite comfortable for a change.

I stayed out of the Operations Center most of the day, checking on the perimeter towers that were assigned to us. I talked with the soldiers, wanting to get a feel for how everyone was doing, accessing their comfort and anxiety levels. No one seemed overly concerned because they were all prepared, armed, and ready. During one of these tower checks, I heard sounds of a fire fight a great distance away.

As routines settled in, I began to walk through the Compound, and visit each Platoon area every day, to check on things while not being intrusive or behaving like I was conducting an inspection. I saw how the Platoons were taking care of themselves, giving me an understanding of how they were doing on a day-by-day basis.

Sergeant Halle was the driver of the vehicle that was hit by an IED when the officer he was driving was wounded. Because Sergeant Halle had to switch vehicles, we lost track of his mileage—but his distance-driven had to be close to, if not the same as, Sergeant Weaver's.

Sergeant Melissa Weaver was the second driver in the same officer's Security team, and she drove the same vehicle the entire time we were deployed. Sergeant Weaver had the highest recorded miles driven in the war zone.

Figure 19.1   Sergeant Melissa Richards-Weaver who logged the most miles driven in Iraq

Figure 19.2   No one had a problem with Sergeant Weaver, as long as you followed her rules

Figure 19.3   From Operations (Front, Left to Right) Specialist Kent
Roeser, Sergeant Jack Earley, Sergeant Melissa
Richards-Weaver, Sergeant Michael Halle (Back, Left
to Right) Private First Class William Zampagleone,
Specialist Mario Mentana, First Sergeant Chaun Jones

Chapter Twenty

THE BRIGADIER GEN. JEREMIAH P. HOWLAND AWARD

We heard an announcement concerning the active-duty 615th Military Police Company that finally allowed us to make sense of all of the rear-echelon crap that had been going on. We learned that the 615th had been trying to earn the Brigadier General Jeremiah P. Howland Award, given each year to the best MP Company in the Army. In order to qualify for the award, a unit must submit packets detailing their achievements in areas such as awards, training, weapons qualification, common task testing, physical fitness testing, schools completed, correspondence courses completed, and many other garrison-type assignments.

This award was created to motivate troops in a garrison environment to strive for and to prepare for battle. The award was not created for troops in a war zone and had no place there (unless your company was devoting its energy to earning the award while you let some other companies do your fighting for you). The 615th won the award[20.1] because the National Guard units from Connecticut, Ohio and Tennessee, and other states did all the patrolling in the streets of Baghdad while the 615th stayed on base qualifying.

I thought that the active-duty 527th was going for this award as well, since battalion was pushing for peace-time training requirements to be completed. Without the Battalion pushing this agenda, very few, if any, of these requirements would have been met, such as finding thousands of rounds of ammunition that the soldiers could fire for qualification.

A short list of requirements that have to be met in order to earn this prestigious award include:

- Training assessment
- Weapons qualification
- Physical fitness
- Noncommissioned officer education
- Military education
- Civilian education
- Reenlistment
- Unit awards
- Individual awards
- Unit discipline
- Foundations of excellence
- External evaluations

ACTIVITY LOG
January 1–January 13, 2004

January 1, 2004

Very little activity was going on, and all the MP units were inside the wire.

Battalion sponsored a New Year's celebration that lasted for a couple of hours. They built a large bonfire inside the Compound and issued each soldier two nonalcoholic beers. Everyone milled around, having a good time, drinking the fake beer, although I later learned that one of the similarities between real beer and fake beer is that both make you wake up at 3:00 a.m. to pee.

I think someone must have snuck some real booze into the party, because I saw at least one soldier get sick.

The bonfire was quite the show, and it was nice to have some decompression time. Thinking back on it gives me some pause, though, considering we had the entire battalion standing around, without any body armor, in an area about the size of a basketball court. If insurgents had known enough to send even just one mortar round over the wall, the consequences could have been devastating.

January 3, 2004

We survived the holidays without any significant hostile activity directed at us.

We were up to eleven Purple Hearts, more than any other Company in the Battalion—and we hadn't even been here for the invasion.

Some units began rotating out of our FOB; they were either headed home or assigned to other locations. This freed up a lot of space inside of the concrete buildings. When the Ohio unit departed, they left behind a large area of the second floor in the main building. We used that building space to house soldiers who had, up until that time, been living in tents. One of our greatest concerns had been that the soldiers living in tents had no protection from mortar or rocket attacks. Being able to move them inside the thick walls of the buildings offered much greater protection.

Most of the Compound's utilities were operational by this time, and everyone's comfort was improving. Food was also getting better, and soldiers made runs to Baghdad International Airport, where they had opened both a Burger King and a Pizza Hut. They also opened a Kellogg, Brown and Root dining facility, which served food that was, quality and variety-wise, light years ahead of the food we had been eating.

Our FOB was so small that we had been eating Tray Pack ever since we had arrived. Tray Pack meals weren't bad, but they were boring, effectively a TV dinner made to serve 25 people. To cook them, they were placed in boiling water for twenty minutes before being opened and served. Each tray contained a single course, and mixing and matching trays allowed for a full meal. One night we might have had a tray with sliced turkey, one with mashed potatoes, another one with some kind of vegetable, and maybe a fourth with gravy.

The military was trying to make Iraq feel more like home by bringing fast food and satellite TV, but I wasn't sure that creature comforts were a good idea. I felt that soldiers should be concentrating on the task at hand, focusing more on trying to survive the next gun battle, and less on creature comforts. I can't say that I didn't enjoy the better food and television, but I felt that focusing on getting those things to American troops in Iraq was the wrong priority. We were there to either beat the insurgents or go home, and we couldn't do both.

January 4, 2004

Everything in the Operations section was coming along smoothly. Over the past eleven months, we had been fine-tuning our procedures in command control, coordination, and reporting. At various times, the Platoons had provided feedback and input, helping us to better structure the way we did business. Things had been humming along for months, with no conflict in how our missions were being presented and coordinated.

That didn't stop an officer from walking in one evening, looking around the Operations Center, and proclaiming that Operations was "all jacked up!"

The officer had come in during shift change, so most of the soldiers who stood watch during the day, as well as evening shift, were present. Everyone was stunned by his words, glancing at one another, and at the officer, trying to figure out what he was talking about.

Being the inquisitive type (and not known for keeping my mouth shut), as well as being the senior NCO, I asked, "What's all jacked up?"

The officer gestured at our two large white boards and easels, and said that they should give him the information he needed to know what was going on. Instead, he explained, the boards told him nothing because they hadn't been updated for weeks. He complained that the first whiteboard was a cluster of confusion, and that the second had absolutely nothing on it.

We were dumbfounded. We had been using the boards and easels since we arrived, posting information on them, and tweaking the information whenever we discovered a better way of doing it. Using these boards, we were able to track an individual soldier at almost any given moment. Reasonably certain that the boards' information was up-to-date, I took a deep breath, and tried to explain how we were using the boards and easels.

The first whiteboard, which he insisted was a cluster of names, listed every soldier by team, squad, and platoon, noting the vehicle to which he or she was assigned. The second whiteboard, which was currently empty, was the mission board. Because no one was currently out on a mission, no one was listed.

I then showed him that each solider and vehicle number was listed on a magnetic strip that we could move from one board to the other, and back again.

I continued to explain that, once a squad leader was ready to depart the Compound, he or she would either come into the Operations Center, or radio in to notify us. We would then move those soldiers and vehicles assigned to that mission from the board on the left onto the mission board, signifying that they were on assignment and no longer available. The mission board was not updated until a unit was ready to depart. Once the unit departed, their departure was posted to the mission board, and listed as a departure in the radio log. When the unit completed its assignment and returned, their labels would be removed from the mission board, and returned to the first board, and that the return would be noted in the radio log.

I showed him how, using these two boards, we were able to determine whether a unit was inside or outside the Compound, what their current assignment was, and who they were with. We might not know their exact physical location from the boards, but we could check the radio log to determine where they had last reported in.

I then took the him over to the two easels, explaining that they were erased every twenty-four hours. The first easel listed the general assignments of the platoons and their squads for the next twenty-four-hour period, while the second easel listed their assignments for the following twenty-four-hour period. Every day, we would erase one of those easels and list new assignments. We gave the assignments to the Platoon Leaders and Sergeants, who then decided which Squad would be posted to each assignment.

I told the officer that the reason the easels looked like no one had changed them was because platoon assignments for the past several weeks had remained almost exactly the same; what a platoon leader or sergeant wrote down today for an assignment often remained the same for several days in a row. The easels with the general assignments did not indicate the specific soldiers going out, because on any given day, an individual soldier might be on sick call, going home on leave, or required to do another assignment. I explained that this was why we used the two white boards to track who was in and outside the Compound.

While I was aware that not everyone enjoyed hearing every detail about our system, I knew that the system had been hammered out over twelve months between Operations and the Platoons. Everyone understood the need for this kind of coordination and monitoring, and went along with our system, even though everyone knew that it wasn't perfect.

Despite my best efforts, the officer continued to insist that our system was "all jacked up."

I knew debating the issue was a waste of time, so I looked at the him and said, "Sir, if you can tell me the changes you'd like us to make, I'll be happy to incorporate them."

He offered no suggestions or constructive criticism, repeated that everything in operations was all jacked up, demanded that we make changes, and left. We stared at one another, shrugged our shoulders and got back to doing what we had been doing since we had arrived in Iraq.

The subject never came up again.

January 10, 2004

Things fell into a steady routine. Everyone wanted to know when we were heading south and getting the hell out of Iraq. Everything indicated that we would be driving back down to Kuwait and departing from there along the same route we had come in, with soldiers flying out and equipment being transported by ship back to the States by April 14th, the day which marked exactly one year since we had arrived in-country.

The upside, if there was one, was that it would take us anywhere from a few days to a week to get organized and pack up our equipment to head south; and it would take us two to three days to travel to Kuwait. Once we reached Kuwait, we were told it could be anywhere from three to four weeks before we would be ready to depart. This gave us a much earlier departure date from Baghdad.

A number of our soldiers went down to Kuwait, either doing supply runs or for short rest and recuperation periods (where they got to relax and maybe watch movies). Almost no one stationed down in Kuwait carried firearms, and those who did didn't tend to load them. This was a big contrast to our daily situation. Even inside our protective compounds, we required each soldier to carry a firearm and one magazine of ammunition, because we just never knew. From time to time, we had Iraqi nationals working inside the Compound, and we had no idea about their true allegiances or how they felt about American soldiers.

January 12, 2004

We had been in Iraq too long, and we were starting to get stale. No one showed much concern or regard for the insurgency anymore, and everyone was so accustomed to daily attacks that they just didn't register as dangerous anymore. Daily attacks became an everyday occurrence in the lives of the 143rd, just another part of the routine.

I had way too much time on my hands and kept thinking about home, which wasn't a good thing. It was important for us to keep our minds in the game, concentrating on what we were doing, otherwise we were going to start making mistakes.

I looked at my daybook and saw that I had written several pages of all of the things that I was looking forward to doing once I returned home. I chided myself and told myself that I had better start concentrating on what I was going to do in Iraq, both to stay alive and to help everyone else get out of here. The last thing that I wanted was to lose someone this late in the game—the Ohio National Guard had already shown us how deadly the last few days in-country could be.

We were now in phase three of our transition of law enforcement to the Iraqi Police. This involved Squads going to the Iraqi Police stations once every three days for inspection.

In the past, we had occupied many forward operating bases; now we were consolidating them into four major compounds: Taji, which was to the north on the main road (actually outside of the

Baghdad city limit); Falcon, our new home (located on the south edge of Baghdad); Camp Victory, which was the major FOB in the area (located at Baghdad International Airport); and the Green Zone.

As part of this consolidation, hundreds of trailers had been set up on the northwest side of the airport compound to be used as housing. Falcon added several hurriedly-constructed barracks to their base. These barracks had heat, air conditioning, and flush toilets, a marked improvement over the tents and bombed-out buildings we had been living in.

The downside of the consolidation was that Coalition forces were no longer patrolling throughout Baghdad. More combat patrols, as well as administrative runs meant Coalition vehicles had to travel all across the city each day. With the consolidation, we also reduced our travels to only a few roadways, and our absence allowed the insurgency to take over the neighborhoods around the back roads.

We had been doing patrols with the Iraqi Police, but now they were more or less on their own. Inspections were short, which meant that our Squads spent only a few hours at each station every few days. Our Military Police were also no longer going out after dark, as night patrols had been delegated to the Infantry (and I didn't know how much time they spent in the city after dark).

We were no longer a presence in Baghdad, and all of the units, from the Military Police to the 3rd Brigade Combat Team, were getting ready to rotate out. That our units were packing up and not patrolling was not lost on the insurgents. In addition, the local Shia Militia began to exert its influence in areas from which the Coalition presence had departed.

The 1st Cavalry began to replace units that were in the process of being rotated out, but they lacked the control that had once been exerted through the city. Even when we had been out in force twenty-four hours a day, fifteen or more attacks per day were common—and now attacks were increasing. 1st Cavalry had their work cut out for them, and we believed that they might have to retake the city at some point.

Even though things were bad on the ground, Mr. Bremer, Mr. Rumsfeld, Mr. Kerik, and Mr. Cheney stuck to their schedule. Mr. Rumsfeld continued to send out press releases stating that the insurgency was limited to no more than 500 people. These press releases were unchanged from the ones he had published in May 2003. If only 500 insurgents were in Iraq, they would have been dead or captured by this point.

January 13, 2004

After being here a year, we were finally starting to get what's called "hillbilly armor" attached to our vehicles. This armor consisted of scrap metal plates bolted to the fiberglass bodies. It was nowhere near as effective as the production up-armored or MRAP vehicles that started to be produced once Mr. Rumsfeld left office.

Of course, we started getting the armor at a time when we were spending less and less time on the roads. Having this armor would have been nice back in the early days, when we were doing regular patrols. It would have cut down on any number of injuries.

Soldiers started to get sloppy, and we were having more accidental weapon discharges. These occurred mainly after soldiers entered the compound, thankfully at the clearing barrels (where soldiers aim weapons in case of accidental discharge while emptying their weapons). Because this procedure was standard, soldiers became complacent, forgetting the step-by-step procedures that must be followed to safely clear and unload weapons.

We needed to rotate out before we got so sloppy that something really bad happened. We had the name of the unit designated as our replacement, but beyond that, no one really knew what was happening.

We were in the final stages of closing down Warrior Compound, and everyone was getting ready to move. Some of us were going home, while others would be rotating to different FOBs.

Chapter Twenty-One

COLONEL GOLD'S MPS

I come in peace, I didn't bring artillery. But I am pleading with you with tears in my eyes: If you fuck with me, I'll kill you all.

Marine General James Mattis
Speaking to Iraqi tribal leaders

ACTIVITY LOG
January 16–January 21, 2004

January 16, 2004

Lieutenant Colonel Garrity and Colonel Gold from the 3rd Brigade Combat Team had a going-away talk to thank the troops. Colonel Gold was a Citadel graduate, an excellent speaker, a hard-charging tanker, and our guys loved working for him and his battalions. Everyone was much happier working for the Armored Unit than they were working for their own Military Police Battalion, because Colonel Gold and his Battalion Commanders treated us as equals. He did not look down on us as inferior National Guard soldiers. While under his command, Colonel Gold, at various times, selected our Military Police officers to be his escort. It meant a lot when a commander, who could have chosen any of the units in his Brigade, chose our company to guard his life.

Figure 21.1   Colonel Russell Gold with (Left to Right) Lieutenant
Grube, Lieutenant Chiverton, and First Sergeant
Jones

During the awards ceremony with the 709th Military Police
Battalion, Colonel Gold presented a few coins to soldiers in every
unit except for the 143rd Military Police Company. Our troops
watched this and became slightly pissed off at being left out. Some
active-duty guys were laughing at us because we weren't receiving
any awards. Once more, we felt like the National Guard had been
put in its place; the second string, part-timers were getting what
they deserved—nothing.

Colonel Gold then dismissed all of the units, and called for the
143rd Military Police Company to fall in. He called us "His MP
Company," and proceeded to give each and every member of the
143rd Military Police Company a coin—his coin. He stated that
the company was as good as—or better than—active-duty Military
Police. With active-duty casually looking on, Colonel Gold related
some of the 143rd's exploits and commended us on the outstanding
job we had done, which seemed to piss off the Battalion Commander
and the Command Sergeant Major to no end.

Figure 21.2   Colonel Gold addressing the 143rd Military Police
Company

Colonel Gold's words meant so much to the members of the 143rd.
We were proud of the fact that someone from the active-duty
appreciated our efforts and was not afraid to voice his opinion.
It was also a relief to know that soon the 709th would be on their
way back to Germany, and we wouldn't have to work with them
much longer.

January 17, 2004

Upon his return, an officer gave his first full company briefing.
The last time he had given a full company briefing was the night
when he'd said we were "lucky," the same night his Squad had
been attacked and he had been injured. This time, when he again
said that we were "lucky," 150+ soldiers groaned out loud. Anyone
who has seen the movie *Memphis Belle* knows that tempting fate
like this officer was doing is never a good idea.

We were able to use the phones more often. They were civilian
phones, of course, not military, which wasn't a bad thing since
calls on military lines almost never went through. And even when
we were able to place a call, it could take anywhere from five to
ten minutes to get a connection; there was always a good chance

that the call could be cut off mid-conversation. Military lines were routed through an Air National Guard unit in Connecticut because they had full-time operators. It seems that the operators were pissed off about transferring the calls from our soldiers who were trying to call home. One soldier said that an operator actually yelled at him for calling home "too many times."

Soon, we had local contractors setting up computer rooms. The speed of their connections was far superior than those provided by the military.

We were told that the unit replacing us would be arriving in Iraq no later than February 24th. Of course, we had been given dates before that had changed, but that didn't stop us from getting our hopes up.

Everyone felt depressed more often than not, and a lot of what we were getting assigned to do was more make-work. Even though we were in the process of disengaging, insurgents were in the process of re-engaging. We kept on trying to push information on the insurgents up the chain of command, but no one seemed to be listening beyond Battalion level. The President's advisors, along with Ambassador Bremer, planned to stick to the timetable, even if that meant losing all the gains we had made in the past year.

The Iraqi judicial system and the Iraqi military were not ready to take over their country. They had made great strides in the past year, but lacked the across-the-board unity and commitment to make the plan work. There were also too many different parties vying for control of the new country. The Sunni and Shia faiths were the two major antagonists, along with criminal elements, but Al Qaeda, the Palestinians, and other foreign fighters had also come into Iraq to defeat "The Great Satan." The hatred that these groups had for America, along with their willingness to martyr themselves for Allah, made them especially dangerous. To them, dying while killing infidels was a great reward, a mind-set that runs counter to stability and future cooperation with any new government.

In our spare time, Battalion came up with a David Letterman-like Top Ten List of "Top Ten Stupid Things to do While in Iraq," which evolved into a "Top Twelve." We took turns reading each item out loud (I read number #12, which was "Removing Green Zone checkpoints and failing to patrol around the CPA because Baghdad is now safe.").

After having so much fun with that, I came up with my own Top Eleven list.

11. Allowing soldiers to drive armored vehicles with the doors off.

10. Allowing soldiers to run for physical training in full view on a river dike, in an area known to have enemy snipers and an enemy mortar position.

9. Testing Iraqi Police cadets in their underwear and bare feet to endear us to the Iraqi people and ensure their support of our presence.

8. Making automatic grenade launchers mandatory, even when no ammunition is available for them.

7. Ordering soldiers to sweep floors and pick up trash in a combat zone rather than letting them rest after a full day of operations.

6. Training soldiers for a desert assignment at Fort Drum, New York in the dead of winter where temperatures reached negative 30°.

5. Failing to supply all soldiers with a full basic load of ammunition.

4. Making the required number of radios more important than making sure they actually work.

3. Maintaining peace-time training standards rather than fighting the insurgency.

2. Ignoring reports of increasing insurgent attacks, and repeating that U.S. soldiers will be in Iraq only a short time.

1. Forgetting to let U.S. forces know that the 143rd MP Company was on its way.

At least number eleven was taken care of in short order. Numerous attacks caused those checkpoints to be put back in place, and patrols to be resumed. Even though the powers-that-be deemed the Green Zone to be safe, they had not consulted with the insurgents. That didn't matter, though. According to their timetable, the Green Zone should have been safe by this point, so down came the checkpoints.

January 18, 2004

Thankfully, the checkpoints had been put back in place. Today, an extremely large blast occurred at Checkpoint One, one of the entrances to the Green Zone. The blast was so large that it sounded like it had been detonated close by, even though Checkpoint One was more than a mile away from our compound. Later in the day, we received a report that the blast had killed eighteen people and wounded twenty-eight. Two of the dead were American contractors. No U.S. soldiers were killed.

In most cases, the outer perimeters of all security checkpoints were manned by Iraqi forces, while American troops formed the inner ring and final defense. It may sound like we were putting the Iraqi security forces at greater risk, and in a sense, we were. In a tactical sense, we made the target less attractive, because the insurgents wanted to kill Coalition forces more than they wanted to kill Iraqi security. Having Iraqi security as the first line of defense meant that attackers could be detected earlier, farther away from Coalition forces, and would have less of a chance of killing anyone from the Coalition. In this case, when the vehicle detonated, it killed more civilians trying to enter the Green Zone than Coalition or Iraqi security forces.

January 21, 2004

There was a lot of small arms fire around the south towers last night.

For the first time that I can remember, the Battalion sent out a foot patrol around the perimeter of the Compound. The south side of the Compound (a limited access highway with several lanes and a median divider) had previously been closed off to traffic, but was now open.

Some very well-off Iraqis lived on the opposite side of the highway from the Compound. They drove new BMW and Mercedes Benz vehicles, had generators for their houses and satellite dishes on their roofs. Most of them dressed in Western-style clothing, with a few mixing head scarfs with fine Italian suits. While the dinar was pretty much valueless, these people had money for vehicles, gas, and the finer things in life.

In this nicer neighborhood was where last night's gun battle took place. The attack didn't look like it was directed at our patrol, but it was so close that patrol felt threatened and the security towers went on high alert to cover their retreat. Tower security fired some parachute flares, which seemed to put a damper on whoever was firing. Fortunately, no one was injured.

The First Sergeant and I went down, and stayed at the towers for about an hour until we felt all danger had passed.

The First Sergeant went to our new location with the 168th Military Police Battalion. Everyone who made the trip said it was much better than Warrior Compound. The new location had real barracks with beds, showers, and flush toilets. It also had a full-service, air-conditioned KBR dining facility, a small gym, a small PX, a dispensary with real doctors and dentists, a very high security wall with numerous guard towers, and a long gauntlet that any vehicle bomber would have to maneuver through if he attempted to get inside the Compound.

We kept having problems getting awards processed through the 709th Military Police Battalion. They provided us with guidance from the highest levels of the U.S. command, outlining what documentation needed to be included for a specific award. Three of these awards were the Silver Star, the Bronze Star with V for Valor, and the Army Commendation Medal with V for Valor ("V" indicating bravery under fire).

Guidance from the 709th included a sample write-up, showing

how to detail what each soldier had done to earn a specific medal. The guidance came through Battalion, but was created much further up the chain of command, and was meant to be used by all the forces in theater. This guidance was written by someone at the General officer rank.

I used these examples as a benchmark to see where our soldiers' actions would fall, and what level of award each soldier had achieved. For example, I read the sample for the Bronze Star with V for Valor award and then compared my soldiers' actions with the one described in the example…and so on. Did our solder risk his life more than, the same as, or less than the soldier in the example? Did our soldier do something that affected the outcome of the action as compared to the example?

I determined that many of them qualified for awards. Based on the guidelines provided, at least one soldier, if not more, qualified for the Silver Star, while several easily met the guidelines for the Bronze Star with V for Valor or the Army Commendation Medal with V for Valor.

During the months we were attached to the 709th Military Police Battalion, a number of active-duty soldiers had been awarded the Bronze Star with V for Valor. This information was all verbal, with no documentation of the actual awards coming from Battalion. Comparing those citations with the citations of our own soldiers' actions, I felt the soldiers of the 143rd Military Police Company's exploits far exceeded those of the active-duty.

In nearly every case, our award requests were denied.

The process of applying for an award was more complicated than writing up a citation, filling out a form, and asking for the medal. The process required numerous forms of official documentation, which included, but was not limited to, sworn statements, official reports, after-action reviews, medical reports, and additional documents to verify the facts and circumstances surrounding the incident and the actions taken by the soldier being proposed for the award. Most award packets were between ten and twenty pages long.

Putting a soldier in for a specific award didn't mean that was the only award the soldier could be considered for. After review, a soldier might be eligible to receive any of several lesser awards appropriate to the situation. Even if it wasn't appropriate to award the Bronze Star with V for Valor, three lesser awards could be considered. That never happened when the soldiers of the 709th reviewed our awards recommendations.

Feeling that we were doing something wrong or missing something in the process, I requested copies of the write-ups that were submitted for the active-duty soldiers. I wanted to review them and determine what was lacking in our requests.

Each time I went to Battalion S-1, I was told that information was unavailable, as it had already been forwarded to Brigade.

Knowing the workings of the personnel units, I felt that it was unlikely that every bit of information had been forwarded to Brigade with no record left at company and battalion levels. The soldier who received the award would also have received a copy of the award certificate and form documenting the award request and detailing the engagement. I felt I was being stonewalled when I was dealing with the Brigade Captain, but I did not see an alternate course of action.

One day, prior to an award ceremony for an active-duty soldier who received the Bronze Star with V for Valor, I went to the Captain in S-1 and requested copies of the award write-up. I was told that they were not available, but that they might be in the possession of whomever would be presenting the award that morning.

As soon as the award ceremony was over, I approached the Captain in S-1 again and asked for copies of the paperwork. He told me he didn't have them. I lost my temper and started calling him just about every four-letter word I knew. Although he didn't challenge me, or try and put me in my place as a Captain normally would when being disrespected by a noncommissioned officer, I knew from that point on that those awards were only for the active-duty.

It didn't matter what the National Guard did, we were never going to see any of those awards. We could have had the bravest soldiers, with accomplishments that made them stand head and shoulders above their active-duty counterparts, and we would still not get recognized.

I stopped submitting award requests altogether—no one in our unit was going to get an award approved. This was disappointing, because the soldiers of the 143rd continued to perform in ways that warranted recognition and were deserving of awards.

Because we did know that just about every soldier would at least be getting an Army Commendation Medal, we began writing individual citations, based on each soldier's individual actions, to be presented along with each award. After completing almost all of these citations, we learned that individual citations would not be included with the awards. Instead, soldiers would receive an award with a generic citation that was based on their assignment. This meant that, for example, every driver would have the same wording on the award, regardless of what he or she had done in Iraq. There were no exceptions to this policy and it included every soldier, from the lowest private to the company commander.

It was up to the Battalion Commander to decide if higher awards were warranted. Even when that happened, the words and justification for the awards for two different platoon leaders receiving two different medals would be identical. I had no idea why this new policy was in place, especially since we had already gone through the trouble of writing up over one hundred award recommendations before they told us about this new policy.

I suppose, from Battalion's standpoint, writing up their own people in this way was easier because they didn't need to identify what each soldier had done to deserve each award. All Battalion needed to do was stick a medal on their soldiers, and they were good to go.

Chapter Twenty-Two

SWEETWOOD, ROBERGE AND BEER

Beer is proof that God loves us and wants us to be happy.

Ben Franklin

Once the powers-that-be decided we would be staying a year, they began a two-week leave rotation, starting with the lower enlisted. Another option offered was a short rest and relaxation trip down to Qatar. In Qatar, soldiers could eat in restaurants, relax in air-conditioned recreational and TV rooms, fish, and enjoy two cold beers a day. Chris Sweetwood and Roger Roberge both opted for, and managed to get, assigned to the same Qatar trip, and Chris insisted that our Supply Sergeant, Roger Severn, join them.

All three knew each other, but were not necessarily running buddies. I could not make the connection as to why Chris wanted Severn to join them until they returned from the trip. Sergeants Severn and Roberge do not drink; Sergeant Sweetwood, on the other hand, has been known to have a beer from time to time. On this trip, he was able to enjoy six beers a day thanks to his two new best friends.

Chapter Twenty-Three

FALCON FOB/ GRACELAND

I am just a poor, poor lad trying to make his way through a troubled, troubled world.

Staff Sergeant Ray Gist, U.S.M.C. 1st Radio Battalion

Falcon FOB was a very large base. Walking in a circuit starting with the barracks, and then going to our Operations Center, to the mess hall, to the laundry facility, and back to barracks was about a mile in length—and this area was only part of the FOB.

During the day, a number of Iraqi contractors and day laborers came into the FOB to work on various jobs inside the perimeter. We received word that some of these workers planned to hide inside the perimeter and attack after dark, and we were warned to watch out for stay-behind civilian workers, and to remain cautious at all times. While we were not permitted to have magazines in our weapons, we were told to each have one readily available to defend ourselves.

Gate security attempted to keep track of every individual entering and exiting the FOB, checking the logs at the end of the day to ensure that all contractors who had signed in had exited. Between the large number of workers coming into the FOB, and the language barrier, keeping an accurate account wasn't always possible. The fact that the

Iraqis didn't want to make keeping track of them easy didn't help.

These contract workers were part of a goodwill gesture/make work policy and were, at times, completely necessary because we didn't have the skills or the manpower required to complete some types of work. Their projects included improvements to make the base more functional and, in some cases, more comfortable. They built a nice-sized gym, along with volleyball and basketball courts.

However, these new recreational facilities also made keeping track of our own soldiers difficult. When soldiers were off duty, they could be at the barracks, the PX, the phone bank, the computer room, the gym, the Operations Center, the dining facility, or any place in between. Each time Falcon was attacked, we had to have a 100% accountability of all soldiers in as brief a period of time as possible. The sheer size and amenities at Falcon made keeping track of everyone difficult.

Consult Your Doctor

We had been looking forward to moving down to Falcon because, among other things, they had a full medical clinic. But then we later learned that Falcon transferred anyone who got sick or hurt to the CSH back in the Green Zone.

Prior to leaving Iraq, we began our processing and had to go through medical screening. I had received dozens of physicals over the years, but never one quite like this physical. They brought us in and had us go through sheet after sheet of paper, writing down everything we could think of about our medical history. We documented our injuries, illnesses, our potential levels of exposure to various chemicals and germs—everything from depleted uranium to carcinogens such as asbestos. Some of the sheets were long "Yes/No" checklists, and we had to explain every "Yes" answer in great detail.

They then sent us to a doctor who reviewed our medical history (sometimes making notes, sometimes not) and then stamped the forms, turning them into official records. The doctor didn't give us an actual physical examination. Soldiers complaining of injuries such as hearing loss, ringing in the ears, strains, sprains, or, in my case, a dislocated shoulder, were not tested or screened in any way.

They explained afterward that we might have a claim with the Veterans Administration. This implied, at least to me, that once I got out I would have the opportunity to go to a VA Hospital and get treatment for the injuries I had sustained in Iraq. I didn't understand the difference between being treated at a VA Hospital for a medical condition, and putting in a claim for monetary compensation with the Veterans Administration. This territory was all new ground to me, even after twenty years of military service.

Figure 23.1   An MP Compound at Graceland FOB sign inside Falcon FOB; all units shown are National Guard/Army

Reserve under a National Guard MP battalion

Figure 23.2   A second sign listing all the MP units assigned to the
168th Battalion

ACTIVITY LOG
February 1–March 31, 2004

February 1, 2004

The Company began operations under the 89th Military Police Brigade, 168th Military Police Battalion.

February 2, 2004

The Company, minus 4th Platoon, relocated out of Warrior FOB down to Falcon FOB to a smaller, interior FOB called Graceland. We were there to perform missions under the Tennessee National Guard. Every unit at Graceland was either Guard or Reserve. The 709th was packing up, heading out to Balad/Anaconda for their flight back to Germany.

February 5, 2004

The weather came full circle. We had a raging storm roll through with thunder, lightning, and downpours. The temperature dropped so low we could see our breath. Temperatures dropped from 120° down to near freezing. Soldiers used the heaters in their vehicles for the first time. This weather was a big change from the summer, when, in the 120° heat, the interiors of those vehicles were a roasting 150°.

We hoped that we would get much better treatment now that we were under a National Guard Military Police Battalion, but that didn't seem to be the case. We were assigned tasks that required twenty-four Military Police teams to execute, even though we only had nineteen teams available. I went over to Battalion and laid it out for them, which caused them to adjust our tasks to those requiring sixteen teams.

I later learned that an officer had previously gotten into a protracted argument with the Battalion's female S-3 major, and that this argument was the key factor in our getting changed from a reasonable number of tasks to a ridiculous number that required personnel we did not have.

Insurgents continued to improve their tactics. By this time, they were attaching IEDs to the backsides of guard rails, thereby raising the IEDs two to three feet off the ground, which made them level with the doors of our vehicles. This change also placed the IEDs sideways, allowing them to blast across the road into vehicles.

February 6, 2004

4th Platoon rejoined the Company at Falcon FOB.

February 7, 2004

Several escorts were scheduled to go out this morning. Some of them started late, but we soon got them all out and running. The Battalion Commander and XO came over to see an officer and First Sergeant, and discovered that they were both participating in the escort missions. Because we didn't have enough soldiers to fill the ranks in the vehicles for all our escort missions, we were forced to have an officer and First Sergeant going along to fill seats—I believe that was the point when the Battalion Commander finally realized how tasked out our Company was.

February 8, 2004

We started to repack shipping containers, getting them ready to move out; we were cleaning all equipment we weren't actively using to prepare them for shipment. We were still expected to go on road missions, and were still trying to get more the hillbilly armor kits installed on our vehicles.

One of our constant precautions whenever we headed out on a mission was to keep the vehicle windows either fully up or nearly closed, as the laminated glass offered some protection (never mind that a "breeze" was actually painful because of the desert heat). Windows up, plus old body armor hanging in the doors, was the only defense that we had for months. Installation of the new armor kits was an improvement, but we still needed to keep the windows up to protect our heads and shoulders. A lot of heat built up inside those vehicles.

The Sadr mission came up again and we were once again tasked with providing escort and security for Special Operations conducting the raid.

We were tasked with escorting the 709th Military Police Battalion from Warrior Compound up to Balad/Anaconda for their flight back to Germany. Battalion allotted us one squad of three vehicles for the escort. Staff Sergeant (Sully) Sullivan and his Squad were assigned the mission.

When Sully heard about the assignment and came into the Operations Center, he was unable to hide the concern on his face and in his voice. He was going to be escorting the 709th through Baghdad to a location several hours to the north, through territory he had never been before. Only one of our Platoons, the 4th, had ever been that far north, and that was eleven months ago during the beginning of our deployment. Sully's Squad would also be out of radio range of just about everyone for almost the entire mission, and they would be responsible for escorting open five-ton trucks loaded with twenty-five soldiers each. These vehicles would make ideal targets for anyone wanting to kill Americans.

Staff Sergeant Sullivan wanted to add a fourth vehicle and a medic to his escort group, so he could have one vehicle in front of the convoy to scout for trouble, one vehicle leading the convoy, one vehicle in the middle, and one vehicle covering the convoy's trail. He also wanted to do this because, even though they would be going up to Anaconda with ten or more vehicles, they would be coming back alone. In that situation, potentially miles away from anyone who could help, Staff Sergeant Sullivan wanted to make sure that his Squad would be able to defend itself and to treat any casualties.

Staff Sergeant Sullivan knew that this escort mission could either turn out to be nothing more dangerous than a ride in the country, or an extremely deadly event. He did not want to take any chances that he didn't have to, and wanted to ensure that he had the protection that he needed. Thankfully, his requests were approved.

February 10, 2004

4th Platoon was assigned an escort mission. On the surface, this mission did not seem to be anything out of the ordinary. It was briefed as a basic escort mission, in which some individuals needed to be brought to a meeting and then returned to the FOB.

We were not briefed that this was, in fact, an NSA escort mission.

4th Platoon went out under the supervision of their Platoon Sergeant, Sergeant First Class Emmerson. They were briefed on their actual mission only once they reached the pickup location. In general terms, it was still an escort mission, but instead of transporting people to a meeting, they were transporting them to a location where they could install eavesdropping devices. The NSA directed the Squad to the location, who set up a roadblock and checkpoint to cover their activities.

Roadblock and checkpoints had been routine early in our deployment, but as time went on, the Military Police were ordered to cease performing roadblocks and checkpoints, as we lacked sufficient firepower and armor protection. U.S. forces were also placed in fixed locations, making them ideal targets for suicide bombers or drive-by shooters. That's why, at the time of this mission, roadblocks and checkpoints were being done only by Armored Infantry units or the Iraqi Police.

The Squad set up a checkpoint and, as the NSA set up their equipment, a vehicle approached the checkpoint at extremely high speed. It refused to stop at the direction of the soldiers manning the checkpoint and so, under the rules of engagement, the Squad opened fire on the vehicle and disabled it. The suspects inside the vehicle attempted to flee on foot, and the Squad engaged them again, killing one individual and wounding another. Tests done on the subjects later found that they had explosive residue on their hands.

The Squad recovered the NSA personnel, returned them to the FOB, and Sergeant First Class Emmerson briefed us on what had transpired. He was pissed off at us because he thought we knew the true purpose of his mission and hadn't told him. We were pissed off because we had only the cover story that we were given, and we had no idea that his Squad was going to be setting up a checkpoint or covering the NSA.

After we hashed it out on a company level, I went to the Battalion and demanded to know why we had not been told all the facts. After talking to the people there, I discovered that they were also unaware of the true purpose of our mission, and had also been kept in the dark.

Anger and the accusations rippled all the way up the chain of command until it finally reached Operations (that generated this mission in the first place). It was discovered that the Brigade S-3 Operations officer had coordinated independently with the NSA agents. This type of mission should have been coordinated with the Armored Brigade who owned the battle space.[23.1]

Once this was discovered, even more people started to demand answers. These people weren't lowly master sergeants from an MP Company, but were colonels and generals from a Military Police brigade and an Infantry division.

The story of what happened next was written about in the book *Warrior Police*, where it was noted that all of the questions were ultimately directed to the Brigade S-3 officer who had coordinated the mission with the NSA. When finally confronted about his part in organizing this mission, the officer collapsed into a fetal position and began moaning incoherently. He was later sent back to Texas and medically discharged.

Had we known at the company level that this was an NSA mission to gather intelligence, we would have substantially reinforced the Squad. Had anyone known that this assignment would entail a roadblock and checkpoint, we would have likely refused based on the rules of engagement, and our duties under the 1st Armored Division.

With what we knew at the time, based on the then-current rules of engagement, the soldiers of 4th Platoon acted appropriately. That did not prevent their every action from being placed under a microscope, of course. Someone at a high level was looking to blame someone besides the S-3 officer.

February 12, 2004

When the Company Commander was evacuated to the States, Lieutenant Grube had stepped up. Today, Colonel Garrity recognized Lieutenant Grube's dedication, determination, leadership, professionalism, and commitment to the Battalion's success by directing that he be put in for a Marechaussee Award. This request was submitted and quickly approved.

Relatively few of these awards were presented each year, and to the best of my knowledge, this was the first Marechaussee Award presented to a National Guardsman.

Prior to taking over the company, Lieutenant Grube had been the 4th Platoon leader, with Sergeant First Class Emmerson as his Platoon Sergeant. When Lieutenant Grube took over the Company, Sergeant First Class Emmerson became the acting Platoon Leader for the 4th Platoon.

February 13, 2004

MP-1 was finally brought back online after several months because parts had not been available. The driver assigned to this vehicle refused to drive it. For this reason, Sergeant Roberge was assigned to drive in any future moves, while I was assigned to be the gunner. I had no problems riding in this vehicle. A jinx wasn't on the vehicle.

Temperatures were starting to warm up again, and we were turning the air conditioners back on.

February 16, 2004

Less than sixty days until we leave beautiful, downtown Baghdad. At least, that was what we thought.

We received word that one of the vehicles from our Battalion had been hit, and a MedEvac helicopter had been called for the wounded. This was not a good sign—if the vehicle had been lightly damaged or the soldiers slightly wounded, driving them to the hospital would have been easier and quicker than calling for a helicopter. Reading between the lines, it was clear that the vehicle had probably been destroyed and whoever was inside was seriously hurt.

We didn't know which company the damaged vehicle belonged to, since every unit, including ours, had sent vehicles in that general direction earlier in the morning. Radio traffic was frantic, but none of it came over our frequencies, which was a sign that the vehicle might not have belonged to us. However, the Battalion CO and XO were both on the radio and we were monitoring their transmissions. This was a bad sign—whenever the big bosses felt the need to get involved, it was never good.

The Squad that had been attacked called in their grid position. We plotted the location on our maps, and realized that they could not be in the location that they had just called in—the helicopter was going to the wrong place.

It was making us nuts that we could not raise any of our Squads on the radio, which only made us more concerned that the Squad that was hit was one of ours. Not until much later were we able to make radio contact with our units to learn that none of them had been hit. The Squad that was attacked was from the 2175th Military Police Company. They lost one soldier, while two others were severely wounded. A deep sadness came over the MP Battalion. While the soldier killed in action wasn't from Connecticut, he was still an MP and one of our brothers. We all felt the loss.

I read the book *Flags of Our Fathers*, which is about the five Marines and Navy Corpsman who raised the flag on Iwo Jima in World War II. In the beginning of the book, Harlon Block, one of the Marines, was in Hawaii getting ready to ship out for Iwo Jima. He left his graduation ring with a friend, and asked him to give the ring to his mother because the Marine didn't want to lose it. Harlon Block never made it off the island.

One of the things I left behind in Connecticut was my FBI Academy ring because I didn't want some Iraqi taking off my finger and waving the ring around like a trophy. It is funny what went through my mind when I was getting ready to deploy. I knew that things could be dangerous, even deadly. I might get killed, but I didn't want to give some SOB a trophy that he could take home and brag about.

Figure 23.3   Lieutenant J. Michael Grube (Left) being congratulated by his Platoon Sergeant, SFC Chris Emmerson, on receiving the Military Police Marechaussee Award

The Battalion Commander wanted someone to put together a program to train the Iraqi Police Chiefs in executive protection. The bulk of them didn't take any precautions to ensure their own safety, and at least one high-ranking Iraqi Police official was being murdered on a weekly basis.

The Iraqis were forever using the term "Insha'Allah" to sum up situations. The term means "God's will," and it was used by the Iraqis in much the same way that we would say, "whatever," or, "shit happens." The Iraqi Police Chiefs used this term to refer to protection. If someone died, they chalked it up to it being God's will, viewing the taking of precautions as a waste of time. In some cases, they really meant that what happened was God's will. In other cases, I saw it as just an excuse for not being prepared.

I broke my own rule about never volunteering for anything and told the Colonel that I would put together the program for him, and spent the next several days putting together a basic executive protection program. I looked at all the prior assassination attempts and tried to identify tactics that could be used to survive them. Most of these tactics were very basic precautions most anyone would use if they knew that someone wanted to kill them. If any of the Iraqi Police Chiefs had watched any of the *The Godfather* movies, they would have recognized a number of the precautions I recommended.

I discovered that most of these attacks took place while police officers were in transit, and that the Iraqis were very rigid about their routines and schedules. They could easily foil many assassination attempts by changing when they visited police stations, as well as varying the routes that they took.

Because they were ranking officers, the Iraqi Police Chiefs carried pistols with them (which would not be of much use in an ambush). So, I suggested that they should carry rifles so that they would have better firepower if they were attacked.

I typed my presentation and presented it to the Colonel, who thought it was a good plan. He had his translator transcribe it into Arabic, so they could hand it out at the presentation. When I presented my program to the Iraqi Police Chiefs, I was surprised that they were totally against it. They were quite adamant about maintaining their travel routes and schedules, and told me that no one was going to tell them what they were going to do, or how they were going to do it. They also held the lofty notion that carrying rifles was beneath them.

I tried to explain that their survival was important, not just for their own sakes, but because they were the hope of the new Iraq. If they were murdered, the country would be without leadership. My plan was still not warmly received.

I went out with the Colonel to meet with the Police command

staff of Western Baghdad. This first ride with him was a real eye-opener. A unit that was coming up on their one-year rotation escorted the Colonel through the city. For my part, I was part of the baggage, not part of the Security team. Since they had been in-country for almost a year and had been selected for the task, I figured they knew what they were doing.

We locked and loaded our weapons after exiting the Compound, but the Security team did not seem at all confident when they performed this procedure. I sat behind the driver in the Colonel's vehicle, next to the translator. The Colonel sat in the front passenger seat next to the driver, and we had a machine gunner up in the turret.

The Colonel read from a map, giving instructions to the driver as we drove for the center of Baghdad. We were lost in short order and ended up on a dead-end street. The Colonel asked the driver to stop so he could get a better look at the map.

I popped out of the door as soon as the vehicle stopped, providing security to the left side of the vehicle. I realized, with some astonishment, that no one else had gotten out of the vehicle with me. They remained inside, not giving any thought to the fact that we were both lost and stopped on a dead-end street, surrounded by people who wanted to kill us.

The two Staff Sergeants on the Colonel's Security team didn't know where we were or how to get to where we needed to go. Neither one of them stepped up to take charge, choosing to instead leave everything up to the Colonel. They didn't bother to get the soldiers out of the vehicles to provide security while the Colonel checked the map, which should have been our number one priority.

The Colonel asked me if I had ever been to Police Headquarters. I had been there on a number of occasions, but, unfortunately, I had always been looking out of the side window and never had a clear picture of the roads we took to get there.

After a while, we finally started moving again, making our way to Police Headquarters. I realized that the Colonel's Security team, despite having spent almost a year in Iraq, didn't know their way around the city. They also hadn't bothered to do map reconnaissance before taking the Colonel out. This simple procedure would have allowed them to plan their route, instead of leaving it to the colonel to figure out where to go on the fly.

The less-than-professional conduct continued when we got to the Police Headquarters. The Colonel left his vehicle and was allowed to walk into the building by himself. I got a hold of one of the Staff Sergeants and told him that the Colonel needed to have someone with him at all times. The Staff Sergeant didn't seem to behave as if escorting the Colonel was terribly important.

I then noticed that everyone in the escort was just relaxing, not bothering to take up security positions. Their lackadaisical attitude was not only figuratively killing me, it could literally have all of us killed. I asked one of the Sergeants to put one of the machine gunners on top of the roof of Police Headquarters for protection.

He didn't seem to understand why security was necessary because we were inside Police Headquarters, and had passed through two security checkpoints just to get here. I pointed out that every ranking police officer in Western Baghdad, along with the American Commander in charge of Police Stations, were all gathered in one building. If I were a car bomber, I would find Police Headquarters at that moment to be an ideal target.

It looked like he was starting to get it, but he still seemed more concerned with relaxing and taking it easy than staying on high alert.

It wasn't just him, though. Everyone was getting short-timer's attitude, even though a soldier had been killed and two more wounded only a few days before. Soldiers weren't taking procedures as seriously, and everyone's mind was on going home, not the task at hand. Every day in this place was dangerous. Something could happen on the first day, on the last, or on any day in between, and you could be killed. No one on the other side was keeping track of how much time we had left in our deployments—they just wanted to kill Americans regardless of the date.

February 26, 2004

One of the intelligence units, possibly the NSA, overheard a phone conversation between locals. They didn't say how the NSA received the information, but that it was credible and convincing. The NSA identified the callers, and we dispatched one of our Squads to pick up the suspects. When our soldiers searched them, they found that they were carrying a handwritten map of the base.

The suspects were locals whom we had dealings with on a day-to-day basis. A small PX, coffee shop, barbershop, and small gift shop were located in the center of Falcon, and they were all run by locals. The two suspects worked in the coffee shop. They and their coworkers weren't dummies, and they had hired some lovely young local ladies to work in the coffee shop.

Many of our soldiers, including a couple of guys from our unit, spent most of their free time in the coffee shop talking with the cute Iraqi girls. One of the soldiers from our unit spent hours there, learning Arabic from one of the girls, and in return, teaching her English.

The owner didn't seem to mind that his employee spent most of her time sitting around flirting with American soldiers, which made me think that she was there for more than just coffee and keeping the place clean. Who knew what was being discussed in the coffee house or what kinds of information they were able to worm out of the soldiers? If they were actively spying on us, this had the potential to become another Tet Offensive.

An investigation cleared all of our Iraqi suspects. They determined that the locals were only looking to expand their operation and not attack the base. I wanted to meet the interrogators because I would have made a lot of money selling them some waterfront property in New Orleans.

Several Iraqi Police vehicles and uniforms were stolen, and there were rumors that Al Qaeda might try to use them to attack our facilities. Even without the concerns that Al Qaeda was behind the thefts, our inability to trust the Iraqi Police had always been an issue. It's not that they were necessarily corrupt, or that they hated Americans. The problem was that no one ever checked into their backgrounds.

Like regular citizens, the Iraqi Police had a love-hate relationship with Americans and Coalition forces. They liked that we removed Saddam from power, that we brought democracy, and a religious freedom they didn't have under the Sunni minority (which Shia were especially happy with). They hated that we had to destroy their Army in order to remove Saddam, that we were occupying their country, and that we were Christian and Jewish infidels.

One example of this love-hate relationship concerned the Festival of Ashura, an important holy day to the Shia Muslims. This holiday is a festival of atonement that honors the life and death of Imam Hussein, who was killed by Sunnis in 680 AD during the Battle of Karbala. Because the Imam was killed by Sunnis, the celebration of Ashura tends to cause a great deal of conflict between Shia and Sunni Muslims.

During part of the Ashura holiday, the Shia cut open their foreheads, bled all over themselves, and then took a pilgrimage to the shrine of Imam Hussein, whipping themselves as they marched in procession. Under Saddam Hussein's rule, the Shia were not permitted to take this pilgrimage. The Coalition forces, wanting to promote understanding and tolerance of both sides of the Islamic faith, allowed the Shia to go on their pilgrimage.

Except, the Shia used their pilgrimage to protest American and Coalition presence in their country, despite the fact that without us, they would not have been permitted to undertake the pilgrimage at all.

February 27, 2004

You can't make this shit up.

We took a ride out to the Brigade supply area. This had once been a sprawling complex, serving as a supply depot for all of Western Baghdad, with several thousand soldiers to justify a KBR dining facility. Tens of thousands of dollars had been spent repairing this facility to turn it into a major base.

The supply area was a ghost town. All the soldiers were gone and virtually was nothing left of the facility. Everything of importance had been shifted to the complex at Baghdad International Airport.

This wasn't the only location where this had happened. Other locations across Western Baghdad were in the process of being abandoned. Everything was being consolidated at the airport, at Camp Falcon, or at Camp Taji.

Falcon FOB kept getting hit on a daily basis. The attacks were random, happening throughout the day and night. With the size of our FOB, it was almost impossible for the insurgents to miss us. Fortunately, the mortars or rockets would impact inside FOB, and would not often hit anything important.

We've also bumped into people firing outgoing rounds. One day, on the way back from the mess hall, I saw an M-113 armored personnel carrier pull to a stop not too far from where I was standing. A few seconds later, it fired four point two inch mortar rounds before moving out. After seeing this, I wondered if we were taking fire from the insurgents or doing the firing ourselves.

February 29, 2004

We received some up-armored Humvees, even though we would be going home in about twenty-eight days. These up-armored vehicles had been left behind by other units who had returned home. We would use the vehicles until we left, turning them over to the unit that would replace us.

Just like our vehicles, these were in pretty rough shape after being in Iraq for an entire year. It also didn't help that the soldiers who left them behind knew that they would never see these vehicles again.

March 2, 2004

I'm not a very religious person, and I usually only go to church for weddings and funerals because I have to. Even so, I received a very appropriate quote from the Tennessee chaplain that I cut out and pasted into my daybook. The heading is, "Rock Steady," and the verse is, "I have fought the good fight, I have finished the race, I have kept the faith." (2 Timothy 4:7)

I hope that I have lived up to that quote.

Our departure schedule changed again. We were told that, instead of leaving from Kuwait, we would now be flying out from Anaconda, which was located to the north of Baghdad.

We continued to perform escort missions and I continued to go out with the Battalion Commander to visit several police stations and meet with ranking police officers in Western Baghdad.

We made our way to the 1st Cavalry's Division Headquarters, located in the northeast corner of Baghdad International Airport. This had previously been an open field, but now housed hundreds of white trailers that were used for sleeping quarters and office space. The Battalion Commander met with both old and new Division Commanders to review all ongoing missions involving the Military Police.

While we were there, we noticed a lot of excited radio activity. Several IEDs were detonated and there was also a broadcast warning the insurgents might be converting ambulances into VBIEDs. Everyone was directed to stop and search all ambulances.

There was also radio activity about a major attack that had occurred earlier that morning. It was initially believed that these attacks had targeted Coalition forces, but more information indicated that all of the casualties were Iraqis. A suicide bomber had attacked a mosque, killing twenty-five and wounding fifty.

We heard reports of additional attacks all across Western Baghdad. These attacks were much more determined and serious than usual, making use of mortars and rockets and RPGs to hit several places simultaneously. Numerous casualties were reported and, again, most of them were Iraqi civilians or Iraqi security forces. We also heard about an indirect fire attack against Iraqi civilians down south in Karbala, which killed 86 people and wounded more than 500.

Insurgents were also taking advantage of us being gone from the police stations and limiting our patrols. So, we stepped up security for ourselves—instead of two vehicle squads, all groups departing FOB were required to have at least three and sometimes four vehicles.

The FOB was mortared again, but this time it was from very close range. We were able to hear the thump of the mortars being launched from the tube, followed by the impact of the round inside the base a couple of seconds later.

We were seeing more Sunni versus Shia attacks now that we were almost completely off the road. There were rumors of rioting, and instances of suicide bombings, car bombings, and the launching of mortars and rockets. So far, there had been no one-on-one confrontations between large groups of individuals, which was a good thing, because those types of confrontations could have turned into real bloodbaths. We would, no doubt, have been caught in the middle.

Staff Sergeant Sullivan's Squad came off the Iraqi Police Academy range. The assignment there had ended and wouldn't begin again for two months, long after we were gone. Staff Sergeant Sullivan and his Squad were reassigned to escort missions as they became available. For the first escort mission, Staff Sergeant Sullivan's Squad was to escort a KBR tractor-trailer to Baghdad International Airport and return with provisions for the dining facility.

I learned that some soldiers in other companies resented KBR drivers because they were civilian contractors who made an awful lot of money driving tractor-trailers in Iraq. I didn't have that problem with private contractors, because they were risking their lives just like us, and they made life a lot more tolerable by providing excellent food.

Staff Sergeant Sullivan had never done this type of mission before, so he came to see me to ask for direction on how to proceed. I thought about it for awhile and concluded that this was just another escort mission, except that it involved a very large target that could not defend itself. We discussed it and decided that he should handle it just like any other escort mission. I told him that he should brief the drivers as to the nature of the mission and go over the route with them ahead of time, highlighting any turns that they would need to make or critical points along the trip.

We then discussed what he would do if the convoy came under attack. I told him to follow standard procedure—if you are past the kill zone, keep moving; if you are in the kill zone, exit the kill zone if possible; if you have not yet entered the kill zone, stay out of the kill zone. This was a procedure that we both knew well, but we both felt that he needed to communicate it to the civilian driver. That way, the driver knew what we would be doing and what was expected of him.

We also discussed what should be done if the tractor-trailer became disabled or if the engagement became too intense. We both agreed that, if things got that bad, they should pick up the driver and get the hell out of there. We could always get another tractor-trailer.

I learned later that Staff Sergeant Sullivan went over all of this with the civilian driver, and in even greater detail than I had suggested. Staff Sergeant Sullivan had always been cautious, but after getting hit by an IED on the way to the Police Academy range, he knew how quickly a simple ride could turn into a deadly confrontation. He even went so far as to put a soldier inside the tractor-trailer, providing additional protection (something that none of the prior escorts had ever done).

The convoy left on time without any problems. When they returned, the civilian driver came into our Operations Center and wanted to talk to me. My first thought was that we had done something wrong, and I tried to think of how I could make it right.

The driver wanted to let me know that this was the first time, in all his trips up to Baghdad International Airport or anywhere else, that a squad leader had completely briefed him. He went on to say that he was impressed with our professionalism and with the obvious concern that the soldiers had for his welfare and for the success of the assignment. He wanted to know who to talk to so that our company, specifically Staff Sergeant Sullivan's Squad, would be the only ones escorting him from then on. I got the impression that his other escorts had just winged it, walking out, mounting up, and going for a ride.

It was nice when a disinterested third party came in and gave us such positive feedback. Like with Colonel Gold, who had selected us over everyone at 3rd Brigade to protect him, it was nice to know that we part-time weekend warriors continued to impress people with our ability to fight a war.

March 8, 2004

Specialist Zampaglione returned to the unit. He had been the gunner when his vehicle was hit suffering a ruptured eardrum and concussion from the blast. He was evacuated to the States, and after treatment, was scheduled to return to Baghdad to complete his tour. For reasons unknown to us, he had been delayed in Germany on his way back to Baghdad. A few days after he was due to arrive, we received an email notifying us that Zampaglione was en route.

I'm not clear why, but in spite of this email, an officer listed Zampaglione as AWOL—one of the worst listings you can place on a soldier (especially one who is in the process of returning to a combat zone after he had been wounded). The only other listing that is worse to receive is a deserter (but in that case, the solider would have to be missing over thirty days). The officer stated that he was sure Zampaglione was hiding out in Germany, intentionally delaying his return.

When Zampaglione returned a few days later. I never asked what he had been doing in Germany or why he had taken so long to return. As far as I was concerned, he had paid his dues and didn't need to explain anything to us. I certainly hoped that he had found an opportunity to remember us while enjoying a couple of beers.

To my surprise, the officer agreed and never inquired about the delay again.

March 12, 2004

The first eighty-two troops of the company that would replace us were scheduled to arrive on Saturday. The soldiers were from the 192nd Chemical Battalion. They weren't MPs, but they were being trained up to perform MP missions.

We were receiving conflicting information on where and when we would be leaving, and soldiers were starting to get wired. The uncertainty of our situation and the constant date changes were causing everyone a lot of stress. Soldiers who had been going out on the road for the entire year were beginning to get superstitious and overly concerned that something bad would happen. They were afraid that they'd never make it home.

The new phone service and email system had its positives and negatives. Now family and friends from home expected soldiers to call and/or email on a more frequent basis, and when soldiers didn't call/email for a while, their family and friends began to worry.

For example, one day we were on a routine escort and were due back in the FOB by 4:00 p.m. Something came up, requiring us to make a couple of extra stops before returning. One of the soldiers became very agitated about the delay, to the point where he looked as if he was going to cry.

I didn't know why he was so upset. We weren't facing any real danger and we were only delayed a couple of hours. I knew that we would be back in the Compound before it got dark, and the dining facility would still be open. When I asked him what was wrong, he told me that he had told his mother he would be back at the FOB at 4:00 p.m.. He promised her that he would email her by 4:30 to let her know that he was back and safe. He was frantic, worried that his mother would think that something had happened to him.

From then on, I began cautioning the troops about making similar promises. Because our situation was dynamic and uncertain, they needed to realize that they might be delayed on missions, our phone and email systems might go down or be suspended, or any one of a number of things that could happen that would limit communications.

Of course, shutting down the email and phone systems every time a soldier was killed didn't help. The systems were shut down as a precautionary measure to ensure that the verification and notification of a soldier's death was conducted through proper channels. The problem was, while the military compiled information to make proper notification, CNN and FOX reported casualties in real time, giving the locations and sometimes the actual units involved. I'm sure these news reports caused our soldiers' stateside families panic every single time, especially for the unfortunate few who had to sit and wait for a Casualty officer to arrive to confirm that their son or daughter had died.

March 18, 2004

By my count, we had about twelve days left.

Insurgents blew up a hotel. All reported casualties were Iraqis, with no Coalition forces involved.

I have been using the word insurgents, but I really had no idea who these attackers really were. They could have been leftover members of the Republican Guard, the Baath Party, Al Qaeda, Sunnis, Shias, Palestinians, organized crime, or just about anybody else with an axe to grind. There was so much hate and contempt between so many different groups that it was hard to pin down who was really doing what to whom.

The only time we were able to identify the attackers was when one of them was captured or killed. We could then use body or fingerprint analysis to determine their identity and who they were working for.

Even though we were scheduled to rotate out in less than two weeks, somehow, we were scheduled for a class on mines, booby-traps, and IEDs (of all things). With two weeks to go, someone decided to train us on the hazards of being in Iraq. The class was quite good and very informative, but wasted on us. Giving this class to the soldiers who were waiting in Kuwait to enter Iraq would have been more effective use of resources. I didn't know what the United States Army was thinking.

For the most part the insurgents—or whoever was shooting at us—stopped using small arms and RPGs. They had to get in close to inflict casualties, and our ability to return fire made this too dangerous a proposition. Now IEDs were their primary choice of weapon for attacking troops on the move, while mortars and rockets were used exclusively to hit the FOBs.

Everyone I have talked with about this period of time agrees that it was a bit surreal. We were performing fewer and fewer missions, living in climate-controlled barracks with an outstanding dining facility, a gym, a PX, and a coffee shop. We even had a library with comfortable chairs where soldiers could read and write letters. Yet, a few hundred yards away was a city teeming with people who wanted to see us dead.

Part of me felt that we should never have left Warrior Compound, because we'd gotten used to a level of comfort and safety that was not in any way in line with the reality outside the Compound walls. The situation continued to become more dangerous every day, with insurgents and criminals continuing to hone their tactics. We saw the danger when we were on the streets, but when we returned to the Compounds, we couldn't shake the feeling that we were nice and safe.

March 21, 2004

It didn't appear that we would be doing much more from this point forward, as most of our equipment had been packed up and shipped out. We had turned over almost all of our vehicles to other units that were arriving in Baghdad and our Operations Center was a ghost town. All our radios had been removed, and we were down to a couple of computers solely for administrative use.

We had been bringing the arriving soldiers to our FOB, turning over equipment, and escorting them to their assigned locations. We were in the middle of the third and final turnover, and I assigned a squad to escort arriving soldiers back to their location. An officer learned about what I was doing, and had me cancel the escort.

When I asked why, he replied that they could find their own way back.

March 22, 2004

Today was my fifty-third birthday.

We were scheduled to get our final Anthrax shot, but the serum had been left in an unplugged refrigerator and was no longer usable.

March 25, 2004

We had a company formation and awards ceremony. Colonel Philips and Lieutenant Colonel Harrison made the presentations. We were allowed to choose between receiving our awards in Baghdad, or having the State of Connecticut present them to us once we returned home. After fondly remembering all of the wonderful things that the Connecticut Army National Guard hadn't done for us, we decided that they would not get the honor of pinning these medals on our chests.

Regardless of how the Connecticut Army National Guard had failed us, we had still had a successful deployment, serving with honor and distinction. We were happy to receive recognition for our accomplishments.

Figure 23.4   Our move to Balad/Anaconda (Left to Right) First
Sergeant Jones, SSG Bispham, Sergeant Earley,
Sergeant Sweetwood, and SPC Roeser

The soldiers from the 1st Cavalry Division started moving in, and their vehicles, equipment, and soldiers were all over our compound. It was being used as a staging area for incoming soldiers, before moving them on to other locations. The scene was chaotic, but things seemed to be moving smoothly.

We were scheduled to move to Anaconda in five-ton trucks, but weren't allowed to leave the Compound until 10:00 a.m. the next day. By that time, traffic would be lighter, and any IEDs would have been found and detonated. Our soldiers would move out with only one magazine each, having turned in all their ammunition to the soldiers coming to Falcon FOB. The machine gunners would have a belt of 200 rounds. A couple of gunners were placed in every vehicle for protection.

The move up to Anaconda was a long, slow, dusty ride through occasional heavy traffic. The soldiers were joking and fooling around quite a bit on the trip, but they would become deadly serious any time we got bogged down in traffic.

Every soldier had a weapon loaded with at least thirty rounds and, from time to time, they trained them on vehicles that got too close. Fortunately, nothing happened and we reached Anaconda without incident.

March 29, 2004

Anaconda was huge and the areas inside were not well marked. We felt lost inside the airbase, but we were well inside the perimeter, and no longer in danger.

Figure 23.5   SPC Matt Hayes, manning a machine gun

We were scheduled to fly out of Anaconda on two U.S. Air Force planes (we didn't know what type) from Iraq to an airbase in Spain. There, both groups would combine to take a civil aviation flight to Fort Drum. They told us we would be leaving at night, so that we could not be targeted by anti-aircraft missiles. Of course, we knew intellectually that we might get shot down. But hearing the words being spoken that we might be shot down, and that precautions were being taken, was a very different feeling.

The 118th Medical Group from the Connecticut National Guard arrived at Anaconda from the United States. Many of us had friends and acquaintances in this unit, and they arranged a going-away cookout. Seeing friendly faces from Connecticut was wonderful, but we felt sorry leaving them behind. In a day or two we would be safe, and they would just be beginning their first year in the dangerous sandbox that was Iraq.

During the party, I had a conversation with the Medical Unit's Colonel, who was from Randolph, Vermont. We discussed the situation in Iraq, including the dangers and the many conflicting ideas of what was going on. I told him that this was not a one-dimensional fight, describing how all of the various groups had their own individual agendas. I also told him that, while our government had a set timetable of what was supposed to happen in Iraq, the plan wasn't working, and no one wanted to admit or deviate from it. I admitted that I had a self-centered view of the situation, as I, along with all of my soldiers, were finally getting out. I wanted to let the Medical Unit know what they were up against, because their problems were just beginning and they might have to pay a heavy price for other people's mistakes.

Our flight dates and times kept changing. The unit that did the coordination and scheduling had just arrived in-country, and seemed to lack concern or respect for those departing units that had been here for an entire year. I asked them to send a runner once the date and time of the flights had been established, but they told me they couldn't do that. They informed me that it was up to me to check in frequently. Apparently it was my responsibility to get my people out of the country.

This was not JFK or O'Hare, with hundreds or thousands of flights a day. At most, there were five or six flights of varying sizes departing Anaconda daily for which this group was responsible. Still, they couldn't be bothered to contact us when our flight was locked in.

I did what I was told, and went to their office every few hours to check the status board. Every time I went in, someone had brought in a fresh batch of food for everyone to eat. It felt like they spent twenty-four hours a day eating, and that scheduling flights for departing soldiers was screwing up their mealtime.

March 31, 2004

The first flight departed with approximately half of the company, while the rest of us waited to see when they would lock in our next flight. The date and time continued to change, as usual. The latest indication was that it was going to be on April Fool's Day, which seemed appropriate.

Our stay in Anaconda was relatively comfortable, and though it had occasionally been rocketed and mortared, we suffered no ground attacks. This was good, as we had turned in all of our body armor and didn't have any ammunition. There wasn't much to do other than to check the scheduling board.

Lieutenant Grube happened to be in the TV tent run by the Air Force and saw that they had flights posted for their people. This Air Force unit was separate from the Army unit that was supposed to be processing us, but Lieutenant Grube noticed that our unit was scheduled on one of their boards. He got a hold of me and told me that we had both a date and departure time.

If we had a departure date, that meant that the clock was ticking, and we didn't have any time to waste out-processing. I went to the Army processing unit and discovered that our unit was still listed on standby, with a flight date sometime after April 4th. I managed to get the attention of the people shoveling food in their mouths and told them that the Air Force had us scheduled for a flight out that night at midnight.

The clerk I was talking to assured me that the date had been posted a while ago, and that I should have checked back more frequently. I called his attention to the soldier who had, in the midst of my explaining things to them, erased the April 4th date on the board and written in April 2nd. I was getting madder by the second, and thought that strangling someone might not be such a terrible idea.

I couldn't believe their arrogance, nor could I imagine how dismissive they were of fellow soldiers who had spent an entire year in the desert. They didn't seem to care about our safety and welfare, or even about doing their job of scheduling six plane flights in a day. All that mattered to them was their nice, air-conditioned building and their unlimited supply of food.

Rather than strangle someone, I decided my time might be better spent getting our troops together so that we could clear customs and get the hell out of Iraq. We had soldiers scattered all over Anaconda because they didn't realize that the clock was ticking. The first step of our departure was to get everyone manifested. In order to do that, we had to have every soldier present as their names were called, and then show their ID cards to the flight schedulers. If we were unable to do this quickly, we would have delayed every other step in our processing, and might have missed getting on the plane.

Lieutenant Grube and I sent teams to round up everyone as quickly as possible. Some were at the library, some were at the gym, others were at the dining facility, and a few were visiting their friends at the 118th. Like Falcon FOB, Anaconda was a sprawling complex and nothing was close. They had to schedule bus routes to facilitate travelling around the base. Even sending several teams, we were worried that we wouldn't be able to round up everyone in time.

Fortunately the soldiers manifesting us were different from the others we had been dealing with. They cared about us and what was going on, and took me at my word that the soldiers who were not present were being rounded up. I promised them that they would be ready to go through customs inspection within the next couple hours. If the schedulers had decided to be chicken shit about the whole thing, they could have sat on our list until we were all present.

They accommodated us; and we were able to make it to the customs inspection area, where they checked our personal effects for contraband and other unauthorized items. Before we got there, Lieutenant Grube, the Platoon Sergeants, and I made it very clear to the soldiers that they were to get rid of any contraband. We said that if anyone tried to sneak anything through customs, we would leave their asses in Iraq. They must have been listening because not one item was seized.

The customs officials thanked us for our cooperation—something that they had been unable to get from units that they had checked in before us. They said that previous units had always given them a hard time, making it difficult for them to be cleared. I think it only helped our cause that we threatened to leave our soldiers behind. It was pointless to try and sneak something out of the country, and none of us wanted to stay in Iraq any longer than necessary.

Someone in charge of customs inspection approached us while we were going through. He wanted to know if we could provide seats for eight other soldiers from an Explosive Ordnance Disposal unit who were looking for a flight out of Iraq. We learned that the flight belonged to the 143rd Military Police Company, and no one else was scheduled to be on it.

The aircraft we were going out on was a C5. While it was a massive aircraft, it had seating for only approximately ninety soldiers in an upper passenger compartment. No one was allowed to sit in the virtually empty cargo bay below.

My first thought was, "Hell, yes." I felt that anyone who had done time in Iraq should be allowed to get the hell out of there, but I also knew that it wasn't my call. Lieutenant Grube and I were on the same wavelength, and he was more than happy to add those eight soldiers to our flight.

I later learned that the EOD unit had been in Iraq for a year and had lost half of their people to IEDs. I had no idea that this had happened to them when we were deciding whether or not to let them on the plane; but once I heard their story, I knew beyond a shadow of a doubt that we had made the right call. After all that they had been through, it would have been criminal to make them sit there and wait for the next flight while we took off with empty seats.

Their final destination was not Fort Drum, but somewhere down south. Even still, Fort Drum was a much better place to be than anywhere in Iraq. The Air Force pilots reassured us that they would get the EOD unit to their final destination.

April 2, 2004

At 2303 hours, our plane was wheels up, and we were on our way out of Iraq.

I think I held my breath the whole time the aircraft taxied out and roared down the runway. I felt the bump as the wheels lost contact with the runway. I thought that there might be a roaring cheer as we left the ground, though I myself had no intentions of cheering—I didn't want to do anything that would jinx that moment or the next several hours. All I wanted was for us to be safe and out of Iraq forever. To my surprise, the cabin remained eerily quiet. I heard only a few deep breaths over the roar of the jet engines, and suspected that everyone felt the same way that I did.

The passenger compartment had airline-like seats. It was relatively comfortable, but crowded. They had the heat on, but it wasn't distributed well. My head felt like it was in 90° heat, but the floor was so cold that my feet had gone numb. The crowding and the weird heating made sleeping difficult—a small price to pay for the plane ride out of Iraq.

At fourteen minutes past midnight on April 3, 2004, we crossed out of Iraqi airspace on our way to Morón Air Base in Spain. The Air Force pilots announced over the intercom that we were no longer in Iraq, and again I anticipated shouting and cheering. Once more, I heard nothing but deep sighs of relief. I knew that everyone was glad that Iraq was getting smaller in our rearview mirror and, with a little bit of luck, we would never see it again. We had no idea what to expect when we got to Spain, but we knew it wasn't Iraq, so it had to be good by comparison.

We landed in pitch blackness. We filed out of the passenger compartment, down to the open rear doors of the plane, and out to buses waiting for us on the tarmac. A rainstorm had just passed through the area, washing everything clean. We couldn't make out any objects in the vastness of the airbase, or the black asphalt of the parking apron. The huge spotlights around the airbase didn't illuminate anything, both because of the rain and because the asphalt absorbed their light.

The first thing we all noticed when we stepped outside was the smell. There was no dirt, oil, or garbage in the air, and everything smelled so clean and fresh. I watched everyone around me as they took in deep breaths of fresh, clean air, something we hadn't done in over a year. Just breathing that air brought a joy and contentment that was hard to describe. It was a feeling of freedom and safety, as well as further reassurance that we were no longer in Iraq.

The buses took us to the Air Force dining facility, though compared to all of the dining facilities we had been in during the last year, the Air Force facility felt more like a restaurant. The local citizens working there served our food, cleared our tables, and made sure all of our needs were met. We had gone from one extreme to the other. By the time we finished our meal, everyone was starting to decompress, and it felt so good.

The other half of the company had gone on to Fort Drum and was waiting for us.

We remained at Morón Air Base for several hours while the Air Force crew got some rest. We went to the waiting lounge, tried to catch naps, and waited for morning. The Air Force offered us barracks space so we could lie down and get some rest, but we were still thinking like the Army. What that meant was that, while we might have been able to lie down for a while, it was drilled into our heads that before we got back onto the plane, we would have to clean and scrub the barracks and turn in our bedding. This would take more time than any rest we might have gotten. So we decided to pass.

But this was an Air Force base, and they had local citizens to take care of all that. Even so, everyone was fine with relaxing in the waiting lounge. We were used to waiting by this point, and at least the lounge had a few TVs.

I glanced at my watch at some point and realized that the sun must have come up. The lounge was an interior room with no windows, so I decided to find my way outside. I was greeted by a beautiful, green, manicured lawn, a nice, cool breeze, and the sight of large, puffy, white clouds hanging over a distant mountain.

After all the dirt, grime, and smog of Baghdad, this scene was just wonderfully beautiful.

A number of people followed my lead, stepping out to admire the beauty of Spain. We liked the view so much that, though they offered us bus rides back to the dining facility for breakfast, most of us chose to walk.

After a leisurely breakfast, we wandered back to the terminal and learned that we had to wait several more hours before the aircrew would be ready. They told us about a little coffee shop a short walk down the tarmac, which overlooked the runway. Several of us went down, sitting at the little bistro tables on the porch, drinking coffee, taking in the lush, colorful scenery.

It was a relief and a comfort to know that everything was behind us by this point. We were happy just to sit and wait for the aircrew. The day was warm and sunny, with an occasional cooling breeze, just the thing for a group of very tired people. We climbed back onto the plane and settled in for the long flight to Fort Drum. By the time we landed, my ass was flat, my feet were frozen, and I hadn't slept, but we were back in the States.

Chapter Twenty-Four

FORT DRUM DE-MOB APRIL 2004

I have fought the good fight, I have finished the race, I have kept the faith.

2 Timothy 4:7

The weather at Fort Drum was no different from the weather on the day, a year ago, when we had headed out to Iraq—cold, rainy, foggy and downright miserable. Fort Drum made us appreciate the beautiful weather in Spain all that much more.

Lieutenant Grube and I stood on the back deck of a C-5 while all the soldiers filed off; he and I were the last two off the airplane. We followed them out, everyone making the short walk in single file to the terminal where a contingent of people from the State of Connecticut, including General Cugno, waited to greet us.

I took everything in, feeling the weight of an entire year melting off my shoulders. I am sure that everyone else had similar feelings. At some point, I realized that I wasn't even in line anymore, just wandering around out on the tarmac near the aircraft. I got a hold of myself and followed everyone inside, where I met and shook hands with General Cugno.

We thought we would start out-processing on April 3, 2004, but as usual we were wrong—the active-duty didn't work on weekends. We sat around and waited over the weekend two days hoping that we wouldn't be inconveniencing the people who had to deal with the long and difficult job of out-processing soldiers in Watertown, New York.

Out-processing was boring. We had to go through a number of briefings and counselling sessions, but nothing with any depth. The meetings were more of a "fill in the blank, check off the box, move to the next station and hurry up" type of situation.

We were told that we were allowed to request physicals. Except, what we would receive wasn't really physicals, only more of the documenting procedure we had gone through in Baghdad. Unless a medical examiner found something obviously wrong, and then we would be stuck at Fort Drum, on active-duty, until the powers-that-be decided to release us. If a medical examiner did find something wrong, they'd ship us off to Fort Bragg in North Carolina for further evaluation. Since being shipped to Fort Bragg could have taken anywhere from a few days to a week (depending on their findings) no one bothered to request a physical.

Once that was settled, we were finally able to leave Fort Drum. We heard that buses would be sent to bring us back to Connecticut and knowing the State, we assumed that they would be putting us on school buses. We were surprised and elated to learn that the Army had ordered our buses, not the State of Connecticut, and they turned out to be comfortable tour buses.

We settled in for the five-hour ride back to Connecticut and, when we hit the Mass Pike, a Massachusetts State Trooper pulled out and escorted us to the state line. We drove south on Interstate-91 and reached the Massachusetts/Connecticut state line, where we were met by a line of several Connecticut State Troopers. They pulled out in formation and escorted us all the way back to our new Armory in West Hartford, Connecticut. The sight of our State Troopers escort brought tears to my eyes. I began to feel that we might actually make it back home. The overwhelming relief from realizing our journey was over is beyond description.

We passed under a huge American flag suspended from a fire truck and pulled into the Armory, where a huge crowd of friends, family and various dignitaries waited to welcome us home. I was grateful someone understood that having a ceremony, official reception, or even having us fall into formation for a welcome home would just be ridiculous—all any of us wanted to do was to see our families and go home. Ceremonies and formations could take place some other time.

To me, everything about that hour is a blur. I know I shook hands with a lot of people and hugged a lot of family and friends, but mostly I just remember feeling so happy that we had made it back, and that this was our final day of Operation Iraqi Freedom.

Since 9/11, some of our company had been on active-duty for just over two years, while the rest had spent fifteen months on active-duty in a war zone. All our soldiers performed real-world duties, both in Connecticut and in Iraq. Our successes and professionalism were obvious, and I expected that the State would treat us differently now that we had proven ourselves in Iraq.

Of course, I was wrong. On our first day back, everyone in the company had three vials of blood taken. I thought that this was unusual because we had been medically screened twice in recent days—first in Iraq and then again at Fort Drum. I spoke with one of the senior NCOs of the medical unit and tried to get some details.

I asked why our blood was being drawn?

The NCO said he didn't know.

I asked if he knew where the blood was being test.

The NCO said he didn't know.

I asked if he knew when could we expect our test results?

He said he didn't know.

In the end, we never did find out why our blood was taken or what our results were. When I obtained my full medical records at the time of my discharge, I could find no mention of that blood test.

Chapter Twenty-Five

IT COULD HAVE BEEN US

I have sometimes been wildly, despairingly, acutely miserable, but through it all I still know quite certainly that just to be alive is a grand thing.

Agatha Christie

We had all made it back home and were in good spirits, but not too much time passed before reality brought us back down to earth. We soon learned that Sergeant Felix Delgreco of Charlie Company, 102nd Infantry, Connecticut Army National Guard had been killed in action April 9, 2004, while on patrol in Baghdad. His unit had been activated on January 8, 2004. It was sent to Fort Hood, Texas, for mobilization and attached to the 39th Infantry Brigade of the Arkansas National Guard.

Sergeant Delgreco was the first Connecticut National Guardsman to be killed in combat in Iraq, ambushed on only his second day in Baghdad. He would not be the last. He was awarded the Purple Heart for wounds received in combat, the Bronze Star for bravery, and the Combat Infantryman's Badge. Sergeant Delgreco had a funeral both befitting and honoring the soldier he was. His death occurred only seven days after the last soldier from the 143rd Military Police Company departed Iraq.

I was always worried that I would have to attend similar funerals for one of our own. Too many times in the middle of the night, the phone in the maintenance area just outside our building would click. We knew that, at that hour, the call wasn't for tires or gas. Calls in the middle of the night were to alert the First Sergeant and me that we needed to get up and go to the Operations Center because someone had been hit. We had no idea that we would continue to wait for more calls like this for the next ten years.

I've attended several more services over the years, paying my respects to the soldiers who lost their lives. I've held back tears during the services, trying to at least look like an old, hard, master sergeant. I clenched my teeth so hard that my jaw ached as I went through receiving lines, telling mothers, fathers, family members, and others how sorry I was for their loss. I often felt so guilty that I had survived and their young family member had not.

In February, 2007, I attended a funeral for a former Connecticut Army National Guardsman who had transferred to the Active Army and was killed in action. I attended the wake, and as I made my way through the receiving line, I saw one of my soldiers standing with the family. I didn't make the connection at first, but I remembered that my soldier often received letters from her fiancée. Sergeant Richard L. Ford, age forty, had left the Guard to become a paratrooper. He was assigned to the 2nd Battalion, 325th Infantry Regiment of the 82nd Airborne Division. He was killed in action on February 20, 2007 in Baghdad on his third combat deployment.

The pain never went away.

Frequently, we reflect on the fact that we did not lose a single soldier during our year in Iraq. Some of the reason for that was because we had good soldiers who knew how to do their jobs, but most of it might have just been luck.

On May 29, 2004, a few short days after returning to Connecticut, we lost Chad Brailey, one of our soldiers, in a head-on motorcycle crash with another vehicle. Almost everyone from the company attended the wake and the following funeral. The crowd was so large the firehouse where the reception was held could not accommodate all of us. After all that we had been through in Iraq, losing Chad to a motor vehicle accident was almost incomprehensible.

The company clustered outside the funeral home waiting for the doors to open, exchanging handshakes and hugs with one another, feeling unity and elation just seeing one another again. As everyone lined up to file inside, the conversations were lighthearted, mostly centering on the things we had done since we had returned. Our lightheartedness abruptly went out the window the moment we stepped inside the funeral parlor and saw Chad's casket with his family next to it. No one spoke as we exited the funeral home…all we could muster was non-comprehending blank stares. Everyone was in shock because, at that point, reality had finally set in.

On June 4, 2004, we buried Chad on a sparkling spring day in his hometown of Waterford, Connecticut. Accepting Chad's death after all that we had been through is still extremely difficult.

Chad was not the only one we lost after our return from Iraq. On September 16, 2008 Staff Sergeant David Rosati succumbed to a long hard battle with cancer. After graduating from high school at the age of seventeen, David spent ten years on active-duty with the United States Air Force. He later enlisted in the Connecticut Army National Guard and served tours of duty all over the world as a Guardsman, and was awarded the Bronze Star while serving in Iraq. Dave was a full-time police officer in the town of Winsted, Connecticut, and attained the rank of master sergeant in the Connecticut Army National Guard prior to his death.

On October 28, 2013, we lost Master Sergeant Brian Young to cancer. Brian served nine years on active-duty as a Military Police officer in the United States Army. After coming off active-duty, Brian enlisted in the Connecticut Army National Guard and served full-time as a training NCO. Brian returned to Baghdad for a second tour, this time accompanied by his daughter who was also a Military Police officer.

On July 18, 2014, we lost Private First Class Levi Saucier to a motorcycle accident. Levi was only 32, and left behind a wife and two small children.

Two other soldiers were critically injured in motorcycle crashes, but fortunately, they survived their injuries. Within ninety days of our return to Connecticut, Private First Class Joel Ethier was seriously injured yet attended an awards ceremony in a wheelchair. Sergeant First Class Marc Pucinski was seriously injured in a motorcycle crash after his third combat deployment to the Middle East.

I Get Out

We were supposed to proceed from the West Hartford Armory down to the East Haven firing range for our annual weapons qualification. We didn't have any vehicles of our own, having left them in Iraq. We were slowly getting in replacement vehicles from the active-duty, but not enough replacements to transport all our soldiers. So we made arrangements to head over to East Haven on buses.

We planned to issue rifles and pistols to our soldiers prior to loading the buses. Someone at the State level learned about our plan and told us that we could not transport weapons and soldiers on the same buses. Keep in mind that for the better part of two years, we had been carrying loaded firearms, both in the State of Connecticut and overseas. For some reason, someone didn't trust us to safely transport firearms and soldiers from West Hartford to East Haven. Maybe this person thought the firearms would fly out the windows by mistake or something.

We were given direct orders to issue weapons to the soldiers once we arrived at the East Haven range. While this order may have been for security purposes, it was in reality far less secure, as no one had ammunition to protect the convoy of weapons going down in separate vehicles.

This ridiculous order was the last straw. I realized that nothing had changed since I had left for Iraq. The time had come for me to go.

In April, 2005, I officially retired with twenty-two years of combined military service between the United States Marine Corps, the Marine Corps Reserve, the Army Reserve, and the Army National Guard. Part of the necessary steps in retiring involved my meeting with a full-time military administrator to calculate my retirement points and my official retirement date based on my military service.

This calculation should have been easy—all the information was to be fed into a computer and the computer should have been able to produce an accurate answer. Not so—after six tries, we were finally able to enter the numbers and dates correctly. I don't know how, but my dates of service and earned retirement points kept on changing even though we were both working from the same spreadsheet. I'm still not quite certain if the final result is correct. But after six attempts, I was just ready to get out of there. The retirement pension seemed adequate enough, so I signed on the dotted line and ended my military career.

And that should have been the end, but it wasn't.

About a year after I retired, my wife came into the house with the mail which contained a large manila envelope from the Army. She asked me what it was, so I took a quick glance at the contents and realized it was a series of awards. The Army had apparently thought so much of my service that they crammed my three medals, along with corresponding award folders, into an envelope and mailed them to me.

I cannot tell you what an honor receiving these prestigious awards in the mail was.

Positive that I was now done with the Army, I was in for an even bigger surprise.

Several months later, I received a phone call from someone at the State level who was acting very chummy like we were old buddies, despite the fact that I had never heard of him. I immediately became suspicious and didn't participate in the chit-chat.

"What do you want?" I asked.

My directness caught him off guard. He became all business, asking if I recalled signing for some items in Iraq.

"What items?"

"Five Ectaco EA B-3s," he answered.

"I don't even know what those items are, and I don't recall ever signing for items that I'm not familiar with."

He explained that they were English-Arabic electronic translators.

I repeated that I couldn't recall signing for the items, and asked him to send me a copy of the documents. He emailed them to me right away, but the scanned copy he emailed wasn't very clear and I couldn't be sure whether what I was seeing was indeed my signature or not. And I still couldn't remember signing for anything even remotely like these items.

By now, I had cleared supply three times: when we left Iraq, when we got back to Connecticut, and when I was honorably discharged. In all three of these cases, no one asked me about the whereabouts of these items and I was never asked to turn them in. Yet, several years after being discharged, I was now being told that the Army was looking for them. More accurately, they didn't want the missing items back so much as they wanted to make someone responsible for their loss and pay for them,

I talked to my JAG lawyer. He took care of the mess, and I never heard from the State regarding the electronic translators again. I later learned that several other soldiers were being questioned about missing items years after we had left Iraq. The nightmare seemed as if it would never end.

The Aftermath

Not until sometime in mid-to-late 2006 did the Bush administration admit that the war in Iraq wasn't going to be as short as they had first hoped, and that they now realized that their current strategy didn't seem to be working (taking them the better part of two and one-half years to figure this out). Despite the fact that General Shinseki, the Army Chief of Staff, had warned them *prior* to the start of the war that the occupation of Iraq was going to be much more difficult than simply defeating Saddam Hussein.

Donald Rumsfeld ignored the facts and stuck with his plan, pushing his agenda through the sheer force of his personality. He stuck to his guns through most of 2006, which was when the Administration decided to replace him. Robert Gates, who had both a lengthy and a distinguished background, was selected as Mr. Rumsfeld's replacement.

In his book *Duty*, Mr. Gates states that he was contacted on October 31, 2006, and asked to meet with the President on Sunday, November 5th. At that meeting plans were put in motion to install Mr. Gates as Secretary of Defense and to modify the U.S. course of action in Iraq. Robert Gates became the new Secretary of Defense on December 18, 2006.

One of Secretary Gates' first actions was to increase the number of combat brigades in Iraq. The plan under Secretary Rumsfeld had been to reduce the number of combat brigades from fifteen to ten by the end of 2006. In his book, Secretary Gates explains that he interviewed various Commanders and learned that they didn't feel that they needed additional troops. I suspect that this attitude was a holdover from the previous Secretary of Defense, and Commanders had been conditioned to not ask for more troops because they knew that more troops were not in the plans.

Secretary Gates not only put his surge into effect, increasing U.S. commitment from fifteen combat brigades to twenty, he also proposed an overall increase in the size of both the Marine Corps (by 27,000+ troops), and the Army (by 65,000+ troops).

Unfortunately, one of the issues that the Commanders neglected to mention to Secretary Gates was that they gave him only the numbers of soldiers who were physically in the combat brigades. Those solders were just the Infantry. The Commanders forgot to mention the number of soldiers needed to support each Infantry brigade, including engineers, military police, medical support, aviation support and numerous other support and supply activities. Secretary Gates believed he had been given accurate numbers, but his totals were far smaller than the actual number of people being sent overseas.

At this point, twenty of the Army's combat brigades were committed to Iraq, leaving only twenty-three available brigades throughout the rest of the world to fulfill our commitments in Korea, Germany, Afghanistan and other locations. These twenty-three brigades were also responsible for training up for their next rotations to Iraq or Afghanistan. The operational tempo far exceeded the available resources, even factoring in the National Guard and the Army Reserve.

Even with the strain on our military resources, the surge did have the desired effect on combat operations in Iraq. Control was steadily and consistently restored, but only after more than three years of chaos and decline.

One of the observations Secretary Gates makes in his book both sticks with and disturbs me. The Bush administration persistently assumed that the Iraq war would not last very long. This assumption was very flawed, and sticking to it led to a war that stretched from months on into years, causing serious problems for the troops on the ground.

No one in the administration was forecasting for a long-term, protracted engagement. No one wanted to spend money on equipment for troop safety and protection, since they believed they would become military surplus in a few months and a waste of money. This mentality resulted in soldiers, like those in the 143rd Military Police Company, operating in unarmored vehicles, using radios that had virtually no range, being armed with limited ammunition, and otherwise being forced to use substandard equipment.

Mr. Gates goes on to state that the Pentagon lost interest in Iraq shortly after the invasion was deemed a success, and switched their focus to potential large land wars in Europe and Korea. High levels in the Pentagon believed that the Iraq war was going to be over soon and chose to repeat this statement for years, unable to admit what was going on in front of them.

Former Secretary Rumsfeld made no apologies for his major blunders.

Army Specialist Thomas Wilson of the 278th Regimental Combat Team, asked, "Now, why do we soldiers have to dig through local landfills for pieces of scrap metal and compromised ballistic glass to up armor our vehicles, and why don't we have those resources readily available to us?"[25.1]

Secretary Rumsfeld replied, "As you know, you go to war with the Army you have, not the Army you might want or wish to have at a later time."[25.2] He had nineteen months after September 11, 2001 to get the Army he needed.

In those nineteen months, thousands of up-armored Humvees could have been built. The up-armored Humvees were already in production, so no lag time for design, testing, or an approval was required. All that was needed was a purchase order. Donald Rumsfeld was the single most powerful person next to the President. He could have changed the training and equipment of the armed forces with the stroke of a pen. He didn't bother.

Years later, under Defense Secretary Robert Gates, the decision was made that the American forces needed better protection from small arms and IEDs than up-armored Humvees provided. On February 14, 2007, the Marine Corps ordered the first Mine-Resistant Ambush Protected (MRAP) vehicles. By January, 2008, 1,000 of these state-of-the-art vehicles had been delivered.

Before February 14, 2007, the MRAP did not exist. Somehow, the Defense Department was able to go from a request to a fighting vehicle in under twelve months. The new MRAP vehicles had a base price of $500,000 each (with the actual price depending was based on the model and additional equipment). Up-armored Humvees cost $140,000 per vehicle while the unarmored Humvees were only about $50,000. I certainly hope the cost difference was not a factor when the Bush administration made the decision to risk our soldiers' lives by providing sub-par vehicles, weapons and equipment.

EPILOGUE

Here is to Us, and those like Us; damn few of Us left.

Traditional Military Toast
from Colonel Edward Lynch
Commanding officer (Retired)
Connecticut State Police

Writing this book took me ten years to complete. During that time, numerous policies have changed in the military, apparently for the better. Once Robert Gates took over, the military began to navigate a different, more determined, course. When the 143rd Military Police Company returned to Connecticut, we returned to a brand-new reserve center, as well as numerous other buildings in construction around the State in support of the National Guard.

At first, I was curious why plenty of funding for buildings and parking lots was available, but funds for the vital equipment soldiers need to survive in battle wasn't. Thankfully, that too began to change. Units activated for deployment now get close to a year's notice to make preparations. Training is specifically directed to their deployment mission, and focus remains on getting the soldiers and their equipment ready for combat.

The 143rd Military Police Company was again slated for deployment, this time to Afghanistan. This country has a somewhat different environment than Iraq, but with a year to prepare, the unit was ready for their mission. I hoped that the soldiers would deploy with the new up-armored Humvees, and was delighted to learn that they were instead deploying in brand-new MRAP vehicles!

As a news junkie and a history buff, I watch a couple of hours of news or footage from the *History* or *Military* channels daily. One night, I watched footage showing soldiers and Marines blazing away at the enemy while a commentator informed me that the battle they were waging had been going on for days. I thought of our limited supply of ammunition and our vulnerable vehicles and wondered how we ever survived that year in Western Baghdad. In the space of twenty seconds, I fired off half the ammunition I was carrying. Only through coincidence, we never became decisively engaged in prolonged gun battle. If we had, we would have quickly run out of ammunition, been overrun and killed.

The 143rd Military Police Company returned from Afghanistan after their third combat deployment, landing at Bradley Field in Hartford, Connecticut, on June 5, 2013. They did not lose a single soldier in battle, and are no longer the only MP Company in Connecticut. Now multiple MP Companies have been established in the State, along with working dog teams, an MP Battalion Headquarters, and a Military Police training unit.

The 143rd Military Police Company is no longer an orphan unit.

AFTERWORD

It ain't over till it's over.

Yogi Berra

February 14, 2015—Almost twelve years have passed since the U.S. and Coalition forces invaded/liberated Iraq.

On May 1, 2003 President Bush declared, "Mission Accomplished." The active resistance from Saddam Hussein and his standing Army had been crushed; and in less than two months, all organized active fighting between the Coalition and the organized armed forces of Iraq had ceased.

The Coalition, spearheaded by U.S. forces, began the rebuilding process. Our unit did its part training Iraqi Police officers, rebuilding police stations and correctional facilities, and re-establishing a criminal justice system based on the American (or western) model.

In December, 2007, the U.S. and Coalition forces began their drawdown, but continued what we had started in 2003: training and supporting the Iraqi government in every way possible. Repeated deployments of U.S. and Coalition partners, training, equipment, support, guidance, money—whatever was needed, the Coalition provided. All told, seven plus years of this dynamic and expensive support, not to mention the lives of numerous soldiers, were spent.

In December of 2011, the Iraqi government insisted that Coalition forces leave. The Iraqi government felt that Iraq was their country, and they were now in a position to take control. And they did. They had certainly received more training and support over the last eight years than any other country in the history of the U.S. So the Coalition forces, along with the U.S. government, finally left Iraq.

Now, if an Iraqi citizen had joined their military or police force in 2003, by the time the U.S. forces officially departed, that individual would have completed eight years of service and training. Eight years of experience policing a location that has been battling an insurgency is unprecedented. In the military and in law enforcement, we call that "practical experience." No U.S. soldiers have ever been in a hostile zone eight years in a row.

At this writing, the Iraqi army and government are now pleading with the United Sates to return to train Iraqi forces and provide air support and equipment. Why?

In 2014, a new, more deadly insurgency began to evolve and take shape: ISIS. To my knowledge from reading news reports, ISIS did not exist as an entity until 2013. Prior to that, ISIS members were part of other terrorist groups. Since 2013, ISIS has managed to mold itself into small but devastating army—one that now controls part of Syria and a some major population centers in Iraq. ISIS has forced Iraqi forces to retreat. In some cases, mass surrender has led to mass beheadings. The Iraqi forces are being defeated by a smaller, more vicious force.

How did this happen?

On December 1, 2014, a CNN article entitled *Iraq's Army Weakened from Within by 50,000 Ghost Soldiers* reported that 50,000 Iraqi soldiers were being paid by the Iraqi government, but were not present for duty. 50,000 "ghost troops" were paying off their commanders to not have to show up. The story explained that Iraqi soldiers paid their commanders up to 50% of their pay to cover their absence. For this reason, a fixed number of Iraqi soldiers is difficult to determine. Press releases now refer to divisions and brigades, but not actual troop strength.

The U.S. currently has 2,600 personnel on the ground in Iraq, and more are being requested. President Obama is asking Congress for a three year commitment to defeat ISIS.

I'm wondering how President Obama came up with three years.

President Bush, at an early stage in the Afghan War (after just a few weeks), was questioned by Diane Sawyer about how long the U.S. was going to be in Afghanistan (implying that three weeks was taking far too long to defeat the Taliban).

The U.S. trained Iraqi troops for eight years before leaving. The Iraqi troops had three more years of autonomous, practical experience fighting Al Qaeda, giving Iraqi troops a total of eleven years of training and experience.

During a decade, a U.S. citizen entering the military as a private would have easily risen to the rank of staff sergeant or sergeant first class. If said individual were deployed to a combat zone for the majority of that decade, he or she would have formidable experience.

Most U.S. soldiers who enlisted around 2003 would have been deployed for about two years, with approximately six to twelve months of training before being sent into combat. Most Iraqi soldiers who enlisted around 2003 received seven to eight years of combat training and experience. One would think that with eight years of combat experience, the Iraqi army would have been well trained and fully qualified to take on any armed adversary. U.S. soldiers are asked to face combat with less than twelve months of training; Iraqi soldiers, who had eight years of practical combat experience, ran.

Like you, I watch the news, but with the keen eye of a soldier.

I see ISIS members driving United States up-armored Humvees and ASVs in the streets, waving American weapons taken from defeated and retreating Iraqi soldiers who fled the battlefield, died, or surrendered. I recall the difficulties we had keeping the Humvees and the ASVs running, sometimes requiring civilian contractors with technical expertise beyond that of our military mechanics.

I see ISIS driving Russian T-72 tanks (a mainstay for the Iraqi Army) and wonder who is doing the maintenance. All those vehicles require skilled, trained maintenance technicians with a vast supply of parts, oil and fuel. Somehow, ISIS has very good command, control, logistic support, and financing.

President George W. Bush declared, "Mission accomplished."

President Obama declared, "Victory."

I fear that I will soon be seeing the sons and daughters of America paying the price for both those statements.

The Hits Just Keep on Coming

At three or more briefings, we had been told that if we were sick, injured or wounded, we might have a claim with the Veterans Administration.

So I made an appointment.

When I arrived, I thought I wouldn't get passed the first floor to the exam room. The hospital was filled with veterans, young and old, some with obvious problems and others with not-so-obvious problems.

As I was making my way towards the elevator, I noticed an older, blind, gentleman facing the elevators. I figured he would need some help getting on the elevator and started toward him. But before I was able to reach him, a second veteran (who also looked to be from the World War II era) called out, "Hey buddy, can I give you a hand?"

I was now standing close enough to them that I could hear their conversation.

"No, that's okay. I'm just listening for the sounds of the elevator so I figure out how to time it, so I can get on by myself."

Now I have some problems from my time in Iraq, but not like the soldiers I had just walked passed, or this blind World War II veteran. While I considered turning around and running for my life, I decided to go upstairs for my evaluation. That's when the real fun began.

A physician's assistant came in to examine my various injuries and ailments. She had me bend over, raise my arms, turn to the left, and turn to the right, and asked an awful lot of questions. When she concluded the evaluation, she sent me for x-rays of my feet. No x-rays were taken of my shoulder (which had been dislocated) or my back (which had been wrenched when I hit the only tree in Baghdad, and re-injured lifting heavy boxes).

Before leaving to go to the x-ray area, I asked the P.A. her thoughts about my injuries. She was noncommittal and said that I would be hearing from the V.A. in a few weeks. She did not give me any indication of what the next step would be, or what treatment, if any, they might offer.

Unbeknownst to me, the V.A. is separated into a treatment section and a claims compensation section. Although I thought that I had made an appointment with the treatment section, I had, in fact, made an appointment with the claims compensation section. Only several months later did I receive the information I needed to understand that I had to go through the entire process again with the treatment section in order to obtain medical care.

What about my claim, you may ask? The information I received that clarified my misunderstanding, and included a detailed letter advising me that parts of my claim had been accepted, and that other parts had been rejected. The letter also stated that I would start receiving compensation and that I could appeal the VA's decision.

The two areas they denied were my back and my shoulder injuries, both of which gave me the most trouble. For the next several months, letters went back and forth between the V.A. and me (I still didn't understanding how drawn-out and technical this process was going to be). I appealed the V.A.'s decision to reject my injury claims and was granted an appeals interview before a V.A. Board.

On December 11, 2007, *two-and-one-half years* after my first evaluation, I found myself in front of a V.A. Appeals Board.

The conference room designed for appeals was on the upper floor, and I had to take an elevator to get there (stairs, for some reason, were not an option). As I got off the elevator, I immediately saw two armed V.A. police officers standing at what looked like an airport security screening station. Fortunately for me, one of the officers had been one of my soldiers in Baghdad.

I was put through an obviously abbreviated formality of being searched, while we talked about old times. When I asked if all this security was really necessary, I was told that we were on the psychiatric floor.

Of all the locations the V.A. could have chosen for these interviews, they chose the psych ward, *with* armed officers *and* search equipment. The decision to use this venue with this level of security is not the V.A.'s only option, and I don't believe for one second that it was made in error. The V.A. chose this location to intimidate and anger veterans who were being forced to fight for compensation.

When I finished stating my case for appeal before the board, I was slightly surprised by their offer for a second evaluation, and quickly agreed, believing, for some reason, that the V.A. would be more thorough with an appealed case. Whomever I would see would certainly order x-rays and possibly MRIs for my shoulder and back.

During the appeals hearing, a board member shared that the V.A. had been awaiting for my medical records from the Connecticut National Guard. The only problem with that request was that I had been discharged over two years ago, and my records were no longer in Connecticut. They were now stored at the Army Records Archive.

In a subsequent letter to the V.A., I included copies of the medical records I received at my time of discharge. I received a letter back stating that copies from me were not sufficient, they had to come from the Connecticut National Guard. The fact that the Connectional National Guard no longer had my records was not important; all that was important was that the records had to come from the Connecticut National Guard.

My next letter explained that, prior to mailing a copy of my medical records to me over two years ago, the Connecticut National Guard was required by procedure to scan and send them to the Army Records

Archive for storage. I asked the V.A. if they were able to obtain the requested medical records from the Army Records Archive. I never received a response to this question.

During these two years, I mentioned how long the claims process was taking, and someone advised me to obtain a counselor from the Connecticut Veterans Administration to assist me with the Federal Veterans Administration—this advice didn't make sense to me, why would I need a state counselor to help me with a Federal counselor? Wasn't the Federal V.A. supposed to be helping me?

In the end, I took the advice, and was able to get a state counselor assigned to me. Although I received a better education of what was going on, the process continued to move very slowly.

On May 23, 2008, I found myself at the V.A. in Newington, Connecticut for an evaluation of my back. This time, I was again evaluated by a nurse practitioner, but at least she ordered x-rays of my back. When I asked the x-ray technician where the films would be sent, and how long reading them would take, he explained that because x-rays are now digital, they would be available online, and that this part of the evaluation could be completed in a few days, a couple of weeks tops. *They are digital.*

I later determined that the V.A. lost the records from this evaluation, including the x-rays. The V.A. has never admitted to losing the records. The only reason I know they were lost is because this visit is not referenced in any documentation that I continue to receive from the V.A. to this day.

So, of course I never received any information from the May 23, 2008, evaluation or x-rays. In fact, I didn't hear a peep from the V.A. until the winter of 2009, when I received a request to return to the V.A. for a third evaluation.

On March 11, 2009, I found myself at the V.A. in Newington, Connecticut, for the exact same evaluation. Although no x-rays were taken during this visit, I was told to expect the coveted results of the evaluation within six weeks.

Over three months later, with no word from the V.A., I decided the time had come to take the situation into my own hands and file a claim with my private insurance company so I could see my own doctors. Instead of being examined by a physician's assistant, I was examined by an actual M.D., as well as an orthopedic surgeon and a licensed physical therapist.

I mailed the following documents to the V.A.:

- December 15, 2008, copies of my physical therapy records
- December 17, 2008, records from the orthopedic surgeon
- December 21, 2008, prescription records
- As available, all updated records

Based on x-rays and an MRI, my private orthopedic surgeon noted problems with my back and shoulder that require extensive physical therapy. I continued mailing updated reports to the V.A. through 2009 with no response.

Five years after I was discharged, I received a letter from the Veterans Appeals Management Center stating that I did, in fact, have problems with my lower back. However, further compensation was not approved.

On August 27, 2009, I appealed this decision.

With no further evaluations, exams, or interview requests from the V.A., my full claim was finally resolved sometime in 2011, after seven years of appeals (dozens of letters were never acknowledged or responded to in any way) and a whole bunch of waiting.

At this point, I wrote letters to my Senators and Congressmen, informing them of my evaluation of the V.A.'s efficiency and effectiveness. Each legislator, in turn, contacted V.A. and each was assured by the V.A. that my claim was being processed. Not one legislator seemed concerned that five years had passed.

Fortunately for me, my civilian employment at the time was not physically demanding. Fortunately for me, I had great civilian health insurance. Throughout my experience with the V.A., I was tempted more times than once to simply walk away.

Anyone who has ever experienced a good old New England shunning will understand: With every passing day that brought nothing but silence from the V.A.—from the very Nation I had gone to war to protect—I became more and more determined to get an answer. Their silence made me stick with my appeals.

I often thought about the large number of veterans who are suffering from PTSD, and maybe also drug, alcohol or other problems that do not allow these veterans the luxury of my tenacity. To quote T.S. Elliot, "And in short, I was afraid." I was, and am, afraid for the number of United States veterans who simply walk, or understandably, run away because they don't have the will power to fight as I had to fight.

American veterans fought for your safety; they should not have to fight for their own.

APPENDICES

COMPANY ROSTER^{A.1}

HEADQUARTERS

First Sergeant Chaun Jones

SFC Stephen Oshana

Staff Sergeant David Konkl

Staff Sergeant Jaqueline Milhomme

Staff Sergeant Roger Severn

Sergeant Erica Buonocre

Sergeant Robert Cociopoli

Sergeant Michael Halle

Sergeant Jeremy McWorter

Sergeant Heath Sheehan

Specialist Silvan Blake

Specialist Daniel Brown

Specialist Jameson Cyr

Specialist Jason Gilbert

Specialist Kathleen Guffre

Specialist David Hernandez

Specialist Carl Joseph

Specialist Eric Lapointe

Specialist Mario Mentana

Specialist Idania Peralta

Specialist Michael Yester

PFC William Zampaglone

PFC Eric Cote

PFC Damion Hewitt

PFC Pharra Hyppolite

PFC Daniel Long

PFC Tanya Simmons

PFC Arkeshia Sparks

PFC Christopher Walsh

OPERATIONS

Master Sergeant Marc Youngquist

SFC Marc Pucinski

Staff Sergeant Mark Bishpham

Staff Sergeant Brian Young

Sergeant Melissa Richards

Sergeant Todd Self

Specialist Daryl Mesaros

PFC Lenworth Williams

Master Sergeant John Minasian

Staff Sergeant John Thompson

Sergeant Jack Earley

Sergeant Roger Roberge

Sergeant Christopher Sweetwood

PFC Melissa Roberts

Specialist Kent Roeser

1st PLATOON (ENFORCER)

Lieutenant Donald Chiverton	Sergeant First Class Roddy Porter
Staff Sergeant Michael Hevey	Staff Sergeant David Rosati
Staff Sergeant Richard Smith	Sergeant Kevin Arrojado
Sergeant Robert Cavin	Sergeant Santo DeFelice
Sergeant Patrick Mondaca	Sergeant Christopher Potts
Sergeant Hallock Youcher	Sergeant Jan Petrie
Specialist Angel Escobales	Specialist Tara Major
Specialist Austin Randolph	Specialist Nicholas Uccello
Specialist Edward Weingart	Specialist Alexander Wilde
Specialist Anna Conigliaro	PFC Chad Brailey
PFC Marissa Foglia	PFC Patrick Hackett
PFC Blake Leonard	PFC David Perrotti

2nd PLATOON (SCORPION)

Lieutenant Michael Rossi	Staff Sergeant Steven Langlais
SFC Robert Mongiat	Staff Sergeant Damon Matus
Staff Sergeant Howard Smith	Sergeant Jason Bjonberg
Staff Sergeant Martin Sullivan	Sergeant Erina Hevey
Sergeant Zachary Freeto	Sergeant Timothy Newell
Sergeant Brian Lozier	Sergeant Michael Styles
Sergeant David Quimby	Specialist Harrison Formiglio
Sergeant Jessica Walsh	Specialist Thadeous Hutchinson
Specialist David Harrel	Specialist Michael Tanguay
Specialist Nathan Soucy	PFC Sarah Conner
Specialist Armando Torres	PFC Patrick McGoldrick
PFC Jacob Mazeika	PFC Chad Dugas
PFC Steven Wabrek	PFC Bartosz Wichowski
PFC Nathan Vaichus	

3rd PLATOON (BANDITS)

Lieutenant Peter Rivera

Staff Sergeant Dominick Derasamo

Staff Sergeant Andrea Cloutier

Sergeant Dawn Andrews

Sergeant Travis Mathews

Sergeant Karl Rhynhart

Sergeant Michael Staron

Specialist Michael Dpietro

Specialist Albert Kim

Specialist Christopher Murphy

Specialist Benjamin Rogers

PFC Jonathan Nemergut

PFC Joshua Clark

Sergeant First Class Daniel Lawler

Staff Sergeant Robert Bachman

Staff Sergeant Joseph Yorski

Sergeant Matthew Major

Sergeant Angel Navarro

Sergeant Timothy Richmond

Specialist Timothy Corcoran

Specialist Darren Kenyon

Specialist Timothy Motola

Specialist Brian Ohler

PFC John Colon   PFC Joel Ethier

PFC Class Levi Saucier

4th PLATOON (VOODOO)

Lieutenant J. Michael Grube

Staff Sergeant Alexander Morales

Sergeant Kristopher Lagor

Sergeant George Magrey

Sergeant Vidal Velasquez

Sergeant Jesse Zettergren

Specialist Sean Dring

Specialist Joseph Herndon

Specialist Marvin Jones

Specialist Christopher Napert

Specialist Michael Piccirllo

Specialist Temistocles Valdes

PFC Brian Nowak

SFC Christopher Emmerson

Sergeant Diana Esposito

Sergeant Jonathan Leonard

Sergeant Kevin Muravnick

Sergeant Jeffery Walsh

Specialist Armando Bettini

Specialist Mathew Hayes

Specialist Christopher Houle

Specialist Arthur Lathrop

Specialist Daniel Pesta

Specialist Tania Quinones

PFC Edgard Montoya

COMBAT ACTION
BADGE

The CAB was approved on May 2, 2005, and was retroactively awarded to soldiers who engaged in combat after September 18, 2001. A soldier must be personally present, and actively engaging or being engaged by the enemy, and performing satisfactorily in accordance with the prescribed rules of engagement. Requirements for direct contact with a hostile enemy are not specified.

BRONZE STAR^{C.1}

The Bronze Star Medal may be awarded by the Secretary of a military department, or the Secretary of Homeland Security (with regard to the Coast Guard when not operating as a service in the Navy), or by such military commanders, or other appropriate officers (as the Secretary concerned may designate) to any person who, while serving in any capacity in or with the Army, Navy, Marine Corps, Air Force, or Coast Guard of the United States, after December 6, 1941, distinguishes, or has distinguished, herself or himself by heroic or meritorious achievement or service, not involving participation in aerial flight:

- While engaged in an action against an enemy of the United States,
- While engaged in military operations involving conflict with an opposing foreign force,
- While serving with friendly foreign forces engaged in an armed conflict against an opposing armed force in which the United States is not a belligerent party.

Lieutenant Grube

Master Sergeant Youngquist

Sergeant First Class Lawler

Sergeant First Class Emmerson

Staff Sergeant Hevey

Staff Sergeant Rosati

Lieutenant Chiverton

First Sergeant Jones

Master Sergeant Minasian

Sergeant First Class Porter

Staff Sergeant Langlais

Sergeant Jeffery Walsh

PURPLE HEART^{D.1}

The Purple Heart Medal is awarded by The President of the United States to any member of the Armed Forces of the United States who, while serving under competent authority in any capacity with one of the U.S. Armed Services after April 5, 1917, has been wounded or killed.

Soldier	Date	Location	Evacuated
PFC Clark	06/29/2003	Route Irish	Yes
SPC Kim	06/29/2003	Route Irish	Yes
PFC Hackett	06/30/2003	Abu Ghraib	No
SGE Halle[D.3]	09/092003	Al Mamun	No[D.2]
PFC Zampaglione	09/09/2003	Al Mamun	Yes[D.2]
PFC Hayes	09/19/2003	Abu Ghraib	No
SPC Ohler[D.3]	11/27/2003	Al Khadra	No
Sergeant Staron	10/27/2003	Al Khadra	No
SPC Kenyon	10/27/2003	Al Khadra	No
Sergeant J. Walsh	12/27/2003	Police Academy	No
PFC Wabrek	12/27/2003	Police Academy	Yes
PFC Bartosz Wichowski	12/27/2003	Police Academy	No
PFC Nemergut	11/16/2003	Baghdad Apt Rd	No

VALOROUS UNIT AWARD

The Valorous Unit Award is awarded to units of U.S. Armed Forces for extraordinary heroism in action against an armed enemy, engaging in military operations involving conflict with an opposing foreign force, or while serving with friendly foreign forces and engaging in an armed conflict against an opposing armed force, in which the U.S. is not a belligerent part for actions, occurring on or after August 3, 1963.

The Valorous Unit Award requires a lesser degree of gallantry, determination, and esprit de corps than is required for the Presidential Unit Citation. Nevertheless, to receive the award, a unit must have performed with marked distinction under difficult and hazardous conditions, accomplishing its mission in a way that sets the unit apart from other units participating in the same conflict. The degree of heroism required is the same as that which warrants award of the Silver Star to an individual—extended periods of combat duty, or participation in a large number of operational missions, either ground or air, is not sufficient.

This award is normally earned by units who have participated in single or successive actions, covering relatively brief time spans.

Presuming that an entire unit can sustain Silver Star performance for extended time periods, under the most unusual circumstances, is not reasonable. For this reason, only on rare occasions can a unit larger than a battalion qualify for this award.

On April 3, 2006, the 143rd Military Police Company of the Connecticut National Guard was a proud recipient of the Valorous Unit Award.

Then State Attorney General Richard Blumenthal, the radio talk show host Jim Vicevich, and the Battalion Commander of the 709th John Garrity, spoke to the soldiers in the great hall of the State Armory, praising guard members for their gallantry in a yearlong tour of duty that started in April 2003.

The State Attorney General Richard Blumenthal said. "I don't know which generation is the greatest, but I know in your generation you're the greatest."[E.1]

Lieutenant Colonel John Garrity, who commanded the 709th MP Battalion that included the 143rd in Iraq, stated, "You patrolled some of the worst parts of a city ravaged by war...where you took your stand against terrorism."[E.2]

The West Hartford-based unit was credited with safeguarding civilians, processing prisoners, capturing terrorist suspects—including the former Iraqi vice president wanted as the "Ten of Diamonds"'—seizing caches of illegal weapons, training 300 Iraqi Police, and rebuilding several police stations, all while under constant attack.

Lieutenant Colonel Garrity shared examples of the direct effect the 143rd personally had on the people of Iraq: a tough Operations Sergeant playing Santa, the relative of a Connecticut fire department dispatcher arranging for firefighter shirts and turnout coats to be donated to the Abu Ghraib fire department, and the impetus of several state troopers in the unit who help start a national highway patrol.

Lieutenant Colonel Garrity praised Staff Sergeant Andrea Cloutier, whose Squad escaped death in a car bomb blast because of their discipline of wearing body armor at all times, for securing the demolished police station area, and caring for the wounded.

Indeed, the unit stood out in his mind as a model, with one exception: the Unit's failure to convert a large tiled sink in their palace base to a hot tub.

The 143rd conferred special honors on Garrity and on WTIC-AM morning show host, the voice of the 143rd MP CO, Jim Vicevich for his public support of the unit.

Master Sergeant Dan Lawler, whose Platoon operated two police stations in Baghdad, said every day was dangerous, and he respected the Iraqi Police trainees. "They were good people. They were great patriotic citizens of their country."[E.3]

Lawler explained how the Captain was able to negotiate with the Iraqi's to move a police department from a destroyed building into a structure occupied by the Kurdish Islamic Party over tea. "Hospitality is a must in their culture. It's like a sin not to offer tea," he said.[E.4]

When most of the guests and honorees had left, Garrity pulled from his breast pocket the dog tags of the eight soldiers from his units who perished. He listed their names and how they died. Most were from the National Guard.

Thankfully, not one was from the 143rd.

ARMY COMMENDATION MEDALS WITH V FOR VALOR[F.1]

The Army Commendation Medal is awarded to any member of the Armed Forces of the United States other than general officers who, while serving in any capacity with the U.S. Army after December 6, 1941, distinguished themselves by heroism, meritorious achievement or meritorious service.

The medal may also be awarded to a member of the Armed Forces of a friendly foreign nation who, after June 1, 1962, distinguishes themselves by an act of heroism, extraordinary achievement, or significant meritorious service which has been of mutual benefit to the friendly nation and the United States.

Soldier	Date	Location
SFC Porter	10/26/2003	Abu Ghraib
SFC Lawler	10/26/2003	Abu Ghraib
SFC Emmerson	02/10/2004	Falcon FOB
SSG Cloutier	10/26/2003	Abu Ghraib
SPC Corcoran	10/26/2003	Abu Ghraib
SPC Roberts	10/26/2003	Abu Ghraib
SPC Colon	10/26/2003	Abu Ghraib
Sergeant Potts	10/31/2003	Abu Ghraib
Sergeant Smith	10/31/2003	Abu Ghraib
Sergeant Walsh	02/10/2004	Falcon FOB

REQUESTED AWARDS

While the following list is not a comprehensive accounting of all award requests, the list includes those for which I was able to locate documentation.

PV2 Patrick S. McGoldrick

For heroic service in military operations against an armed enemy force in Iraqi in support of Operation Iraqi Freedom on 13 July 2003. Private McGoldrick distinguished himself while serving as a gunner with 1st Squad, 2nd Platoon, 143rd Military Police Company, in the area of Al Khadimya Hospital in Baghdad, Iraq. Private McGoldrick displayed true courage under fire when his Squad was taken under fire by several hostile forces that had been involved in a gun battle at the Hospital and in the area adjacent to the hospital. Private McGoldrick's Squad was fired upon by four to five Iraqi males. Private McGoldrick, in his exposed position in the turret of the vehicle, returned well-aimed bursts of fire at the attackers, striking the vehicle they were in and wounding at least one of the attackers who was later captured. Private McGoldrick's well-aimed fire broke up the attack on his Squad and caused the attackers to flee. Throughout the engagement, Private McGoldrick displayed exceptional valor, professional conduct, and courage under fire, exposing himself to defend his Squad. Private McGoldrick's actions reflect great credit upon himself, the 18th Military Police Brigade and the United States Army.

DENIED

Specialist Armando Torres

For heroic service in military operations against an armed enemy force in Iraq in support of Operation Iraqi Freedom on 30 August 2003. Specialist Torres distinguished himself while serving as a gunner with 2nd Squad, 2nd Platoon, 143rd Military Police Company. Specialist Torres displayed true courage under fire during patrol operations in the vicinity of MB 377899, Baghdad, Iraq. Specialist Torres' Squad was responding to a "shots fired" call when they came upon a carjacking situation where the suspect was assaulting the victim. The suspect injured the driver of the vehicle and then entered the vehicle and fled. The Military Police Squad gave chase. Specialist Torres, in his exposed gunner's position, was directed to fire a burst into the rear of the vehicle to disable the vehicle without injuring the suspects in the vehicle. Specialist Torres fired a controlled burst into the trunk of the vehicle as directed from his moving Humvee. The chase continued, with the suspects attempting to ram the military vehicle. The suspect driver then drew a handgun, attempting to bring it to bear on the pursuing Military Police vehicle. At this point, Specialist Torres again engaged the suspect with a controlled burst of fire, striking the armed assailant and ending the engagement. A second individual who was in the suspect vehicle was then taken into custody by the Military Police Squad. Throughout the engagement, Specialist Torres demonstrated exceptional valor, sound judgment, and professional courage in a highly charged situation. Specialist Torres' conduct on the night of 30 August 2003 reflects great credit upon himself, the 18th Military Police Brigade, and the United States Army.

DENIED

Sergeant Jessica Walsh

For heroic service in military operations against an armed enemy force in Iraq in support of Operation Iraqi Freedom. On 25 August 2003 Sergeant Walsh was serving as Squad Leader for 2nd Squad, 2nd Platoon, 143rd Military Police Company. Sergeant Walsh's Squad was responding to a report of shots being fired when they came upon a carjacking in progress. Sergeant Walsh observed the suspect assaulting the victim before removing the injured victim from the vehicle and fleeing in the stolen car. Sergeant Walsh ordered the Squad to give chase in an attempt to apprehend the suspects. The chase continued, with the suspects attempting to ram the military vehicle. Sergeant Walsh directed the gunner to engage the vehicle with a controlled burst of fire in an attempt to disable the vehicle. The gunner placed a controlled well-aimed burst of fire into the vehicle, but the suspects continued to flee. The driver of the suspect vehicle then drew a handgun and attempted to bring it to bear on the pursuing Military Police vehicle. Sergeant Walsh then directed the gunner to engage the driver of the suspect vehicle. The resulting burst of fire from the gunner struck the driver, ending the chase. The Squad dismounted and apprehended the second suspect without incident. Throughout the engagement, Sergeant Walsh demonstrated exceptional valor and sound professional judgment in a highly charged and dangerous situation, reflecting great credit upon herself, the 18th Military Police Brigade, and the United States Army.

DENIED

Private First Class William Zampaglione

For heroic service in military operations against an armed enemy force in Iraq in support of Operation Iraqi Freedom on 09 September 2003. Private First Class Zampaglione distinguished himself while serving as the gunner for an officer's Security team, 143rd Military Police Company, while on patrol in the vicinity of grid, MB 3831484934, Baghdad, Iraq. Private First Class Zampaglione displayed true courage under fire during this mission. Private First Class Zampaglione's patrol had just left the Al Mamun Patrol Station when the patrol was struck by an improvised explosive device. Private First Class Zampaglione's vehicle sustained the brunt force of the blast and Private First Class Zampaglione was wounded in the attack. Though dazed by the effects of the concussion and injured in the blast, Private First Class Zampaglione remained in his exposed position, covering the vehicles as they exited the danger zone and moved to a place of relative safety. Private First Class Zampaglione remained in his exposed position covering the two teams while the officer was being treated for his injuries and other Military Police units were dispatched to evacuate the wounded officer and recover the disabled vehicle. Private First Class Zampaglione remained vigilant during this time, fearing a second follow-on attack of the disabled vehicle. Private First Class Zampaglione did not seek medical treatment until all parties were safe in Warrior Compound and all vehicles recovered. It was only then that Private First Class Zampaglione went to the Medics to seek treatment for his head injuries. Throughout this mission, Private First Class Zampaglione demonstrated exceptional valor and courage while under fire, in spite of his injuries. Private First Class Zampaglione's exceptional devotion to duty reflects great credit upon himself, the 18th Military Police Brigade, and the United States Army.

DENIED

Specialist Angel Escobales

For heroic service in military operations against an armed enemy force in Iraq in support of Operation Iraqi Freedom on 22 June 2003. Specialist Escobales distinguished himself while serving as a gunner with 1st Squad, 143rd Military Police Company in the area of Abu Ghraib Market. Specialist Escobales displayed true courage under fire when his Squad was attacked by hostile forces the evening of 22 June 2003. While on patrol in the marketplace, an area with a history of hostile action, Specialist Escobales' vehicles became separated from the other team by civilians on foot in the crowded marketplace. This move may have been a deliberate tactic by the attacking force in order to divide the Military Police Squads' ability to defend themselves and destroy one of the teams. Once separated, an individual appeared from the crowd and threw a hand grenade at Specialist Escobales' vehicle. The grenade detonated underneath Specialist Escobales' vehicle, damaging the vehicle and causing injury to all the team members including Specialist Escobales. Though dazed by the blast and suffering concussion and hearing loss, Specialist Escobales remained in his exposed position in the turret of the vehicle, covering his team members as they dismounted and established security on the damaged vehicle. A second grenade was thrown, which landed in front of the vehicle but failed to detonate. A third grenade was thrown, striking the second vehicle as it moved forward. This grenade also failed to detonate. Specialist Escobales remained vigilant in his exposed position, covering his team until the other half of the Squad was able to make their way forward and cover Specialist Escobales' team's exit from the market. Throughout the engagement, Specialist Escobales displayed exceptional valor, sound judgment, professional conduct, and courage under fire, exposing himself to the hostile force to defend his teammates.

DENIED

Private First Class Patrick Hackett

For heroic service in military operations against an armed enemy force in Iraq in support of Operation Iraqi Freedom on 22 June 2003. Private First Class Hackett distinguished himself while serving as a driver with 1st Squad, 143rd Military Police Company in the area of the Abu Ghraib Market, Baghdad, Iraq. Private First Class Hackett displayed true courage under fire when his Squad was attacked by hostile forces the evening of 22 June 2003. While on patrol in the market place, an area with a history of hostile action, Private First Class Hackett's vehicle became separated from the other vehicle of the Squad by civilians on foot in the crowded marketplace. This move may have been a deliberate tactic by the attacking force in order to divide the Military Police Squads' ability to defend themselves and enable the attackers to destroy one of the two teams. Once the teams were separated, an individual appeared from the crowd and threw a hand grenade at Private First Class Hackett's vehicle. The grenade detonated under the vehicle, heavily damaging it and wounding Private First Class Hackett. Though dazed by the effects of the blast and having sustained an injury to his left arm, Private First Class Hackett maintained his composure, taking direction from his team and Squad Leaders, and successfully maneuvering the vehicle out of the danger zone while a second grenade was thrown, but failed to detonate. Even though grenades were being thrown, the crowd continued to press in on the Military Police vehicles, presenting a very chaotic situation and preventing the Military Police officers from engaging the hostile attackers. Throughout the engagement, Private First Class Hackett displayed exceptional valor, sound judgment, professional conduct and courage under fire by successfully getting his vehicle and team members out of the danger zone and to a position of relative safety.

DENIED

Staff Sergeant David Rosati

For heroic service in military operations against an armed enemy force in support of Operation Iraqi Freedom on 22 June 2003. Staff Sergeant Rosati distinguished himself while serving as a Squad Leader with 1st Squad, 143rd Military Police Company in the area of the Abu Ghraib Market, Baghdad, Iraq. Staff Sergeant Rosati displayed true courage under fire when his Squad was attacked by a hostile force the evening of 22 June 2003. While on patrol in the marketplace, an area with a history of hostile action, Staff Sergeant Rosati's vehicle became separated from the second vehicle by the crowd in the market place. This move may have been a deliberate tactic by the attacking force in order to divide the Military Police Squads' ability to defend themselves and destroy one of the teams. Once the vehicles were separated, an individual appeared from the crowd and threw a hand grenade at Staff Sergeant Rosati's' vehicle. The grenade detonated underneath the vehicle, causing injuries to Staff Sergeant Rosati and the other soldiers in his vehicle. Though dazed by the blast and suffering hearing loss and a concussion, Staff Sergeant Rosati began directing his Squad in order to disengage the Squad from the attack and exit the danger zone. Staff Sergeant Rosati established security and attempted to identify the attackers. Staff Sergeant Rosati maintained control of his Squad as the crowd continued to press in, even after the grenade detonated. A second grenade was thrown but failed to detonate. Despite the chaotic situation, Staff Sergeant was able to reestablish squad integrity and exited the danger zone without further incident and without loss of personnel or equipment. Staff Sergeant Rosati demonstrated great restraint in the use of deadly force and positive control of his troops in a highly-charged and volatile situation. Once clear of the danger zone, Staff Sergeant Rosati directed the medical treatment of the injured, recovery of the damaged vehicle, and the relaying of pertinent information to higher headquarters. Throughout the engagement, Staff Sergeant Rosati displayed exceptional valor, sound judgment, professional conduct, and courage under fire.

DENIED

Private First Class David Perrotti

For valorous service in military operations against an armed enemy force in support of Operation Iraqi Freedom on 22 June 2003. Private First Class Perrotti distinguished himself while serving as a driver with 1st Squad, 143rd Military Police Company in the area of the Abu Ghraib Market in Baghdad, Iraq. Private First Class Perrotti displayed true courage under fire when his Squad was attacked by hostile forces the day of 22 June 2003. While on patrol in the marketplace Private First Class Perrotti' vehicle became separated from the other vehicle of the Squad by civilians on foot in the crowded marketplace. This move may have been a deliberate tactic by the attacking force in order to divide the Military Police Squads' ability to defend themselves and enable the attackers to destroy one of the two teams. Once the teams became separated, an individual appeared from the crowd and threw a hand grenade at the vehicle in front of Private First Class Perrotti. The grenade detonated underneath the lead vehicle, injuring the occupants and damaging the vehicle. With total disregard for his own personal safety, Private First Class Perrotti maneuvered his vehicle through the crowd to a position close to the damaged vehicle to cover the injured parties as they attempted to get the disabled vehicle running and out of the danger zone. As Private First Class Perrotti negotiated his vehicle through the crowd, a second grenade was thrown, striking Private First Class Perrotti's vehicle but failing to detonate. Undeterred, Private First Class Perrotti was able to bring his vehicle up to a position close to the damaged vehicle and, after a time, both vehicles were able to withdraw out of the danger zone. Once out of the danger zone, Private First Class Perrotti positioned his vehicle to secure the eastern end of the market and maintained security until relieving units arrived. Throughout the engagement, Private First Class Perrotti displayed exceptional valor, sound judgment, courage under fire, and a deep commitment to the safety and well-being of his fellow soldiers.

DENIED

Private First Class Melissa Roberts

For exceptionally valorous service in military operations against an armed enemy force in support of Operation Iraqi Freedom on 22 June 2003. Private First Class Roberts distinguished herself while serving with 1st Squad, 143rd Military Police Company in the area of the Abu Ghraib Market, Baghdad, Iraq. Private First Class Roberts displayed true courage under fire when her Squad was attacked by a hostile force on the evening of 22 June 2003. While on patrol in the marketplace, an area with a history of hostile action, Private First Class Roberts's vehicle became separated from the trail vehicle by the crowd in the market place. This move may have been a deliberate tactic by the attacking force in order to divide the Military Police Squads' ability to defend themselves and destroy one of the teams. Once the vehicles were separated, an individual appeared from the crowd and threw a hand grenade at Private First Class Roberts's vehicle. The grenade detonated under the vehicle, causing injury to all parties in the vehicle. Though dazed by the explosion and suffering from hearing loss and a concussion, Private First Class Roberts exited the vehicle, taking up a defensive position, securing the vehicle, and keeping the crowd back that was pressing in on the disabled vehicle. While covering the crowd, Private First Class Roberts began radio transmissions to the second vehicle and higher headquarters, keeping them advised of the unfolding situation. A second grenade was thrown and landed just in front of Private First Class Roberts's vehicle. Private First Class Roberts took cover but, a short time later, when the grenade failed to detonate, Private First Class Roberts resumed her position covering the right side of the vehicle, transmitting update reports on the Squad's status. Once the second vehicle was able to make its way forward to Private First Class Roberts's vehicle, the team was able to get the vehicle running and backed out of the danger zone, through the hostile crowd that had surrounded the vehicles. Once clear of the market, Private First Class Roberts's Squad established security until relief elements were able to make their way to them and recover all vehicles and Squad members. Throughout the engagement, Private First Class Roberts displayed exceptional valor, sound judgment, professional conduct, and courage under fire.

DENIED

Specialist David Harrell

For valorous service in military operations against an armed enemy force in support of Operation Iraqi Freedom on 22 June 2003. SPC Harrell distinguished himself while serving as a gunner with 1st Squad, 143rd Military Police Company in the area of the Abu Ghraib Market, Baghdad, Iraq. Specialist Harrell displayed true courage under fire when his Squad was attacked by a hostile force on the evening of 22 June 2003. While on patrol in the marketplace, an area with a history of hostile action, Specialist Harrell's vehicle became separated from the lead vehicle by the crowd in the marketplace. This move may have been a deliberate tactic by the attacking force in order to divide the Military Police Squads' ability to defend themselves and destroy one of the teams. Once the vehicles were separated, an individual appeared from the crowd threw a hand grenade at the lead vehicle, which detonated under the vehicle, injuring all the soldiers in the vehicle. Specialist Harrell, in his exposed position in the turret, began sweeping the crowd in search of the attackers as his team moved up to the disabled vehicle to render assistance and recover the vehicle and injured soldiers. While moving up, a grenade was thrown at Specialist Harrell's vehicle, striking the vehicle near Specialist Harrell's exposed position. Specialist Harrell maintained his position in the turret and covered the link up and subsequent withdrawal of the damaged vehicle and injured soldiers to a position of relative safety. Throughout the engagement, Specialist Harrell maintained security in his exposed position, protecting his Squad from further attack and displaying true courage, sound judgment, and professional conduct under fire.

DENIED

Sergeant Robert Cavin

For valorous service in military operations against an armed enemy force in support of Operation Iraqi Freedom on 22 June 2003. Sergeant Cavin distinguished himself while serving as a Military Police officer with 1st Squad, 143rd Military Police Company in the area of the Abu Ghraib Market, Baghdad, Iraq. Sergeant Cavin displayed true courage under fire when his Squad was attacked by a hostile force on the evening of 22 June 2003. While on patrol in the marketplace, an area with a history of hostile action, Sergeant Cavin's team became separated from the lead vehicle by the crowd in the marketplace. This move may have been a tactic by the attacking force in order to divide the Military Police Squads' ability to defend themselves and destroy one of the teams. Once the vehicles were separated, an individual appeared from the crowd and threw a hand grenade at the lead vehicle. The grenade detonated under the vehicle, damaging the vehicle and injuring the soldiers inside. Sergeant Cavin coordinated security and, with his team, moved forward to secure the damaged vehicle and injured soldiers. A second grenade was thrown at Sergeant Cavin's vehicle as it moved forward, striking the vehicle but failing to detonate. A third grenade was thrown near the lead vehicle, which also failed to detonate. While the hostile forces continued to press their attack, Sergeant Cavin and his team continued to move forward, securing the damaged vehicle and linking up with the injured soldiers. Once the link up was complete, the first team was able to start their vehicle and the Squad was able to break contact and exit the danger zone to a position of relative safety, where the damaged vehicle was recovered and the injured soldiers evacuated. Throughout the engagement, Sergeant Cavin displayed valor, sound judgment, professional conduct, and courage under fire.

DENIED

Sergeant Jan Petrie

For valorous service in military operations against an armed enemy force in support of Operation Iraqi Freedom on 22 June 2003. Sergeant Petrie distinguished himself while serving as a Military Police Team Leader with 1st Squad, 143rd Military Police Company in the area of the Abu Ghraib Market, Baghdad, Iraq. Sergeant Petrie displayed true courage under fire when his Squad was attacked by a hostile force on the evening of 22 June 2003. While on patrol in the marketplace, an area with a history of hostile action, Sergeant Petrie's team became separated from the lead vehicle by the crowd in the marketplace. This move may have been a tactic by the attacking force in order to divide the Military Police Squads' ability to defend themselves and destroy one of the Teams. Once the vehicles were separated, an individual appeared from the crowd and threw a hand grenade at the lead vehicle. The grenade detonated under the vehicle, damaging the vehicle and injuring the soldiers inside. Sergeant Petrie coordinated security and led his team forward to secure the damaged vehicle and injured soldiers. A second grenade was thrown at Sergeant Petrie's vehicle as it moved forward, striking the vehicle but failing to detonate. A third grenade was thrown near the lead vehicle, which also failed to detonate. While the hostile forces continued to press their attack, Sergeant Petrie and his team continued to move forward, securing the damaged vehicle and linking up with the injured soldiers. Once the link up was complete, the first team was able to start their vehicle and the Squad was able to break contact, exiting the danger zone to a position of relative safety where the damaged vehicle was recovered and the injured soldiers evacuated. Throughout the engagement, Sergeant Petrie displayed valor, sound judgment, professional conduct, and courage under fire.

DENIED

Staff Sergeant Andrea Cloutier

For heroic service in military operations against an armed enemy force in Iraq in support of Operation Iraqi Freedom on 26 October 2003. Staff Sergeant Cloutier distinguished herself while serving as a Squad Leader with 3rd Squad, 3rd Platoon, 143rd Military Police Company in the area of the Abu Ghraib Police Station. Staff Sergeant Cloutier displayed true courage under fire when the Abu Ghraib Police Station was attacked. On the night of 26 October 2003, Staff Sergeant Cloutier was assigned to the commanders' escort detail and was conducting an inspection visit to the Abu Ghraib Police Station. Staff Sergeant Cloutier and several individuals were seated in their vehicle near the north wall of the Compound when the station came under attack. The first explosion occurred just a short distance from Staff Sergeant Cloutier's vehicle. The explosion seriously injured three soldiers. Though dazed by the concussion, Staff Sergeant Cloutier heard the injured soldiers' cries for help and immediately exited her vehicle. Upon exiting the vehicle, Staff Sergeant heard and felt several more explosions. With a total disregard for her own safety, Staff Sergeant Cloutier and several other soldiers made their way under fire to the injured soldiers, removed them from the vehicle and then, while still under fire, moved them across the exposed area of the parking lot and into the relative security of the Police Station where lifesaving first aid was performed, resulting in two soldiers lives being saved. Throughout the attack, Staff Sergeant Cloutier displayed exceptional valor, sound judgment, and an uncompromising devotion to her fellow soldiers, risking her own life to save theirs.

AWARDED

Sergeant First Class Daniel Lawler

For heroic service in military operations against an armed enemy force in Iraq in support of Operation Iraqi Freedom on 26 October 2003. Sergeant First Class Lawler distinguished himself while serving as a Platoon Sergeant with 3rd Platoon, 143rd Military Police Company in the area of the Abu Ghraib Police Station. Sergeant First Class Lawler displayed true courage under fire when the Abu Ghraib Police Station was attacked. On the night of 26 October 2003, Sergeant First Class Lawler was assigned to the commanders' escort detail and was conducting an inspection visit to the Abu Ghraib Police Station. Sergeant First Class Lawler and several individuals were seated in their vehicle near the north wall of the Compound when the station came under attack. The first explosion occurred just a short distance from Sergeant First Class Lawler's vehicle and seriously injured three soldiers. Though dazed by the concussion from the explosion, Sergeant First Class Lawler heard the injured soldiers' cries for help and immediately exited his vehicle. Upon exiting the vehicle, Sergeant First Class Lawler heard and felt several more explosions. With a total disregard for his own safety, Sergeant First Class Lawler and several other soldiers made their way under fire to the injured soldiers, removed them from the vehicle and then, while still under fire, moved them across the exposed area of the parking lot and into the relative security of the Police Station where lifesaving first aid was performed, resulting in two soldiers lives being saved. Throughout the attack, Sergeant First Class Lawler displayed exceptional valor, sound judgment, and an uncompromising devotion to his fellow soldiers risking his own life to save theirs.

AWARDED

Specialist Timothy Corcoran

For heroic service in military operations against an armed enemy force in Iraq in support of Operation Iraqi Freedom on 26 October 2003. Specialist Corcoran distinguished himself while serving as a driver with 3rd Squad, 3rd Platoon, 143rd Military Police Company in the area of the Abu Ghraib Police Station. Specialist Corcoran displayed true courage under fire when the Abu Ghraib Police Station was attacked. On the night of 26 October 2003, Specialist Corcoran was assigned to the commanders' escort detail and was conducting an inspection visit to the Abu Ghraib Police Station. Specialist Corcoran and several individuals were seated in their vehicle near the north wall of the Compound when the station came under attack. The first explosion occurred just a short distance from Specialist Corcoran' vehicle. The first explosion seriously injured three soldiers. Though dazed by the concussion from the explosion, Specialist Corcoran heard the injured soldiers' cries for help and immediately exited his vehicle. Upon exiting the vehicle, Specialist Corcoran heard and felt several more explosions. With a total disregard for his own safety, Specialist Corcoran and several other soldiers made their way under fire to the injured soldiers, removed them from the vehicle and then, while still under fire, moved them across the exposed area of the parking lot and into the relative security of the Police Station where life-saving first aid was performed, resulting in two soldiers lives being saved. Throughout the attack, Specialist Corcoran displayed exceptional valor, sound judgment, and an uncompromising devotion to his fellow soldiers risking his own life to save theirs.

AWARDED

Private First Class John Colon

For heroic service in military operations against an armed enemy force in Iraq in support of Operation Iraqi Freedom on 26 October 2003. Private First Class Colon distinguished himself while serving as a Gunner with 3rd Squad, 3rd Platoon, 143rd Military Police Company in the area of the Abu Ghraib Police Station. Private First Class Colon displayed true courage under fire when the Abu Ghraib Police Station was attacked. On the night of 26 October 2003, Private First Class Colon was assigned to the commanders' escort detail and was conducting an inspection visit to the Abu Ghraib Police Station. Private First Class Colon and several individuals were seated in their vehicle near the north wall of the Compound when the station came under attack. The first explosion occurred just a short distance from Private First Class Colon' vehicle. The explosion seriously injured three soldiers. Though dazed by the concussion from the explosion, Private First Class Colon heard the injured soldiers' cries for help and immediately exited his vehicle. Upon exiting the vehicle, Private First Class Colon heard and felt several more explosions. With a total disregard for his own safety, Private First Class Colon and several other soldiers made their way under fire to the injured soldiers, removed them from the vehicle and then, while still under fire, moved them across the exposed area of the parking lot and into the relative security of the Police Station where lifesaving first aid was performed, resulting in two soldiers lives being saved. Throughout the attack, Private First Class Colon displayed exceptional valor, sound judgment, and an uncompromising devotion to his fellow soldiers risking his own life to save theirs.

AWARDED

Specialist Melissa Roberts

For heroic service in military operations against an armed enemy force in Iraq in support of Operation Iraqi Freedom on 26 October 2003. Specialist Roberts distinguished herself while serving as a Gunner for an officer's escort team, 143rd Military Police Company in the area of the Abu Ghraib Police Station. Specialist Roberts displayed true courage under fire when the Abu Ghraib Police Station was attacked. On the night of 26 October 2003, Specialist Roberts was assigned to the commander's escort detail and was conducting an inspection visit to the Abu Ghraib Police Station. Specialist Roberts and several individuals were seated in their vehicles near the north wall of the Compound when the station came under attack. The first explosion occurred just a short distance from Specialist Roberts's vehicle, striking the vehicle she was in and causing damage to the vehicle. The explosion seriously injured three soldiers. Though dazed by the concussion, Specialist Roberts heard the injured soldiers' cries for help and immediately exited her vehicle. Upon exiting the vehicle, Specialist Roberts heard and felt several more explosions. With a total disregard for her own safety, Specialist Roberts and several other soldiers made their way under fire to the injured soldiers, removed them from the vehicle and then, while still under fire, moved them across the exposed area of the parking lot and into the relative security of the Police Station, where lifesaving first aid was performed resulting in 2 soldiers lives being saved. Throughout the attack, Specialist Roberts displayed exceptional valor, sound judgment and an uncompromising devotion to her fellow soldiers, risking her own life to save theirs.

AWARDED

Private First Class Levi Saucier

For distinguished valorous service in military operations against an armed enemy force in Iraq in support of Operation Iraqi Freedom on 27 October 2003. Private First Class Saucier distinguished himself while serving as a Gunner with 3rd Squad, 3rd Platoon, 143rd Military Police Company at the Al Khadra Police Station. Private First Class Saucier displayed a high degree of professionalism and attention to duty while performing rooftop security. At approximately 0910 hours, Private First Class Saucier observed a lone Iraqi male operating an SUV in the area of the Police Station. Private First Class Saucier detected that there was something wrong with the way the vehicle was being operated by the lone male and began visually tracking the vehicle. When the vehicle moved out of line of fire that Private First Class Saucier had his SAW positioned, he re-positioned the weapon to maintain acquisition of the vehicle in case he had to engage the vehicle. The lone male observed Private First Class Saucier's actions, and it is believed that Private First Class Saucier' actions caused the driver of the vehicle to attempt his attack prematurely. The result was that the driver turned before he had a clear run on the station and the vehicle became immobile on the protective barrier. Private First Class Saucier was about to engage the vehicle when the suicide bomber detonated the vehicle bomb, causing extensive damage and injuries. Private First Class Saucier's actions caused the attack to fail to the degree that it was intended. The result was that the vehicle bomb exploded at a greater distance from the Police Station, resulting in less damage and less injuries to the Military Police officers and Iraqi Police officers on duty,

DENIED

Sergeant First Class Roddy Porter

For heroic service in military operations against an armed enemy force in Iraq in support of Operation Iraqi Freedom on 26 October 2003. Sergeant First Class Porter distinguished himself while serving as a Platoon Sergeant with 143rd Military Police Company in the area of the Abu Ghraib Police Station. Sergeant First Class Porter displayed true courage under fire when the Abu Ghraib Police Station was attacked. On the night of 26 October 2003, Sergeant First Class Porter was assigned as the NCOIC of the Abu Ghraib Police Station. Sergeant First Class Porter was outside the Police Station building in the area of the north wall when the station came under attack. The first explosion occurred just a short distance from where Sergeant First Class Porter was standing. The first explosion seriously injured three soldiers. Though dazed by the concussion from the explosion, Sergeant First Class Porter heard the injured soldier's cries for help and immediately made his way to their vehicle. While moving towards the injured soldiers, Sergeant First Class Porter heard and felt several more explosions. With a total disregard for his own safety, Sergeant First Class Porter and several other soldiers made their way under fire to the injured soldiers, removed them from the vehicle and then, while still under fire, moved them across the exposed area of the parking lot and into the relative security of the Police Station where lifesaving first aid was performed, resulting in two soldiers lives being saved. Throughout the attack, Sergeant First Class Porter displayed exceptional valor, sound judgment, and an uncompromising devotion to his fellow soldiers, risking his own life to save theirs.

AWARDED

Staff Sergeant Andrea Cloutier

For heroic service in military operations against an armed enemy force in Iraq in support of Operation Iraqi Freedom on 27 October 2003. Staff Sergeant Cloutier distinguished herself while serving as a Squad Leader with 3rd Squad, 3rd Platoon, 143rd Military Police Company in the area of the Al Khadra Police Station. Staff Sergeant Cloutier displayed true courage under fire when the Al Khadra Police Station was attacked. On the 27 October 2003, Staff Sergeant Cloutier was assigned NCOIC of the monitoring detail and was conducting an inspection visit to the Al Khadra Police Station. Staff Sergeant Cloutier and her Squad were in and around the building at approximately 0915 hours when the station came under attack. Staff Sergeant Cloutier was entering the rear of the building when a suicide vehicle bomber attempted to ram his vehicle into the Police Station. The suicide bomber, in his attempt to strike the building, became immobilized on one of the vehicle barriers. The bomber detonated the bomb short of the wall of the Compound, killing a number of Iraqi civilians and an Iraqi Police officer. Dozens of Iraqi Police and civilians were wounded, including two Military Police officers. Though dazed by the concussion from the bomb, Staff Sergeant Cloutier immediately began assessing the damage and injuries and organizing a defense of the damaged facility, fearing a second attack was imminent. Staff Sergeant Cloutier began an accounting of all personnel and insured all injured were treated and evacuated to a proper medical facility. Staff Sergeant Cloutier ensured that communications with Company and Battalion were reestablished and critical information was relayed to higher Headquarters to facilitate appropriate recovery operations. Staff Sergeant Cloutier continued her efforts as the NCOIC on scene until relieved by her platoon leader. Staff Sergeant Cloutier remained on scene assisting with security and the recovery mission until late that evening. This was the second major engagement that Staff Sergeant Cloutier had been in during the past twelve hours.

DENIED

Staff Sergeant Cloutier had received one award the day before, and she could not receive two.

Specialist Timothy Corcoran

For heroic service in military operations against an armed enemy force in Iraq in support of Operation Iraqi Freedom on 27 October 2003. Specialist Corcoran distinguished himself while serving as a Driver with 3rd Squad, 3rd Platoon, 143rd Military Police Company in the area of the Al Khadra Police Station. Specialist Corcoran displayed true courage under fire when the Al Khadra Police Station was attacked by a suicide vehicle bomber. On the morning of 27 October 2003, Specialist Corcoran was on duty at the Al Khadra Police Station, manning the vehicle radio as the Squad conducted a monitoring inspection of the station. At approximately 0915 hours the Al Khadra Police Station was attacked by a suicide bomber who attempted to ram his vehicle into the station. In his attempt to strike the building, the suicide bomber struck a vehicle barrier and became immobile a short distance from the Police Station wall. The explosion killed a number of Iraqi civilians, an Iraqi Police officer, and wound dozens of civilians, Iraqi Police officers and two Military Police officers. Though dazed by the explosion, Specialist Corcoran maintained his position, relaying critical information to responding units and higher headquarters, ensuring a swift and coordinated response. Shortly after the attack, Specialist Corcoran was sent one of the injured Military Police officers. Specialist Corcoran performed first aid on the injured soldier until the soldier could be evacuated to a hospital. Specialist Corcoran remained on post until relieved late that afternoon. This was the second major attack Specialist Corcoran had been involved in the past twelve hours.

DENIED

Specialist Corcoran received an award the day before and could not receive two.

Specialist Alexander Wilde

For distinguished service in military operations against an armed enemy force in Baghdad Iraq in support of Operation Iraqi Freedom on 26 October 2003. Specialist Wilde distinguished himself while serving as the Desk Sergeant with 1st Squad, 143rd Military Police Company at the Abu Ghraib Police Station, Baghdad, Iraq. Specialist Wilde was on duty the night of 26 October 2003 when the station was attacked by hostile forces firing mortars at the Compound. The first round impacted inside the Compound, seriously injuring three soldiers. The three injured soldiers were moved into the Police station for treatment of their injuries. Specialist Wilde, who is a Combat Life Saver, immediately responded to the room and began assessing the injuries and directing lifesaving medical aid. Specialist Wilde noted that two of the three soldiers had sustained serious, life-threatening injuries to their legs which, if not treated promptly, would cause them to quickly bleed to death. Specialist Wilde directed tourniquets be placed on the legs which stopped the flow of blood. Specialist Wilde then started an IV on the most seriously injured soldier, who had lost a large amount of blood and was going into shock. Specialist Wilde continued to treat the injured until they were evacuated to the medical facility. Specialist Wilde' swift action was instrumental in the saving the lives of two serious casualties.

AWARDED

Sergeant First Class Roddy Porter

For heroic service in military operations against an armed enemy force in Iraq in support of Operation Iraqi Freedom on 26 October 2003. Sergeant First Class Porter distinguished himself while serving as a Platoon Sergeant with 143rd Military Police Company in the area of the Abu Ghraib Police Station. Sergeant First Class Porter displayed true courage under fire when the Abu Ghraib Police Station was attacked. On the night of 26 October 2003, Sergeant First Class Porter was assigned as the NCOIC of the Abu Ghraib Police Station. Sergeant First Class Porter was outside the Police Station building in the area of the north wall when the station came under attack. The first explosion occurred just a short distance from where Sergeant First Class Porter was standing. The first explosion seriously injured three soldiers. Though dazed by the concussion from the explosion, Sergeant First Class Porter heard the injured soldier's cries for help and immediately made his way to their vehicle. While moving towards the injured soldiers, Sergeant First Class Porter heard and felt several more explosions. With a total disregard for his own safety, Sergeant First Class Porter and several other soldiers made their way under fire to the injured soldiers, removed them from the vehicle and then, while still under fire, moved them across the exposed area of the parking lot and into the relative security of the Police Station where lifesaving first aid was performed, resulting in two soldiers lives being saved. Throughout the attack, Sergeant First Class Porter displayed exceptional valor, sound judgment, and an uncompromising devotion to his fellow soldiers, risking his own life to save theirs.

AWARDED

Sergeant First Class Roddy Porter

For heroic service in military operations against an armed enemy force in Iraq in support of Operation Iraqi Freedom on 31 October 2003. Sergeant First Class Porter distinguished himself while serving as a Platoon Sergeant with 143rd Military Police Company in the area of the Abu Ghraib Police Station. Sergeant First Class Porter displayed true courage under fire when the Abu Ghraib Police Station was attacked. On 31 October 2003, Sergeant First Class Porter was assigned as the NCOIC of the Abu Ghraib Police Station. At approximately 1030 hours on the morning of 31 October 2003, a disturbance began in the market east of the Abu Ghrab Police Station. Sergeant First Class Porter directed soldiers of 143rd Military Police Company to take up defensive positions should the disturbance move in their direction. During the morning and into the afternoon, the disturbance turned into a full-fledged armed confrontation between Coalition forces and hostile forces in the market. At approximately 1225 hours, a mortar attack was launched against the Abu Ghrab Station. Two rounds impacted inside the Abu Ghrab Station compound and a third impacted outside the Compound. At this point, the individuals began an advance on the Police Compound. Armor elements just east of the Abu Ghrab Station, in defense of the station, began receiving fire from small arms and rocket propelled grenades. The Abu Ghrab Police Station was also fired on from buildings to the east of the station. With a total disregard for his own personal safety, Sergeant First Class Porter directed his Military Police officers to engage the hostile force, firing small arms and M-203 grenade rounds at the attacking force. With small arms fire impacting around the Military Police officers, Sergeant First Class Porter's soldiers continued to fire on the attackers and forced them to break contact and retreat without causing any injuries to those occupying the Police station. With the attackers neutralized, the Armored Unit was able to move forward and clear the market of the attacking force.

DENIED

Sergeant First Class Porter had already received an ARCOM with V from a prior engagement.

Sergeant Kevin Arrojado

For heroic service in military operations against an armed enemy force in Iraq in support of Operation Iraqi Freedom on 31 October 2003. Sergeant Arrojado distinguished himself while serving as a Team Leader with 3rd Squad, 143rd Military Police Company in the area of the Abu Ghraib Police Station. Sergeant Arrojado displayed true courage under fire when the Abu Ghraib Police Station was attacked. On 31 October 2003 Sergeant Arrojado was assigned to the Abu Ghrab Police Station. At approximately 1030 hours the morning of 31 October 2003, a disturbance began in the market east of the Abu Ghrab Police Station. Sergeant Arrojado and other members of 143rd Military Police Company, took up defensive positions should the disturbance move in their direction. During the morning and into the afternoon, the disturbance turned into a full-fledged armed confrontation between Coalition forces and hostile forces in the market. At approximately 1225 hours, a mortar attack was launched against the Abu Ghrab Station. Two rounds impacted inside the Abu Ghrab Station compound and a third impacted outside the Compound. At this point, the individuals began an advance on the Police Compound. Armor elements just east of the Abu Ghrab Station, in defense of the station,began receiving fire from small arms and rocket propelled grenades. The Abu Ghraib Police Station was also fired on from buildings to the east of the station. With a total disregard for his own personal safety, Sergeant Arrojado engaged the hostile force, firing small arms and M-203 grenade rounds at the attacking force. With small arms fire impacting around the Military Police officers, Sergeant Arrojado continued to fire on the attackers and forced them to break contact and retreat without causing any injuries to those occupying the Police station. With the attackers neutralized, the Armored Unit was able to move forward and clear the market of the attacking force.

AWARDED

Sergeant Christopher Potts

For heroic service in military operations against an armed enemy force in Iraq in support of Operation Iraqi Freedom on 31 October 2003. Sergeant Potts distinguished himself while serving as a Team Leader with 3rd Squad, ,143rd Military Police Company in the area of the Abu Ghraib Police Station. Sergeant Potts displayed true courage under fire when the Abu Ghraib Police Station was attacked. On 31 October 2003, Sergeant Potts was assigned to the Abu Ghraib Police Station. At approximately 1030 hours the morning of 31 October 2003, a disturbance began in the market east of the Abu Ghrab Police Station. Sergeant Potts and other members of 143rd Military Police Company took up defensive positions in case the disturbance moves in their direction. During the morning and into the afternoon, the disturbance turned into a full-fledged armed confrontation between Coalition forces and hostile forces in the market. At approximately 1225 hours, a mortar attack was launched against the Abu Ghrab Station. Two rounds impacted inside the Abu Ghrab Station compound and a third impacted outside the Compound. At this point, the individuals began an advance on the Police Compound. Armor elements just east of the Abu Ghrab Station in defense of the station began receiving fire from small arms and rocket propelled grenades. The Abu Ghrab Police Station was also fired on from buildings to the east of the station. With a total disregard for his own personal safety, Sergeant Potts engaged the hostile force, firing small arms rounds at the attacking force. With small arms fire impacting around the Military Police officers, Sergeant Potts continued to fire on the attackers and forced them to break contact and retreat without causing any injuries to those occupying the Police station. With the attackers neutralized, the Armored Unit was able to move forward and clear the market of the attacking force.

AWARDED

Staff Sergeant Richard Smith

For heroic service in military operations against an armed enemy force in Iraq in support of Operation Iraqi Freedom on 31 October 2003. Staff Sergeant Smith distinguished himself while serving as a Squad Leader with 143rd Military Police Company in the area of the Abu Ghraib Police Station. Staff Sergeant Smith displayed true courage under fire when the Abu Ghraib Police Station was attacked. On 31 October 2003, Staff Sergeant Smith was assigned to the Abu Ghraib Police Station. At approximately 1030 hours the morning of 31 October 2003, a disturbance began in the market east of the Abu Ghrab Police Station. Staff Sergeant Smith and other members of 143rd Military Police Company took up defensive positions in case the disturbance moved in their direction. During the morning and into the afternoon the disturbance turned into a full-fledged armed confrontation between Coalition forces and hostile forces in the market. At approximately 1225 hours, a mortar attack was launched against the Abu Ghrab Station. Two rounds impacted inside the Abu Ghrab Station compound and a third impacted outside the Compound. At this point, the individuals began advancing on the Police Compound. Armor elements just east of the Abu Ghrab Station in defense of the station began receiving fire from small arms and rocket propelled grenades. The Abu Ghrab Police Station was also fired on from buildings to the east of the station. With a total disregard for his own personal safety, Staff Sergeant Smith engaged the hostile force firing small arms rounds at the attacking force. With small arms fire impacting around the Military Police officers Staff, Sergeant Smith continued to fire on the attackers and forced them to break contact and retreat without causing any injuries to those occupying the Police station. With the attackers neutralized, the Armored Unit was able to move forward and clear the market of the attacking force.

AWARDED

Specialist Angel D. Escobales

For heroic service in military operations against an armed enemy force in Iraq in support of Operation Iraqi Freedom on 21 September 2003. Specialist Escobales distinguished himself while serving as a gunner with 1st Squad 143rd Military Police Company, assigned to force protection duty at the Abu Ghraib Police Station, Baghdad, Iraq. Specialist Escobales displayed true courage under fire while providing rooftop security in support of joint police operations in the area of the Abu Ghraib Police Station. While on duty, Specialist Escobales observed movement to the north of the police station at a location known as the Milk Factory. Specialist Escobales gave the alarm and notified other Military Police officers and soldiers assigned to force protection. Specialist Escobales then observed three individuals armed with AK-47 assault rifles and rocket propelled grenades. Specialist Escobales opened fire with his weapon, striking one of the individuals who was in the process of firing a rocket propelled grenade at the police station. The impact of the rounds fired by Specialist Escobales caused the rocket to fire wildly up into the air, missing the police station. Other Military Police officers and force protection soldiers then joined in the defense of the station, suppressed the hostile fire, and drove the attackers from the Milk Factory. A follow up sweep of the Milk Factory revealed the body of the dead attacker and three un-fired rocket propelled grenades. Throughout the engagement, Specialist Escobales demonstrated exceptional valor under fire, and used sound judgment and professional courage to defend his fellow Military Police officers, soldiers, and Iraqi Police officers at the Abu Ghraib Police Station. His actions were instrumental in breaking up the attack and driving off the hostile force. His actions reflect great credit upon himself, the 18th Military Police Brigade and the United States Army.

DENIED

Lieutenant Michael Grube

For exceptional meritorious service in military operations against an armed enemy force in Iraq in support of Operation Iraqi Freedom from 19 October 2003 to 27 October 2003. Lieutenant Grube distinguished himself while serving as the company commander for the 143rd Military Police Company. Shortly after taking command of the 143rd Military Police Company, Lieutenant Grube began making assessments of the four Iraqi Police Stations in his area of responsibility. Lieutenant Grube, working with his platoon leaders, identified areas that were deficient in the area of force protection and security at the four stations and immediately began implementing upgraded force protection measures and security barriers. At the Al Khadra Police Station, Lieutenant Grube noted that the Iraqi Police officers had removed certain vehicle barriers that left the facility open to a hostile, vehicle-borne improvised explosive device. Lieutenant Grube attempted to procure pre-manufactured barriers but was unable to locate any. Undeterred, Lieutenant Grube located decorative concrete planters that were no longer being utilized and, with the company wrecker and 2.5 ton trucks, began transporting them to the Police Station and arranging them to block the access of a suicide vehicle bomber. From 19 October 2003 until 21 October 2003, Lieutenant Grube directed the movement and placement of the concrete barriers. On the morning of 27 October 2003, a suicide bomber driving an SUV attempted to ram through the protective barrier in order to blow up the Police Station. The SUV became immobile on the concrete barriers and the suicide bomber detonated the vehicle bomb approximately 25 feet from the wall of the station, approximately 50' from the Police Station Building. The blast was so intense that it left a crater 12' wide and 7' deep, destroying numerous vehicles and businesses on the street. The blast injured two Military Police officers, several Iraqi Police officers, and killed one Iraqi Police officer. Had the barriers not been in place, the Suicide Bomber could have been able to get closer to the Police Station and the results would have been catastrophic in loss of life and damage to the structure. Lieutenant Grube's keen insight, resourcefulness, dedication to duty, and mission focus prevented what could have been a horrible tragedy.

DENIED

Lieutenant Grube would not let the request go forward, stating that he was only doing his job, and that award request would be denied.

Lieutenant Jeremy Kerfoot

For exceptional meritorious service in military operations against an armed enemy force in Iraq in support of Operation Iraqi Freedom from 19 October 2003 to 27 October 2003. Lieutenant Kerfoot distinguished himself while serving as the platoon leader for 3rd Platoon, 143rd Military Police Company. Shortly after being assigned as the officer in charge of the Al Khadra Police Station, Lieutenant Kerfoot began making assessments of the Iraqi Police Station. Lieutenant Kerfoot made recommendations and identified areas that were deficient in the area of force protection and security at the Al Khadra Station and immediately began implementing upgraded force protection measures and security barriers. At the Al Khadra Police Station, it was noted that the Iraqi Police officers had removed certain vehicle barriers that left the facility open to a hostile vehicle-borne improvised explosive device. Lieutenant Kerfoot attempted to procure pre-manufactured barriers but was unable to locate any. Undeterred, Lieutenant Kerfoot and the company commander, Lieutenant Grube, located decorative concrete planters that were no longer being utilized and with the Company wrecker and the Company's 2.5 ton trucks began transporting them to the Police Station and arranging them to block the access of a suicide vehicle bomber. From 19 October 2003 until 21 October 2003, Lieutenant Kerfoot coordinated the placement of the concrete barriers. On the morning of 27 October 2003, a suicide bomber driving an SUV attempted to ram through the protective barrier in order to blow up the Police Station. The SUV became immobile on the concrete barriers and the suicide bomber detonated the vehicle bomb approximately 25 feet from the wall of the station, approximately 50' from the Police Station Building. The blast was so intense that it left a crater 12' wide and 7' deep destroying numerous vehicles and businesses on the street. The blast injured two Military Police officers, several Iraqi Police officers, and killed one Iraqi Police officer. Had the barriers not been in place, the suicide bomber could have been able to get closer to the Police Station and the results would have been catastrophic in loss of life and damage to the structure. Lieutenant determination to secure the facility, keen insight, resourcefulness, and dedication to duty, and mission focus prevented what could have been a horrible tragedy.

DENIED

Lieutenant Kerfoot would not let the request go forward, stating that he was only doing his job, and that the award request would be denied.

Specialist Angel Escobales

For heroic service in military operations against an armed enemy force in Iraq in support of Operation Iraqi Freedom on 21 September 2003. Specialist Escobales distinguished himself while serving as a gunner with 1st Squad, 143rd Military Police Company assigned to force protection at the Abu Ghraib Police Station, Baghdad, Iraq. Specialist Escobales displayed true courage under fire while providing roof top security in support of joint police operations in the area of the Abu Ghraib Police Station. While on duty, Specialist Escobales observed movement to the north of the police station at a location known as the Milk Factory. Specialist Escobales gave the alarm and notified other Military Police officers and soldiers assigned to force protection. Specialist Escobales then observed three individuals who were armed with AK-47 assault rifles and rocket propelled grenades. Specialist Escobales opened fire with his weapon, striking one individual who was in the process of firing a rocket propelled grenade at the police station. The impacting of Specialist Escobales's rounds into the attacker caused the rocket to be fired wildly up into the air, missing the police station. At this time, other Military Police officers and force protection soldiers joined in the defense of the station, suppressing the hostile fire and driving the attackers from the Milk Factory. A follow up sweep of the Milk Factory revealed the body of the dead attacker and three un-fired rocket propelled grenades. Throughout the engagement Specialist Escobales demonstrated exceptional valor while under fire, using sound judgment and professional courage to defend his fellow Military Police officers, soldiers and the Iraqi Police officers of the Abu Ghraib Police Station. His actions were instrumental in breaking up the attack and driving off the hostile force. His actions reflect great credit upon himself, the 18th Military Police Brigade, and the United States Army.

AWARDED

KILLED IN ACTION DURING OUR TOUR

Nine Active-duty/Twenty Guard & Reserve

Here is to us, and those like us, damn few of us left.

Colonel Edward Lynch
Connecticut State Police (retired)

SOLDIER	DATE	UNIT	ACTIVE GUARD/ RESERVE[H.1]
PVT David J. Evans[1]	05/25/2003	977 MP CO	AD
SSG Brett Petriken[2]	05/26/2003	501 MP CO	AD
PVT Kenneth Nalley[3]	05/26/2003	501 MP CO	AD
SGT Travis Burkhardt[4]	06/06/2003	170 MP CO	AD
SPC Richard Orengo[5]	06/26/2003	755 MP CO	NG PR
SGT Jaror Puello-Coronado[6]	07/13/2003	310 MP BN	AR NY
SGT Heath McMilli[7]	07/27/2003	105 MP CO	NG NY

SOLDIER RESERVE[H.1]	DATE	UNIT	ACTIVE GUARD/
PFC Brandon Ramsey[8]	08/08/2003	933 MP CO	NG IL
SSG David Perry[9]	08/10/2003	649 MP CO	NG CA
SGT Eric Hall[10]	08/18/2003	210 MP CO	AR PA
SSG Bobby Franklin[11]	08/20/2003	210 MP CO	NG NC
SSG Joseph Camara[12]	09/01/2003	115 MP CO	NG RI
SGT Charles Caldwell[13]	09/01/2003	115 MP CO	NG RI
SPC Michael Andrade[14]	09/24/2003	115 MP CO	NG RI
SGT Darrin Potter[15]	09/29/2003	223 MP CO	NG KY
LTC Kim Orlando[16]	10/16/2003	716 MP BN	AD
CPL Sean Grilley[17]	10/16/2003	716 MP BN	AD
SSG Joseph Bellavia[18]	10/16/2003	716 MP BN	AD
SPC Michael Williams[19]	10/17/2003	105 MP CO	NG NY
PFC Rachel Bosveld[20]	10/26/2003	527 MP CO	AD
SGT Aubrey Bell[21]	10/27/2003	214 MP CO	NG AL
SGT Nicholas Tomko[22]	11/09/2003	307 MP CO	NG PA
SSG Aaron Reese[23]	12/10/2003	135 MP CO	NG OH
SPC Todd Bates[24]	12/10/2003	135 MP CO	NG OH
SPC Michael Mihalakis[25]	12/26/2003	270 MP CO	NG CA
SSG James Mowris[26]	01/29/2004	805 MP CO	AR NC
SPC Eric Ramirez[27]	02/12/2004	670 MP CO	NG CA
SPC Christopher Taylor[28]	02/16/2004	1165 MP CO	NG AL

SSG Wentz Shanaberger[29]   02/24/2004   21 MP CO   AD

1. Memorial page for PVT David J. Evans
   http://www.fallenheroesmemorial.com/oif/profiles/evansjrdavid.html

2. Memorial page for SSG Brett Petriken
   http://www.ourfallensoldier.com/PetrikenBrettJ_MemorialPage.html

3. Memorial page for PVT Kenneth Nalley
   http://www.fallenheroesmemorial.com/oif/profiles/nalleykennetha.html

4. Memorial page for SGT Travis Burkhardt
   http://www.fallenheroesmemorial.com/oif/profiles/burkhardttravisl.html

5. Memorial page for SPC Richard Orengo
   http://www.fallenheroesmemorial.com/oif/profiles/orengorichardp.html

6. Memorial page for SGT Jaror Puello-Coronado
   http://www.fallenheroesmemorial.com/oif/profiles/puellocoronadojarorc.html

7. Memorial page for SGT Heath McMilli
   http://www.forevermissed.com/sgt-heath-a-mcmillin/#about

8. Memorial page for PFC Brandon Ramsey
   http://www.fallenheroesmemorial.com/oif/profiles/ramseybrandon.html

9. Memorial page for SSG David Perry
   http://www.honoredmps.org/perry-david.html

10. Memorial page for SGT Eric Hall
    http://thefallen.militarytimes.com/army-spc-eric-r-hull/256757

11. Memorial page for SSG Bobby Franklin
    http://www.fallenheroesmemorial.com/oif/profiles/franklinbobbyc.html

12. Memorial page for SSG Joseph Camara
    http://www.fallenheroesmemorial.com/oif/profiles/camarajoseph.html

13. Memorial page for SGT Charles Caldwell
    http://www.fallenheroesmemorial.com/oif/profiles/caldwellcharlest.html

14. Memorial page for SPC Michael Andrade
    http://www.fallenheroesmemorial.com/oif/profiles/andrademichael.html

15. Memorial page for SGT Darrin Potter
    http://www.fallenheroesmemorial.com/oif/profiles/potterdarrink.html

16. Memorial page for LTC Kim Orlando
    http://www.fallenheroesmemorial.com/oif/profiles/orlandokims.html

17. Memorial page for CPL Sean Grilley
    http://www.fallenheroesmemorial.com/oif/profiles/grilleyseanr.html

18. Memorial page for SSG Joseph Bellavia
    http://www.fallenheroesmemorial.com/oif/profiles/bellaviajosephp.html

19. Memorial page for PFC SPC Michael Williams
    http://www.honoredmps.org/williams-michael.html

20. Memorial page for PFC Rachel Bosveld
    http://www.fallenheroesmemorial.com/oif/profiles/bosveldrachelk.html

21. Memorial page for SGT Aubrey Bell
    http://www.fallenheroesmemorial.com/oif/profiles/bellaubreyd.html

22. Memorial page for SGT Nicholas Tomko
    http://www.fallenheroesmemorial.com/oif/profiles/tomkonicholasa.html

23. Memorial page for SSG Aaron Reese
    http://www.fallenheroesmemorial.com/oif/profiles/reeseaaront.html

24. Memorial page for SPC Todd Bates
http://www.forevermissed.com/todd-m-bates/#about

25. Memorial page for SPC Michael Mihalakis
http://www.honoredmps.org/mihalakis-michael.html

26. Memorial page for SSG James Mowris
http://thefallen.militarytimes.com/army-staff-sgt-james-d-mowris/263002

27. Memorial page for SPC Eric Ramirez
http://www.honoredmps.org/ramirez-eric.html

28. Memorial page for SPC Christopher Taylor
http://www.fallenheroesmemorial.com/oif/profiles/taylorchristopherm.html

29. Memorial page for SSG Wentz Shanaberger
http://www.fallenheroesmemorial.com/oif/profiles/shanabergeriiiwentzjeromehenry.html

MILITARY POLICE ORGANIZATION

When we deployed, we had at one point 151 soldiers, five of whom were officers. Most platoons that should have had one officer and thirty-two soldiers often had one officer and twenty-six soldiers.

All sections of the military were equally short on personnel. As the deployment went on, we lost soldiers on a monthly basis—before leaving Fort Drum, we had already lost three soldiers.

MILITARY POLICE PLATOON

A Team consists of a team leader normally a Sergeant, a driver and a gunner all assigned to a Humvee.

A squad consists of three MP teams plus a squad leader normally a staff sergeant.

An MP platoon consists of three squads plus the platoon command element that consists of a platoon leader, lieutenant, a platoon sergeant, a sergeant first class and a driver, also assigned to a separate vehicle from the squads.

MILITARY POLICE COMPANY

Four MP platoons make up the largest portion of a Military Police Company.

Added to the platoons are the Headquarters and Operations Platoons.

Headquarters

Headquarter is one section that includes:

- company commander
- first sergeant
- driver
- vehicle

Headquarter also includes a support staff:

- medics
- clerks
- food service
- vehicle maintenance and support
- communications
- nuclear, biological and chemical warfare specialist
- supply

Operations

A separate section, Operations is the coordinating hub for the entire unit, and consist of:

- senior military police NCOs
- MP support
- administrative clerks

ENDNOTES

8.1 Garry Trudeau, Doonesbury, (gocomics.com, accessed August 1, 2015, http://www.gocomics.com/doonesbury/2007/02/18) doonesbury/2007/02/18), 94-95

9.1 Refers to the Battle of Hunayn in 630 (8 AH or January AD); i.e. having one foot in the past, 129

15.1 With great apologies to Adam Busby, the author and publisher have been unable to locate his military rank. 196

15.2 Alanis Morissette, *Ironic*, (Beverly Hills, CA, Maverick Records, June 9, 1995), 196

16.1 *Took a knee* is a military expression that refers to going down on one knee, as opposed to diving for cover. 208

20.1 PFC Lynne M. Steely, 18th Military Police Brigade, "V Corps Military Police Company Named Best in Army," (December 31, 2003, accessed August 1, 2015, http://www.globalsecurity.org/military/library/news/2003/12/mil-031231-vcorps01.htm), 244

23.1 Iraq was divided up into sections and subsection with separate Armored Brigades controlling different subsections. Individual brigades had supreme authority over their sectors, and all units below them had to operate under their guidelines and control. These sectors are referred to as "battle space." 274

25.1 Wolf Blitzer, "Troops put Rumsfeld in the hot seat," (Washington, DC, CNN, December 8, 2004, 2014, accessed August 1, 2015, http://www.cnn.com/2004/US/12/08/rumsfeld.kuwait/), 311

25.2 Ibid. 312

A.1 Some lists may not be complete. 327

C.1 Ibid. 338

D.1 Ibid. 341

D.2 Returned to duty in Iraq. 342

D.3 Received Purple Heart after returning from Iraq. 342

E.1 Stephanie Summers, Courant Staff Writer, "National Guard Company Honored In Armory, West Hartford-based MPs Served In Iraq," *The Hartford Courant*, April 3, 2006, (accessed August 1, 2015, http://articles.courant.com/2006-04-03/news/0604030407_1_iraqi-police-iraqi-command-car-bomb-blast), 346

E.2 Ibid. 346

E.3 Ibid. 347

E.4 Ibid. 347

F.1 This list may not be complete. 349

H.1 AD—Active-duty full-time army
AR—The Army Reserve
NG—The National Guard
AL, CA, IL, KY, NC, NY, OH, PA, PR, RI—State abbreviations

BIBLIOGRAPHY

Woodward, Bob *State of Denial: Bush at War, Part III*, (New York: Simon and Schuster Paperbacks, 2007)

Gates, Robert *Duty: Memoirs of a Secretary at War*, (New York: Penguin Random House LLC, 2014)

Bradley, James and Powers, Ron *Flags of our Fathers*, (New York: Bantam Dell, 2000)

Forester, C.S. *The African Queen*, (Boston, MA: Little, Brown and Company, 1935)

Cucullu, Gordon and Fontana, Chris Fontana *Warrior Police: Rolling with America's Military Police in the World's Trouble Spots* (New York: St. Martin's Press, 2011)

Moore, Harold and Galloway, Joseph *We Were Soliders Once…And Young* (New York: Random House, 1992)

Milne, A. A. *The Complete Tales of Winnie-the-Pooh* (New York: Dutton Children's Books, 1994)

GLOSSARY

Active-duty	The full-time military (also called AD)
AK-47	Standard issue for the Iraqi Infantry, rifle 7.62-35mm
ARCOM	Army Commendation Medal
Article 15	Allows commanders to inflict discretionary punishments without the need for judicial proceedings.
ASV	Armored Security Vehicles
AWOL	Absent Without Leave
Battalion	A large body of troops ready for battle (especially an Infantry unit forming part of a brigade), typically commanded by a lieutenant colonel.
BCC	Battlefield Control Unit
BCT	Brigade Combat Team
BMW	Bayerische Motoren Werke AG, commonly known as BMW (or BMW AG), a German automobile, motorcycle, and engine manufacturer founded in 1916.

Call Signs	See *Radio Calls*
Clearing Barrels	A 55 gallon drum filled with sand that is used as a target in case of accidental discharge when clearing a weapon.
CPA	Coalition Provisional Authority—a transitional government in Iraq that followed the March 19, 2003 Coalition invasion. The Coalition included the United States, United Kingdom, Australia and Poland.
CO	Commanding officer
CROWS	Common Remotely Operated Weapons Station
CS	Combat Support
CSH	Combat Surgical Hospital
Deterrent Patrolling	Making a military presence at random times to deter insurgent activities.
EOD	Explosive ordnance disposal; EOD soldiers are bomb technicians who are responsible for disabling and disarming explosive devices.
Flank Security	Protection to the sides
FLR	Forward Looking Infrared Targeting System
FOB	Forward Operating Base
Forming Up	Participating in an orderly physical arrangement
Green Zone	Secure area where the provisional Coalition compound was located
HMFIC	Head Mother-Fucker In charge

Humvees	High Mobility Multi-purpose Wheeled Vehicles produced by AM General—the standard military vehicle that replaced the jeep. Many variations are available. Also called a Hummer.
IG	Inspector General—the eyes, ears, voice and conscience of the Army across the spectrum of operations
IED	Improvised Explosive Device
ISIS	Islamic State, Islamic State of Iraq and Syria, or the Islamic State of Iraq and Ahrar ash-Sham
Induction Center	The facility where people who have enlisted in all branches of the military are processed.
Insurgents	Militant fighters—most were from Iraq, but not all.
JAG	Judge Advocate General's Corps, also known as JAG or JAG Corps, refers to the legal branch or specialty of a military concerned with military justice and military law. Officers serving in a JAG Corps are typically called Judge Advocates.
Litter	A hospital stretcher
LZ	Landing Zone
KBR	Kellogg, Brown and Root—U.S. contractors who ran the dining facilities and other support activities.
KP	Key Processor or Kitchen Police (soldiers assigned to mess duty)
LZ	Landing Zone
M-2	50-caliber heavy machine gun

M-4	The carbine version of the M-16 rifle, 5.56mm
M-9	Standard U.S. issue Beretta 9mm pistol
M-16	Standard U.S. issue rifle, 5.56mm
M-240 SAW	Squad Automatic Light Machine Gun—fires the same round as the M-16 and M-4
Make-Work Details	Tasks that were not really necessary, but someone decided you needed something to do to keep busy.
MK-19	40mm automatic grenade launcher
Massif	A mountain or block of the earth's crust bounded by faults or flexures and displaced as a unit without internal change.
Main Side	The central location of a base (as opposed to the outlying areas).
MedEvac	Medical Evacuation
MOB	Mobilization
MP-5	9mm submachine gun
MRAP	Mine Resistant Ambush Protected Vehicle
MRE	Military Readiness Exercise; Meals Ready to Eat
MTA	Metropolitan Transit Authority
MTOE	Military Table of Organization
NCO	Non-Commissioned Officers—officers who usually obtained their position by promotion through the enlisted ranks. The NCO corps usually includes all grades of corporal and sergeant; in some non-U.S. countries, warrant officers also carry out the duties of NCO.

NCOIC	Non-Commissioned officer In Charge
NSA	National Security Agency
NVA	North Vietnamese Army
OGA	Other Government Agency—used when the an individual does not want to identify which government agency they work for (e.g. CIA, NSA, Delta Force, SEALS, etc.).
OIF	Operation Iraqi Freedom
Ordnance	A general term referring to weapons, ammunition, artillery shells and other explosives.
Platoon	A military unit—See Appendix I *Military Organizational Chart* for more information.
PFC	Private First Class
PX	Post Exchange—the military version of a store
QRF	Quick Reaction Force
Radio Calls	Radio Calls are code names used to identify individuals over the radio. Some radio calls are assigned and some are earned. My assigned radio call was Wolf Eight because the company commander decided our company radio call would be called Wolf Pack. My earned call sign was Teddy Bear Eight (which I preferred). Also called "call signs."
Reception Center	The facility where soldiers are processed for the Army.
RPG	Rocket Propelled Grenade
RPK	Standard Iraqi issue light machine gun, 7.62-35mm

Running the Range	Performing the management duties required to supervise a firearms qualification range.
SAW	See *M-240 SAW*
SINGARS	Single-Channel Ground-Air Radio System
SKS	A light assault rifle
SFC	Sergeant First Class
SPC E4	SPC refers to an enlisted soldier, the third promotion after enlisting (normally attained in about two years). E4 refers to the Specialist's pay grade.
Suppressive Fire	A tactic used when being fired upon. Suppressive fire involves sending back a lot more rounds than are coming in. The three main goals of suppressive fire are to: (1) kill the enemy (2) force the enemy to duck and stop shooting at you, or (3) make the enemy think that shooting at you wasn't a great idea and cause him to run away.
TDA	Temporary Duty Assignment
Tet Offensive	The 1968 major attack on South Vietnam.
TOC	(1) Tactical Operations Center; (2) Theater of Operations Command
Took a Knee	A military expression that refers to going down on one knee, as opposed to diving for cover
Train Up	To train for a new skill or train to a higher level.
Tray Pack	Bulk/precooked meals that only require heating.
VBIED	Vehicle-Borne Improvised Explosive Devices

Wahhabism	A religious movement, or branch of Sunni Islam
Warrior Compound	The name given to our first FOB. "Warrior" came from the motto of the 709th Military Police, who called themselves "Warriors."
Wire, the	Perimeter of a military compound—when an individual leaves the Compound, he is outside "the wire."
XO	Executive officer

INDEX

T

U

V

W

Y

Z

ABOUT THE AUTHOR

(Left to Right) Sergeant Jack Earley, Author Master Sergeant Marc Youngquist

Marc Youngquist enlisted in the Marines in April, 1969, and went off to Parris Island on August 18th of that year. For the next four years, he served all over the Western Pacific (with a very limited time and no direct combat experience in Vietnam). In July, 1973, Marc was discharged from active-duty as a Sergeant, and in 1975, was honorably discharged from the Marine Corps Reserve.

In 1974, Marc became a police officer attaining the rank of Lieutenant. During that time, he attended the University of New Haven, obtaining a B.A. in Criminal Justice. In 1979, he graduated from the Federal Bureau of Investigations' National Academy in Quantico, Virginia.

Marc went on to work as a contractor for the Department of Energy and returned to school to earn an M.S. in Criminal Justice/Public Administration. He later enlisted in the Army Reserve as a Drill Sergeant, and two years later transferred to the Military Police in the Connecticut Army National Guard, where he served the rest of his military career.

While an MP, Marc held every position from driver to First Sergeant, and was deployed to Panama, the Dominican Republic, 9/11 airport security, and then finally, Iraq.

Since retiring in 2012 as a Special Investigator for the Insurance industry, Marc has been spending his time traveling with his wife and three dogs, and resides in Connecticut where he writes and builds stunning kayaks.

If you want to keep up with what Marc's doing, feel free to visit his website at marcyoungquist.com. Marc also welcomes hearing from his readers. If you'd like to write to him, he can be reached at info@ marcyoungquist.com.

Visit us at
emeraldlakebooks.com

Made in the USA
Middletown, DE
30 April 2022